PRENTICE HALL

SCIENCE EXPLORER

Teacher's Edition

From Bacteria to Plants

PRENTICE HALL
Needham, Massachusetts
Upper Saddle River, New Jersey

ISBN 0-13-434571-1
3 4 5 6 7 8 9 10   03 02 01 00 99

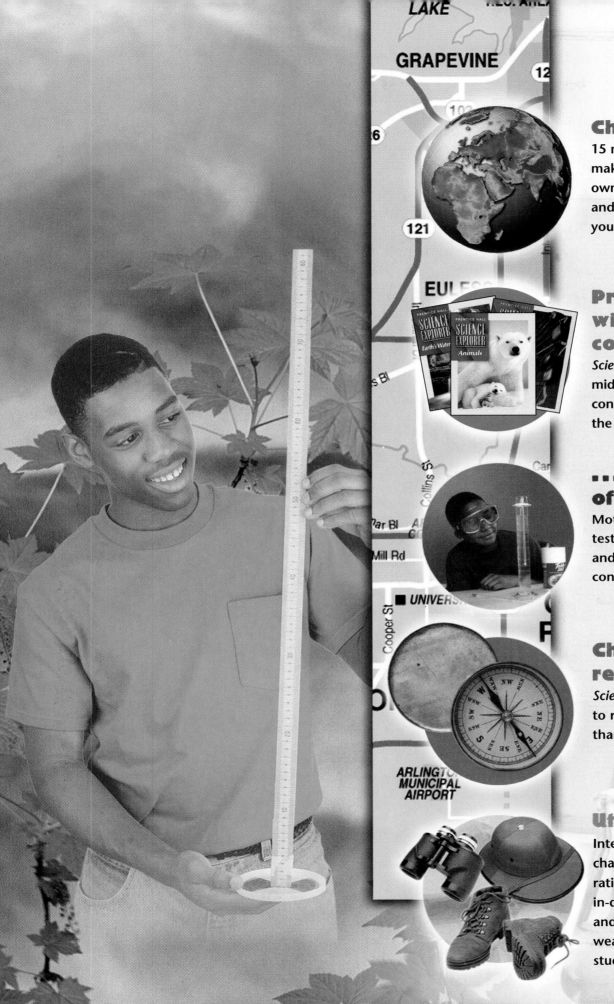

Chart your own course.

15 motivational hardcover books make it easy for you to create your own curriculum; meet local, state, and national guidelines; and teach your favorite topics in depth.

Prepare your students with rich, motivating content...

Science Explorer is crafted for today's middle grades student, with accessible content and in-depth coverage of all the important concepts.

...and a wide variety of inquiry activities.

Motivational student- and teacher-tested activities reinforce key concepts and allow students to explore science concepts for themselves.

Check your compass regularly.

Science Explorer gives you more ways to regularly check student performance than any other program available.

Utilize a variety of tools.

Integrated science sections in every chapter and Interdisciplinary Explorations in every book allow you to make in-depth connections to other sciences and disciplines. Plus, you will find a wealth of additional tools to set your students on a successful course.

Chart the course you want with 15 motivating books that easily match your curriculum.

Each book in the series contains:
- Integrated Science sections in every chapter
- Interdisciplinary Explorations for team teaching at the end of each book
- Comprehensive skills practice and application—assuring that you meet the National Science Education Standards and your local and state standards

For custom binding options, see your local sales representative.

EXPLORATION TOOLS: BASIC PROCESS SKILLS

Observing

Measuring

Calculating

Classifying

Predicting

Inferring

Graphing

Creating data tables

Communicating

LIFE SCIENCE TITLES

From Bacteria to Plants
1 Living Things
2 Viruses and Bacteria
3 Protists and Fungi
4 Introduction to Plants
5 Seed Plants

Animals
1 Sponges, Cnidarians, and Worms
2 Mollusks, Arthropods, and Echinoderms
3 Fishes, Amphibians, and Reptiles
4 Birds and Mammals
5 Animal Behavior

Cells and Heredity
1 Cell Structure and Function
2 Cell Processes and Energy
3 Genetics: The Science of Heredity
4 Modern Genetics
5 Changes Over Time

Human Biology and Health
1 Healthy Body Systems
2 Bones, Muscles, and Skin
3 Food and Digestion
4 Circulation
5 Respiration and Excretion
6 Fighting Disease
7 The Nervous System
8 The Endocrine System and Reproduction

Environmental Science
1 Populations and Communities
2 Ecosystems and Biomes
3 Living Resources
4 Land and Soil Resources
5 Air and Water Resources
6 Energy Resources

Integrated Science sections in every chapter

EXPLORATION TOOLS: ADVANCED PROCESS SKILLS

- **Posing questions**
- **Forming operational definitions**
- **Developing hypotheses**
- **Controlling variables**
- **Interpreting data**
- **Interpreting graphs**
- **Making models**
- **Drawing conclusions**
- **Designing experiments**

EARTH SCIENCE TITLES

Inside Earth
1 Plate Tectonics
2 Earthquakes
3 Volcanoes
4 Minerals
5 Rocks

Earth's Changing Surface
1 Mapping Earth's Surface
2 Weathering and Soil Formation
3 Erosion and Deposition
4 A Trip Through Geologic Time

Earth's Waters
1 Earth: The Water Planet
2 Fresh Water
3 Freshwater Resources
4 Ocean Motions
5 Ocean Zones

Weather and Climate
1 The Atmosphere
2 Weather Factors
3 Weather Patterns
4 Climate and Climate Change

Astronomy
1 Earth, Moon, and Sun
2 The Solar System
3 Stars, Galaxies, and the Universe

PHYSICAL SCIENCE TITLES

Chemical Building Blocks
1 An Introduction to Matter
2 Changes in Matter
3 Elements and the Periodic Table
4 Carbon Chemistry

Chemical Interactions
1 Chemical Reactions
2 Atoms and Bonding
3 Acids, Bases, and Solutions
4 Exploring Materials

Motion, Forces, and Energy
1 Motion
2 Forces
3 Forces in Fluids
4 Work and Machines
5 Energy and Power
6 Thermal Energy and Heat

Electricity and Magnetism
1 Magnetism and Electromagnetism
2 Electric Charges and Current
3 Electricity and Magnetism at Work
4 Electronics

Sound and Light
1 Characteristics of Waves
2 Sound
3 The Electromagnetic Spectrum
4 Light

 Integrated Science sections in every chapter

Place your students in the role of science explorer through a variety of inquiry activities.

Motivational student- and teacher-tested activities reinforce key concepts and allow students to explore science concepts for themselves. More than 350 activities are provided for each book in the Student Edition, Teacher's Edition, Teaching Resources, Integrated Science Lab Manual, Inquiry Skills Activity Book, Interactive Student Tutorial CD-ROM, and *Science Explorer* Web Site.

STUDENT EDITION ACTIVITIES

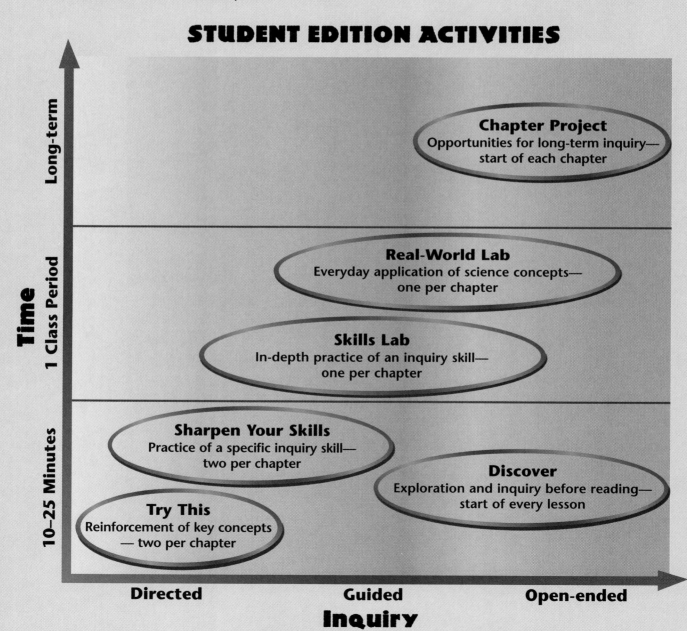

Time

Long-term

Chapter Project
Opportunities for long-term inquiry—
start of each chapter

1 Class Period

Real-World Lab
Everyday application of science concepts—
one per chapter

Skills Lab
In-depth practice of an inquiry skill—
one per chapter

10–25 Minutes

Sharpen Your Skills
Practice of a specific inquiry skill—
two per chapter

Discover
Exploration and inquiry before reading—
start of every lesson

Try This
Reinforcement of key concepts
— two per chapter

Directed   Guided   Open-ended

Inquiry

Check your compass regularly with integrated assessment tools.

Prepare for state exams with traditional and performance-based assessment.

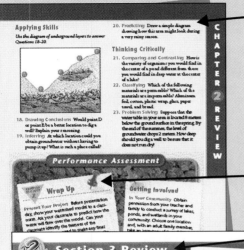

Comprehensive Chapter Reviews include a wide range of question types that students will encounter on standardized tests. Types include multiple choice, enhanced true/false, concept mastery, visual thinking, skill application, and critical thinking. Also includes Chapter Project "Wrap Up."

Chapter Projects contain rubrics that allow you to easily assess student progress.

Section Reviews provide "Check your Progress" opportunities for the Chapter Project, as well as review questions for the section.

Additional *Science Explorer* assessment resources:

- **Assessment Resources with CD-ROM**
- **Resource Pro® with Planning Express® CD-ROM**
- **Standardized Test Practice Book**
- **On-line review activities** at www.phschool.com
  See page T9 for complete product descriptions.

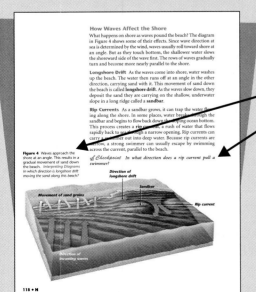

Self-assessment opportunities help students keep themselves on course.

- **Caption Questions** throughout the text assess critical thinking skills.

- **Checkpoint Questions** give students an immediate content check as new concepts are presented.

- **Interactive Student Tutorial CD-ROM** provides students with electronic self-tests, review activities, and Exploration activities.

- **Got It! Video Quizzes** motivate and challenge students with engaging animations and interactive questions.

- **www.science-explorer.phschool.com** provides additional support and on-line test prep.

Utilize a wide variety of tools.

Easy-to-manage, book-specific teaching resources

15 Teaching Resource Packages, each containing a Student Edition, Teacher's Edition, Teaching Resources with Color Transparencies, Guided Reading Audiotape, Materials Kit Order form, and Correlation to the National Science Education Standards.

15 Teacher's Editions with a three-step lesson plan—*Engage/Explore, Facilitate,* and *Assess*— that is ideal for reaching all students. Chapter planning charts make it easy to find resources, as well as to plan for block scheduling and team teaching.

15 Teaching Resource Books with Color Transparencies offer complete support organized by chapter to make it easy for you to find what you need—when you need it.

15 Guided Reading Audiotapes (English and Spanish) provide section summaries for students who need additional support.

15 Explorer Videotapes allow students to explore concepts through spectacular short videos containing computer animations. Available in Spanish.

Program-wide print resources

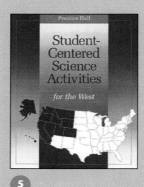

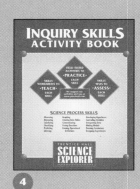

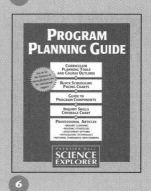

1. **Materials Kits**—Prentice Hall and Science Kit, Inc. have collaborated to develop a Consumable Kit and Nonconsumable Kit for each book. Ordering software makes it easy to customize!

2&3. **Integrated Science Laboratory Manual with Teacher's Edition**—74 in-depth labs covering the entire curriculum, with complete teaching support.

4. **Inquiry Skills Activity Book**—additional activities to teach, practice, and assess a wide range of inquiry skills.

5. **Student-Centered Science Activities**—five activity books for the Northeast, Southeast, Midwest, Southwest, and West.

6. **Program Planning Guide**—course outlines, block scheduling pacing charts, correlations, and more.

7. **Product Testing Activities by *Consumer Reports***—19 student-oriented testing activities turn students into real-world explorers.

Additional print resources...

8. **Reading in the Content Area**—with Literature Connections
9. **Standardized Test Practice**—review and self-tests to prepare for statewide exams.
10. **15 Prentice Hall Interdisciplinary Explorations**
11. **How to Assess Student Work**
12. **How to Manage Instruction in the Block**
13. ***Cobblestone, Odyssey, Calliope,* and *Faces* Magazines**

Program-wide technology resources

1. **Resource Pro® CD-ROM**—the ultimate management tool with easy access to blackline masters and lab activities for all 15 books. Planning Express® software lets you customize lesson plans by day, week, month, and year. Also includes Computer Test Bank software.

2. **Assessment Resources with CD-ROM**—*Computer Test Bank* software with Dial-A-Test® provides you with unparalleled flexibility in creating tests.

3. *Science Explorer* **Web Site**—activities and teaching resources for every chapter at www.science-explorer.phschool.com

4. **Interactive Student Tutorial CD-ROMs**—provide students with self-tests, helpful hints, and Explorations. Tests are scored instantly and provide complete explanations to all answers.

5. **An Odyssey of Discovery CD-ROMs**—interactive labs encourage students to hypothesize and experiment. (Life and Earth Science).

6. **Interactive Earth CD-ROM**—explore global trends, search the media library, and zoom in on a 3-D globe.

7. **Mindscape CD-ROMs**—*The Animals!™, Oceans Below,* and *How Your Body Works* bring science alive with compelling videoclips, 3-D animations, and interactive databases.

8. **A.D.A.M. The Inside Story**—take an entertaining tour of each body system, designed for middle grades students.

9. **Interactive Physics**—explore physics concepts with computer simulations that encourage what-if questions.

10. **Explorer Videotapes and Videodiscs**—explore and visualize concepts through spectacular short documentaries containing computer animations (Spanish audio track).

11. **Event-Based Science**—series of NSF-funded modules that engage students with inquiry-based projects. Includes video.

Options for Pacing *From Bacteria to Plants*

The Pacing Chart below suggests one way to schedule your instructional time. The *Science Explorer* program offers many other aids to help you plan your instructional time, whether regular class periods or **block scheduling**. Refer to the Chapter Planning Guide before each chapter to view all program resources with suggested times for Student Edition activities.

Pacing Chart

	Days	Blocks		Days	Blocks
Nature of Science: Disease Detective Solves Mystery	1	$\frac{1}{2}$	**Chapter 4 Introduction to Plants**		
Chapter 1 Living Things			Chapter 4 Project Become a Moss Expert	Ongoing	Ongoing
Chapter 1 Project Mystery Object	Ongoing	Ongoing	1 The Plant Kingdom	5	2–3
1 What Is Life?	4–5	$2\frac{1}{2}$	2 Integrating Physics: Photosynthesis and Light	$2\frac{1}{2}$	1–2
2 Integrating Earth Science: The Origin of Life	$1\frac{1}{2}$	1	3 Mosses, Liverworts, and Hornworts	$2\frac{1}{2}$	1–2
3 Classifying Organisms	6	3	4 Ferns and Their Relatives	$2\frac{1}{2}$	1–2
4 The Six Kingdoms	$1\frac{1}{2}$	1	Chapter 4 Review and Assessment	1	$\frac{1}{2}$
Chapter 1 Review and Assessment	1	$\frac{1}{2}$	**Chapter 5 Seed Plants**		
Chapter 2 Viruses and Bacteria			Chapter 5 Project Cycle of a Lifetime	Ongoing	Ongoing
Chapter 2 Project Be a Disease Detective	Ongoing	Ongoing	1 The Characteristics of Seed Plants	5	$2\frac{1}{2}$
1 Viruses	4	2	2 Gymnosperms	3	$1\frac{1}{2}$
2 Bacteria	6	3	3 Angiosperms	4	2
3 Integrating Health: Viruses, Bacteria, and Your Health	3–4	$1\frac{1}{2}$	4 Plant Responses and Growth	2	1
Chapter 2 Review and Assessment	1	$\frac{1}{2}$	5 Integrating Technology: Feeding the World	$1\frac{1}{2}$	$\frac{1}{2}$–1
Chapter 3 Protists and Fungi			Chapter 5 Review and Assessment	1	$\frac{1}{2}$
Chapter 3 Project A Mushroom Farm	Ongoing	Ongoing	Interdisciplinary Exploration: Corn the Amazing Grain	2–3	1–2
1 Protists	5	$2\frac{1}{2}$			
2 Integrating Environmental Science: Algal Blooms	$2\frac{1}{2}$	1–2			
3 Fungi	5	$2\frac{1}{2}$			
Chapter 3 Review and Assessment	1	$\frac{1}{2}$			

RESOURCE PRO®

The Resource Pro® CD-ROM is the ultimate scheduling and lesson planning tool. Resource Pro® allows you to preview all the resources in the *Science Explorer* program, organize your chosen materials, and print out any teaching resource. You can follow the suggested lessons or create your own, using resources from anywhere in the program.

Thematic Overview of *From Bacteria to Plants*

The chart below lists the major themes of *From Bacteria to Plants*. For each theme, the chart supplies a big idea, or concept statement, describing how a particular theme is taught in a chapter.

	Chapter 1	Chapter 2	Chapter 3	Chapter 4	Chapter 5
Patterns of Change	The composition of air changed as a result of the presence of living organisms.	Bacteria were responsible for altering Earth's early atmosphere.			The life cycle of seed plants involves pollination, fertilization, seed development, dispersal of seeds, and growth of a new plant.
Scale and Structure	Classification groups form a hierarchy in which the largest groups (kingdoms) are the most general and the smallest groups (species) are the most specific.	Viruses are considered to be nonliving, but have genetic material necessary to reproduce. The cells of bacteria differ in structure from other cells.	Protists are unicellular organisms that contain nuclei. Most are microscopic. Most fungi are made of threadlike fibers called hyphae.	Plants are made up of cells that have cell walls and chlorophyll. All plants have adaptations for obtaining and transporting water and other materials, support, and reproduction.	All seed plants have vascular tissue and seeds that allow seed plants to grow tall and survive in many different environments.
Unity and Diversity	Differences between organisms are used as a means of classifying them into different groups.	All bacteria have a similar cellular structure. However, bacteria are divided into two kingdoms based on chemical differences.	All protists are eukaryotes but they vary in size and in how they obtain food. Fungi are alike in the way they reproduce and obtain food.	Although each kind of plant has unique adaptations, all plants share basic characteristics.	While all seed plants share specific characteristics, many different species of seed plants exist.
Systems and Interactions		Some bacteria are producers, decomposers, or parasites. Early bacteria probably altered Earth's atmosphere.	Some protists are parasitic and can harm crops and cause disease in humans. Fungi interact with the living world in a variety of ways.		Many angiosperms rely on animals for pollination and seed dispersal.
Evolution	Life has evolved over time. Modern classification systems are based on evolutionary history.	The first forms of life on Earth were similar to bacteria.		Land plants evolved from green algae. Vascular plants are better suited to drier conditions than are nonvascular plants.	Gymnosperms were the first group of seed plants to evolve. Angiosperms first appeared about 100 million years ago. Seed plants have evolved adaptations to different environments.
Energy	All living things must have a source of energy to survive. Different organisms obtain energy in different ways.		Some protists make their own food, while other protists consume other organisms. Fungi obtain energy by absorbing food from living organisms.	Plants use energy from sunlight to make food during photosynthesis. Peat and coal resources formed from the ancient remains of mosses and ferns.	Plants use light energy to change water and carbon dioxide into carbohydrates and oxygen. Plants store energy in their roots, stems, leaves, fruits, and seeds.
Stability	All organisms must be alive to keep the conditions inside their bodies constant.				Photosynthesis helps to maintain the atmospheric balance of oxygen and carbon dioxide.

Inquiry Skills Chart

The Prentice Hall *Science Explorer* program provides comprehensive teaching, practice, and assessment of science skills, with an emphasis on the process skills necessary for inquiry. The chart lists the skills covered in the program and cites the page numbers where each skill is covered.

Basic Process SKILLS				
	Student Text: Projects and Labs	Student Text: Activities	Student Text: Caption and Review Questions	Teacher's Edition: Extensions
Observing	14–15, 24, 38–39, 55, 66–67, 78–79, 93, 100–101, 108–109, 118–119, 129, 138–139, 162–163, 167	16, 18, 25, 28, 32, 40, 48, 61, 74, 80, 84, 87, 94–95, 97, 110, 120, 125, 130, 132, 140, 142, 150, 153, 156, 164, 168, 182	60	18, 26, 29, 41, 57, 60, 63–64, 69, 72, 81, 86, 88, 96, 98–99, 104, 111–112, 114–116, 121, 126–127, 131, 141, 146–148
Inferring	14–15, 38–39, 66–67, 93, 100–101, 108–109, 129, 162–163	25, 48, 56, 68, 84, 110, 130, 132, 153, 164, 182	22–27, 35, 54, 73, 96, 107, 112, 137, 142, 161, 172	18, 30, 41, 60, 63, 69, 70, 72, 96, 113, 144, 146–147, 157, 165, 170
Predicting	24, 55, 93, 100–101, 118–119	22, 25, 68, 87, 90, 97, 125, 146, 168, 182	45, 107, 137, 149, 172	34, 68–69, 72, 86, 88, 99, 102, 113, 116, 126, 143, 148, 156, 165
Classifying	14–15, 38–39, 46–47	16, 18, 28, 37, 40, 110, 140, 150, 183	29, 41–42, 45, 77, 99, 104, 117, 124, 160	29, 31, 37, 42, 57, 133, 144
Making Models	55, 108–109	51, 56, 68, 90, 98, 168, 183		18, 21, 26, 33, 50, 85–86, 91, 143, 151, 165
Communicating	14–15, 38–39, 46–47, 55, 66–67, 78–79, 108–109, 129, 138–139, 167	16, 18, 25, 28, 30, 40, 63, 68, 70, 74, 94, 103, 123, 127, 140, 158, 168, 183	44, 76, 106, 136, 172	16, 18–19, 23, 25–28, 31, 40, 50, 52, 54, 60, 62–63, 65, 69–70, 72, 83, 85–86, 89–92, 96, 102, 104, 112, 117, 121, 123, 130, 133, 140, 143, 147, 149– 150, 155, 160, 164, 168, 170
Measuring	55, 100–101, 129, 162–163	146, 150, 184–185		
Calculating	55	56, 146, 184–185	50	148
Creating Data Tables	24, 66–67, 78–79, 93, 100–101	45, 137, 192		60
Graphing	46–47, 78–79	59, 181, 192–194	137	
Advanced Process SKILLS				
Posing Questions	14–15, 46–47, 78–79, 108–109, 138–139	186		
Developing Hypotheses	78–79, 100–101, 167	186	45, 77	60, 83
Designing Experiments	24, 46–47, 66–67, 78–79, 93, 100–101, 118–119, 167	22, 179, 187	45, 77	60, 83, 102, 123

Advanced Process SKILLS (continued)

	Student Text: Projects and Labs	Student Text: Activities	Student Text: Caption and Review Questions	Teacher's Edition: Extensions
Controlling Variables	24, 46–47, 78–79, 93, 118–119	187	45	21, 60
Forming Operational Definitions	14–15	16, 40, 156, 187		81
Interpreting Data	46–47	59, 113, 187	107, 172	
Drawing Conclusions	24, 46–47, 55, 66–67, 78–79, 93, 100–101, 118–119, 167	22, 59, 87, 113, 187	37, 137, 172	42, 63–64, 83, 123, 133

Critical Thinking SKILLS

Comparing and Contrasting	14–15, 38–39, 66–67, 167	95, 188	18, 77, 81, 107, 128, 137, 152, 155	22, 26, 35, 49, 51, 57, 69, 83, 85, 96, 112–113, 141, 159–160
Applying Concepts	24, 38–39, 55, 66–67, 93, 162–163	94, 98, 188	22–23, 37, 45, 64–65, 89, 107, 121, 133–134, 137, 141, 166, 169–170, 172	18, 30, 34, 52, 73, 126
Interpreting Diagrams, Graphs Photographs, and Maps	38–39	32, 70, 175, 188	33, 42, 58, 71, 77, 87, 111, 117, 126, 147–148, 157	
Relating Cause and Effect	24, 78–79, 100–101, 118–119	18, 188	45, 69, 72, 85, 91, 107, 124, 137, 172	
Making Generalizations	16	188	17, 31, 102, 165	112
Making Judgments	14–15, 66–67	48, 74, 94, 168, 188	89, 173	169
Problem Solving	14–15, 55	10–13, 74, 94, 188	77, 92	31

Information Organizing SKILLS

Concept Maps		190	44, 172	156
Compare/Contrast Tables		190	136	21, 40, 68, 80, 125
Venn Diagrams		191	76	21, 128, 134
Flowcharts		191	106	26, 52, 92, 120, 161
Cycle Diagrams		191		

The *Science Explorer* program provides additional teaching, reinforcement, and assessment of skills in the Inquiry Skills Activities Book and the Integrated Science Laboratory Manual.

Throughout the *Science Explorer* program, every effort has been made to keep the materials and equipment *affordable, reusable,* and *easily accessible.*

The *Science Explorer* program offers an abundance of activity options so you can pick and choose those activities that suit your needs. To help you order supplies at the beginning of the year, the Master Materials List cross-references the materials by activity. If you prefer to create your list electronically, use the electronic order forms at:
www.science–explorer.phschool.com

There are two kits available for each book of the *Science Explorer* program, a Consumable Kit and a Nonconsumable Kit. These kits are produced by **Science Kit and Boreal Laboratories,** the leader in providing science kits to schools. Prentice Hall and Science Kit collaborated throughout the development of *Science Explorer* to ensure that the equipment and supplies

in the kits precisely match the requirements of the program activities.

The kits provide an economical and convenient way to get all of the materials needed to teach each book. For each book, Science Kit also offers the opportunity to buy equipment and safety items individually. For a current listing of kit offerings or additional information about materials to accompany *Science Explorer,* please, contact Science Kit at:
1-800-828-7777
or at their Internet site at:
www.sciencekit.com

Master Materials List

Consumable Materials

*	Description	Quantity per class	Textbook Section(s)	*	Description	Quantity per class	Textbook Section(s)
C	Alcohol, isopropyl (rubbing) 500 mL	1	2-2 (Lab)	SS	Leaves, average-rainfall environment	5	4-1 (DIS)
C	Aluminum foil, roll 12" × 25 ft	1	2-1 (TT) 3-1 (SYS)	SS	Leaves, desert environment	5	4-1 (DIS)
SS	Animal, live, small	5	1-2 (DIS)	SS	Leaves, set	5	5-2 (DIS)
C	Bag, plastic zip lip 6" × 8" (1 qt.)	30	1-1 (Lab) 3-3 (DIS)	SS	Lemon, slice	5	1-1 (TT)
C	Baking soda, 454 g	1	4-1 (Lab)	C	Lens paper, pkg. of 50, 4" × 6"	1	5-3 (Lab)
C	Balloons, round, 9", pkg. of 35	1	3-3 (TT) 3-3 (Lab)	C	Marking pencil, black wax	5	2-2 (Lab) 3-2 (Lab) 3-3 (Lab) 4-1 (Lab) 5-4 (Lab)
SS	Bread without preservatives, slice	5	1-1 (Lab)				
SS	Bread, slice	5	3-3 (DIS)	C	Methylene blue chloride biostain, 1% aq. solution, 100 mL	1	2-2 (TT)
SS	Celery stalk	5	5-1 (SYS)	C	Moss clump, live	1	4-3 (Lab)
C	*Chlorella*, live	1	3-1 (TT)	SS	Mushroom	5	1-4 (DIS) 3-3 (TT)
C	Clay, modeling (cream), 1 lb.	1	2-1 (TT) 3-3 (TT) 5-4 (Lab)	C	Nutrient agar plates, pkg. of 15	1	2-2 (Lab)
C	Cone, pine	5	5-2 (TT)	C	Paper clips, box of 100	1	2-1 (TT)
C	Cotton balls, pkg. of 300	1	3-1 (TT) 3-3 (TT)	SS	Paper towel roll	1	5-3 (Lab) 5-4 (Lab)
C	Cup, medicine type, graduated, 30 mL	10	4-3 (DIS)	SS	Paper, construction	1	2-1 (TT) 3-2 (DIS)
C	Cup, paper, 200 mL	40	2-2 (DIS)	SS	Paper, long strips (10-m length total)	5	2-1 (Lab)
C	Cup, clear plastic, 300 mL	50	2-3 (DIS)	SS	Paper, sheet	20	1-3 (Lab) 3-3 (TT) 4-2 (DIS) 5-2 (TT)
C	Disinfectant, spray, 15 oz.	1	2-2 (Lab)				
C	*Elodea*, live (12 sprigs)	1	4-1 (Lab)				
C	*Euglena*, live	1	3-1 (SYS)	C	*Paramecium caudatum*, live	1	3-1 (TT)
SS	Fern plant	5	4-4 (TT)	C	Peat moss	1	4-3 (DIS)
C	Fertilizer, granular, 8 oz.	1	3-2 (Lab)	SS	Pencil	5	1-3 (Lab) 2-1 (Lab)
SS	Flower, large	5	5-3 (Lab)	C	Phenol red sodium salt, 100 mL, (indicator, pH 6.8 − 8.2)	1	2-3 (DIS)
C	Food coloring, dark red, 30 mL	1	4-4 (DIS) 5-1 (SYS)	C	Pipe cleaners, white, 6", pkg. of 30	1	2-1 (TT)
SS	Food items	5	5-1 (DIS)	SS	Plant, common house	5	1-2 (DIS) 1-4 (DIS) 5-4 (DIS)
SS	Fruit	5	3-3 (DIS)				
SS	Fruits, 3 different kinds	5	5-3 (DIS)				
SS	Glue	5	2-1 (TT) 4-2 (DIS)	SS	Plant, sensitive (e.g., Venus flytrap or Mimosa)	5	5-4 (DIS)
SS	Graph paper, sheet	5	2-2 (SYS)				

KEY: **DIS**: Discover; **SYS**: Sharpen Your Skills; **TT**: Try This; **Lab**: Lab
* Items designated **C** are in the Consumable Kit, **NC** are in the Nonconsumable Kit, and **SS** are School Supplied.

Quantities based on 5 lab groups per class.

Master Materials List

Consumable Materials (cont.)

*	Description	Quantity per class	Textbook Section(s)	*	Description	Quantity per class	Textbook Section(s)
C	Plates, paper 9", pkg. of 50	1	1-1 (Lab)	C	Straws, plastic (wrapped), pkg. of 50	1	2-1 (TT) 3-3 (Lab)
C	Pond culture, mixed, live	1	3-1 (DIS)	C	String, cotton, 200 ft.	1	2-1 (TT)
SS	Potato, slice	5	1-1 (SYS)	C	Sugar, granulated, 454 g	1	3-3 (Lab)
SS	Rubber bands, pkg.	1	2-1 (TT)	C	Tape, brown packing, 60 ft.	1	1-1 (Lab) 3-3 (DIS)
C	Salt, non-iodized, 737 g	1	3-3 (Lab)				
C	Sand, fine, 1 kg	1	4-3 (DIS)	SS	Tape, masking, 3/4" × 60 yd	2	2-1 (TT) 2-1 (Lab) 3-3 (TT) 5-3 (Lab) 5-4 (Lab)
SS	Sea animal (e.g. urchin, anemone, or cultivated coral)	5	1-4 (DIS)				
C	Seeds, black bean, 1 lb. (approx. 1700 seeds)	1	2-2 (DIS)				
C	Seeds, lima bean, 30 g	1	5-1 (TT)	SS	Tape, transparent, 3/4" × 27 ft.	1	2-2 (Lab)
C	Seeds, pea, Alaska (smooth), 1 oz.	1	5-1 (TT)	C	Toothpicks, flat, box of 750	1	4-3 (Lab)
				SS	Water, aquarium	5	3-2 (Lab)
C	Seeds, corn, 30 g	1	5-4 (Lab)	SS	Water, tap, aged	5	3-2 (Lab)
C	Sodium hydroxide, 0.1 N solution, 100 mL	1	2-3 (DIS)	SS	Worm or insect	5	1-4 (DIS)
				SS	Yeast, pkg.	5	3-3 (Lab)
C	Spoons, plastic, pkg. of 24	1	3-2 (DIS) 5-1 (SYS)	SS	Yogurt, plain	1	2-2 (TT)

Nonconsumable Materials

*	Description	Quantity per class	Textbook Section(s)	*	Description	Quantity per class	Textbook Section(s)
SS	Bag	1	5-5 (DIS)	NC	Dropper, plastic	30	1-1 (Lab) 2-2 (TT) 2-2 (Lab) 2-3 (DIS) 3-1 (DIS) 3-1 (TT) 4-3 (Lab) 4-4 (TT) 5-3 (Lab)
NC	Beaker, Pyrex, 400 mL	5	3-3 (Lab) 4-1 (Lab)				
SS	Bottles, narrow-necked, small	25	3-3 (Lab)				
NC	Capillary tubes, melting point, vial/100	1	4-4 (DIS)				
SS	Clock	1	2-2 (Lab)				
SS	Cold medication packages, empty	30	2-1 (DIS)	SS	Hair dryer	5	1-1 (SYS)
				SS	Hole punch	5	3-2 (DIS)
NC	Cylinder, graduated, polypropylene, 10 × 0.2 mL	5	3-2 (Lab) 3-3 (Lab) 4-3 (DIS)	SS	Items, desk, assortment	5	1-3 (DIS)

KEY: **DIS**: Discover; **SYS**: Sharpen Your Skills; **TT**: Try This; **Lab**: Lab
* Items designated **C** are in the Consumable Kit, **NC** are in the Nonconsumable Kit, and **SS** are School Supplied.

Nonconsumable Materials (cont.)

*	Description	Quantity per class	Textbook Section(s)	*	Description	Quantity per class	Textbook Section(s)
NC	Jar, plastic, 16 oz., 89 mm diameter	20	1-2 (DIS) 3-2 (Lab) 3-3 (TT) 5-1 (SYS)	SS	Scissors	5	2-1 (Lab) 5-4 (Lab)
NC	Lid, metal, 89 mm, screw type	20	1-2 (DIS) 3-2 (Lab)	NC	Shoe box	5	4-2 (DIS)
NC	Magnifying glass, 3X and 6X	5	3-3 (DIS) 3-3 (TT) 4-1 (DIS) 4-3 (Lab) 4-4 (TT) 5-1 (TT) 5-2 (DIS) 5-2 (TT) 5-3 (DIS) 5-3 (Lab)	NC	Slides, plastic cover glass set, (72 slides & 100 cover glasses)	1	2-2 (TT) 3-1 (DIS) 3-1 (TT) 5-3 (Lab)
				NC	Sticks, craft, pkg. of 30	1	3-3 (TT)
				SS	Tags	30	5-5 (DIS)
				NC	Test tube, 18 × 150 mm, 27 mL	10	4-1 (Lab)
				NC	Toy, wind-up	5	1-1 (DIS)

Equipment

*	Description	Quantity per class	Textbook Section(s)
NC	Meter stick, half-length (50 cm)	5	2-1 (Lab)
NC	Mirror, plastic, 7.5 × 12.5 cm	5	1-1 (TT) 4-2 (DIS)
NC	Petri dish, polystyrene, sterile, 100 × 15 mm, pkg. of 20	1	3-1 (SYS) 3-2 (DIS) 4-4 (DIS) 5-4 (Lab)
NC	Pins, straight, steel, pkg. of 150	1	2-1 (Lab) 3-3 (TT)
NC	Prism, equilateral, plastic, 25 mm	5	4-2 (DIS)
SS	Ruler, plastic	5	4-3 (Lab) 5-1 (SYS) 5-2 (DIS) 5-3 (DIS) 5-3 (Lab)
NC	Scalpel, steel, 140 mm	5	5-3 (Lab)

*	Description	Quantity per class	Textbook Section(s)
SS	Apron	30	2-2 (TT) 2-3 (DIS) 5-1 (SYS)
SS	Balance, triple beam	5	1-1 (SYS)
SS	Calculator	5	2-1 (Lab)
SS	Gloves, laboratory, box	1	2-3 (DIS)
SS	Goggles, chemical splash, class set	1	2-2 (Lab) 2-3 (DIS) 3-2 (Lab) 4-4 (DIS)
SS	Lamp (optional)	5	4-1 (Lab)
SS	Microscope	5	2-2 (TT) 3-1 (DIS) 3-1 (TT) 5-3 (Lab)

KEY: **DIS**: Discover; **SYS**: Sharpen Your Skills; **TT**: Try This; **Lab**: Lab
* Items designated **C** are in the Consumable Kit, **NC** are in the Nonconsumable Kit, and **SS** are School Supplied.

PRENTICE HALL SCIENCE EXPLORER

From Bacteria to Plants

Program Resources

Student Edition
Annotated Teacher's Edition
Teaching Resources Book with Color Transparencies
From Bacteria to Plants Materials Kits

Program Components

Integrated Science Laboratory Manual
Integrated Science Laboratory Manual, Teacher's Edition
Inquiry Skills Activity Book
Student-Centered Science Activity Books
Program Planning Guide
Guided Reading English Audiotapes
Guided Reading Spanish Audiotapes and Summaries
Product Testing Activities by Consumer Reports™
Event-Based Science Series (NSF funded)
Prentice Hall Interdisciplinary Explorations
Cobblestone, Odyssey, Calliope, and *Faces* Magazines

Media/Technology

Science Explorer Interactive Student Tutorial CD-ROMs
Odyssey of Discovery CD-ROMs
Resource Pro® (Teaching Resources on CD-ROM)
Assessment Resources CD-ROM with Dial-A-Test®
Internet site at www.science-explorer.phschool.com
Life, Earth, and Physical Science Videodiscs
Life, Earth, and Physical Science Videotapes

Science Explorer Student Editions

- *From Bacteria to Plants*
- *Animals*
- *Cells and Heredity*
- *Human Biology and Health*
- *Environmental Science*
- *Inside Earth*
- *Earth's Changing Surface*
- *Earth's Waters*
- *Weather and Climate*
- *Astronomy*
- *Chemical Building Blocks*
- *Chemical Interactions*
- *Motion, Forces, and Energy*
- *Electricity and Magnetism*
- *Sound and Light*

Staff Credits

The people who made up the *Science Explorer* team—representing editorial, editorial services, design services, field marketing, market research, marketing services, on-line services/multimedia development, product marketing, production services, and publishing processes—are listed below. Bold type denotes core team members.

Kristen E. Ball, **Barbara A. Bertell,** Peter W. Brooks, **Christopher R. Brown, Greg Cantone,** Jonathan Cheney, **Patrick Finbarr Connolly,** Loree Franz, Donald P. Gagnon, Jr., **Paul J. Gagnon, Joel Gendler,** Elizabeth Good, Kerri Hoar, **Linda D. Johnson,** Katherine M. Kotik, Russ Lappa, Marilyn Leitao, David Lippman, **Eve Melnechuk, Natania Mlawer,** Paul W. Murphy, **Cindy A. Noftle,** Julia F. Osborne, Caroline M. Power, Suzanne J. Schineller, **Susan W. Tafler,** Kira Thaler-Marbit, Robin L. Santel, Ronald Schachter, **Mark Tricca,** Diane Walsh, Pearl B. Weinstein, Beth Norman Winickoff

ISBN 0-13-434490-1
3 4 5 6 7 8 9 10   05 04 03 02 01 00 99

Cover: A Panama Pacific water lily blooms in a Florida lake.

Teacher's Edition ISBN 0-13-434571-1

Program Authors

Michael J. Padilla, Ph.D.
Professor
Department of Science Education
University of Georgia
Athens, Georgia

Michael Padilla is a leader in middle school science education. He has served as an editor and elected officer for the National Science Teachers Association. He has been principal investigator of several National Science Foundation and Eisenhower grants and served as a writer of the National Science Education Standards.

As lead author of *Science Explorer,* Mike has inspired the team in developing a program that meets the needs of middle grades students, promotes science inquiry, and is aligned with the National Science Education Standards.

Ioannis Miaoulis, Ph.D.
Dean of Engineering
College of Engineering
Tufts University
Medford, Massachusetts

Martha Cyr, Ph.D.
Director, Engineering
   Educational Outreach
College of Engineering
Tufts University
Medford, Massachusetts

Science Explorer was created in collaboration with the College of Engineering at Tufts University. Tufts has an extensive engineering outreach program that uses engineering design and construction to excite and motivate students and teachers in science and technology education.

Faculty from Tufts University participated in the development of *Science Explorer* chapter projects, reviewed the student books for content accuracy, and helped coordinate field testing.

Book Author

Jan Jenner, Ph.D.
Science Writer
Talladega, Alabama

Contributing Writers

James Robert Kaczynski, Jr.
Science Teacher
Barrington Middle School
Barrington, Rhode Island

Evan P. Silberstein
Science Teacher
Spring Valley High School
Spring Valley, New York

Joseph Stukey, Ph.D.
Department of Biology
Hope College
Holland, Michigan

Reading Consultant

Bonnie B. Armbruster, Ph.D.
Department of Curriculum
   and Instruction
University of Illinois
Champaign, Illinois

Interdisciplinary Consultant

Heidi Hayes Jacobs, Ed.D.
Teacher's College
Columbia University
New York, New York

Safety Consultants

W. H. Breazeale, Ph.D.
Department of Chemistry
College of Charleston
Charleston, South Carolina

Ruth Hathaway, Ph.D.
Hathaway Consulting
Cape Girardeau, Missouri

Tufts University Program Reviewers

Behrouz Abedian, Ph.D.
Department of Mechanical
    Engineering

Wayne Chudyk, Ph.D.
Department of Civil and
    Environmental Engineering

Eliana De Bernardez-Clark, Ph.D.
Department of Chemical Engineering

Anne Marie Desmarais, Ph.D.
Department of Civil and
    Environmental Engineering

David L. Kaplan, Ph.D.
Department of Chemical Engineering

Paul Kelley, Ph.D.
Department of Electro-Optics

George S. Mumford, Ph.D.
Professor of Astronomy, Emeritus

Jan A. Pechenik, Ph.D.
Department of Biology

Livia Racz, Ph.D.
Department of Mechanical Engineering

Robert Rifkin, M.D.
School of Medicine

Jack Ridge, Ph.D.
Department of Geology

Chris Swan, Ph.D.
Department of Civil and
    Environmental Engineering

Peter Y. Wong, Ph.D.
Department of Mechanical Engineering

Content Reviewers

Jack W. Beal, Ph.D.
Department of Physics
Fairfield University
Fairfield, Connecticut

W. Russell Blake, Ph.D.
Planetarium Director
Plymouth Community
    Intermediate School
Plymouth, Massachusetts

Howard E. Buhse, Jr., Ph.D.
Department of Biological Sciences
University of Illinois
Chicago, Illinois

Dawn Smith Burgess, Ph.D.
Department of Geophysics
Stanford University
Stanford, California

A. Malcolm Campbell, Ph.D.
Assistant Professor
Davidson College
Davidson, North Carolina

Elizabeth A. De Stasio, Ph.D.
Associate Professor of Biology
Lawrence University
Appleton, Wisconsin

John M. Fowler, Ph.D.
Former Director of Special Projects
National Science Teacher's Association
Arlington, Virginia

Jonathan Gitlin, M.D.
School of Medicine
Washington University
St. Louis, Missouri

Dawn Graff-Haight, Ph.D., CHES
Department of Health, Human
    Performance, and Athletics
Linfield College
McMinnville, Oregon

Deborah L. Gumucio, Ph.D.
Associate Professor
Department of Anatomy and Cell Biology
University of Michigan
Ann Arbor, Michigan

William S. Harwood, Ph.D.
Dean of University Division and Associate
    Professor of Education
Indiana University
Bloomington, Indiana

Cyndy Henzel, Ph.D.
Department of Geography
    and Regional Development
University of Arizona
Tucson, Arizona

Greg Hutton
Science and Health
    Curriculum Coordinator
School Board of Sarasota County
Sarasota, Florida

Susan K. Jacobson, Ph.D.
Department of Wildlife Ecology
    and Conservation
University of Florida
Gainesville, Florida

Judy Jernstedt, Ph.D.
Department of Agronomy and Range Science
University of California, Davis
Davis, California

John L. Kermond, Ph.D.
Office of Global Programs
National Oceanographic and
    Atmospheric Administration
Silver Spring, Maryland

David E. LaHart, Ph.D.
Institute of Science and Public Affairs
Florida State University
Tallahassee, Florida

Joe Leverich, Ph.D.
Department of Biology
St. Louis University
St. Louis, Missouri

Dennis K. Lieu, Ph.D.
Department of Mechanical Engineering
University of California
Berkeley, California

Cynthia J. Moore, Ph.D.
Science Outreach Coordinator
Washington University
St. Louis, Missouri

Joseph M. Moran, Ph.D.
Department of Earth Science
University of Wisconsin–Green Bay
Green Bay, Wisconsin

Joseph Stukey, Ph.D.
Department of Biology
Hope College
Holland, Michigan

Seetha Subramanian
Lexington Community College
University of Kentucky
Lexington, Kentucky

Carl L. Thurman, Ph.D.
Department of Biology
University of Northern Iowa
Cedar Falls, Iowa

Edward D. Walton, Ph.D.
Department of Chemistry
California State Polytechnic University
Pomona, California

Robert S. Young, Ph.D.
Department of Geosciences and
    Natural Resource Management
Western Carolina University
Cullowhee, North Carolina

Edward J. Zalisko, Ph.D.
Department of Biology
Blackburn College
Carlinville, Illinois

Teacher Reviewers

Stephanie Anderson
Sierra Vista Junior
    High School
Canyon Country, California

John W. Anson
Mesa Intermediate School
Palmdale, California

Pamela Arline
Lake Taylor Middle School
Norfolk, Virginia

Lynn Beason
College Station Jr. High School
College Station, Texas

Richard Bothmer
Hollis School District
Hollis, New Hampshire

Jeffrey C. Callister
Newburgh Free Academy
Newburgh, New York

Judy D'Albert
Harvard Day School
Corona Del Mar, California

Betty Scott Dean
Guilford County Schools
McLeansville, North Carolina

Sarah C. Duff
Baltimore City Public Schools
Baltimore, Maryland

Melody Law Ewey
Holmes Junior High School
Davis, California

Sherry L. Fisher
Lake Zurich Middle
    School North
Lake Zurich, Illinois

Melissa Gibbons
Fort Worth ISD
Fort Worth, Texas

Debra J. Goodding
Kraemer Middle School
Placentia, California

Jack Grande
Weber Middle School
Port Washington, New York

Steve Hills
Riverside Middle School
Grand Rapids, Michigan

Carol Ann Lionello
Kraemer Middle School
Placentia, California

Jaime A. Morales
Henry T. Gage Middle School
Huntington Park, California

Patsy Partin
Cameron Middle School
Nashville, Tennessee

Deedra H. Robinson
Newport News Public Schools
Newport News, Virginia

Bonnie Scott
Clack Middle School
Abilene, Texas

Charles M. Sears
Belzer Middle School
Indianapolis, Indiana

Barbara M. Strange
Ferndale Middle School
High Point, North Carolina

Jackie Louise Ulfig
Ford Middle School
Allen, Texas

Kathy Usina
Belzer Middle School
Indianapolis, Indiana

Heidi M. von Oetinger
L'Anse Creuse Public School
Harrison Township, Michigan

Pam Watson
Hill Country Middle School
Austin, Texas

Activity Field Testers

Nicki Bibbo
Russell Street School
Littleton, Massachusetts

Connie Boone
Fletcher Middle School
Jacksonville Beach, Florida

Rose-Marie Botting
Broward County
    School District
Fort Lauderdale, Florida

Colleen Campos
Laredo Middle School
Aurora, Colorado

Elizabeth Chait
W. L. Chenery Middle School
Belmont, Massachusetts

Holly Estes
Hale Middle School
Stow, Massachusetts

Laura Hapgood
Plymouth Community
    Intermediate School
Plymouth, Massachusetts

Sandra M. Harris
Winman Junior High School
Warwick, Rhode Island

Jason Ho
Walter Reed Middle School
Los Angeles, California

Joanne Jackson
Winman Junior High School
Warwick, Rhode Island

Mary F. Lavin
Plymouth Community
    Intermediate School
Plymouth, Massachusetts

James MacNeil, Ph.D.
Concord Public Schools
Concord, Massachusetts

Lauren Magruder
St. Michael's Country
    Day School
Newport, Rhode Island

Jeanne Maurand
Glen Urquhart School
Beverly Farms, Massachusetts

Warren Phillips
Plymouth Community
    Intermediate School
Plymouth, Massachusetts

Carol Pirtle
Hale Middle School
Stow, Massachusetts

Kathleen M. Poe
Kirby-Smith Middle School
Jacksonville, Florida

Cynthia B. Pope
Ruffner Middle School
Norfolk, Virginia

Anne Scammell
Geneva Middle School
Geneva, New York

Karen Riley Sievers
Callanan Middle School
Des Moines, Iowa

David M. Smith
Howard A. Eyer Middle School
Macungie, Pennsylvania

Derek Strohschneider
Plymouth Community
    Intermediate School
Plymouth, Massachusetts

Sallie Teames
Rosemont Middle School
Fort Worth, Texas

Gene Vitale
Parkland Middle School
McHenry, Illinois

Zenovia Young
Meyer Levin Junior
    High School (IS 285)
Brooklyn, New York

PRENTICE HALL
SCIENCE EXPLORER

Contents

From Bacteria to Plants

Nature of Science: Disease Detective Solves Mystery 10

Chapter 1 Living Things 14
    1 What Is Life? 16
    2 Integrating Earth Science: The Origin of Life 25
    3 Classifying Organisms 28
    4 The Six Kingdoms 40

Chapter 2 Viruses and Bacteria 46
    1 Viruses 48
    2 Bacteria 56
    3 Integrating Health: Viruses, Bacteria, and Your Health 68

Chapter 3 Protists and Fungi 78
    1 Protists 80
    2 Integrating Environmental Science: Algal Blooms 90
    3 Fungi 95

Prepare your students with rich, motivating content

Science Explorer is crafted for today's middle grades student, with accessible content and in-depth coverage. Integrated Science Sections support every chapter and the Interdisciplinary Exploration provides an engaging final unit.

Chapter 4 **Introduction to Plants** 108
  1 The Plant Kingdom 110
  2 Integrating Physics: Photosynthesis and Light 120
  3 Mosses, Liverworts, and Hornworts 125
  4 Ferns and Their Relatives 130

Chapter 5 **Seed Plants** 138
  1 The Characteristics of Seed Plants 140
  2 Gymnosperms 150
  3 Angiosperms 156
  4 Plant Responses and Growth 164
  5 Integrating Technology: Feeding the World 168

Interdisciplinary Exploration:
  Corn—The Amazing Grain 174

Reference Section
  Skills Handbook 182
    Think Like a Scientist 182
    Making Measurements 184
    Conducting a Scientific Investigation 186
    Thinking Critically 188
    Organizing Information 190
    Creating Data Tables and Graphs 192
  Appendix A: Laboratory Safety 195
  Appendix B: Using the Microscope 198
  Glossary 200
  Index 203
  Acknowledgments 208

Activities

Inquiry Activities

CHAPTER PROJECT
Opportunities for long-term inquiry

Chapter 1: Mystery Object 15
Chapter 2: Be a Disease Detective 47
Chapter 3: A Mushroom Farm 79
Chapter 4: Become a Moss Expert 109
Chapter 5: Cycle of a Lifetime 139

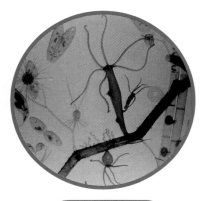

DISCOVER
Exploration and inquiry before reading

Is It Living or Nonliving? 16
How Can the Composition of Air Change? . . .25
Can You Organize a Junk Drawer? 28
Which Organism Goes Where? 40
Can You Cure a Cold? 48
How Quickly Can Bacteria Multiply? 56
How Do Infectious Diseases Spread? 68
What Lives in a Drop of Pond Water? 80
How Can Algal Growth Affect Pond Life? 90
Do All Molds Look Alike? 95
What Do Leaves Reveal About Plants? 110
What Colors Make Up Sunlight? 120
Will Mosses Absorb Water? 125
How Quickly Can Water Move Upward? 130
Which Plant Part Is It? 140
Are All Leaves Alike? 150
What Is a Fruit? 156
Can a Plant Respond to Touch? 164
Will There Be Enough to Eat? 168

Sharpen your Skills
Practice of specific science inquiry skills

Designing an Experiment 22
Observing 32
Graphing 59
Predicting 87
Interpreting Data 113
Calculating 146

TRY THIS
Reinforcement of key concepts

React! 18
Modeling a Virus 51
Bacteria for Breakfast 61
Feeding Paramecia 84
Making Spore Prints .97
Spreading Spores 98
Examining a Fern 132
The In-Seed Story 142
The Scoop on Cones 153

Draw upon the world around you.

Interdisciplinary Activities connect to every discipline and give science a meaningful, real-world context.

Guide your students to become science explorers.

A wide range of **student-tested** activities, from **guided to open-ended**, with options for **short-** **and long-term** inquiry.

Skills Lab

In-depth practice of inquiry skills

Please Pass the Bread! .24
How Many Viruses Fit on a Pin? 55
What's for Lunch? 100
Eye on Photosynthesis 118
Masses of Mosses 129
Which Way Is Up? 167

Real-World Lab

Everyday application of science concepts

Living Mysteries 38
Do Disinfectants Work? 66
An Explosion of Life .93
A Close Look at Flowers 162

Interdisciplinary Activities

Science and History
Bacteria and Foods of the World 62
Unraveling the Mysteries of Photosynthesis .122

Science and Society
Antibiotic Resistance—An Alarming Trend . .74
Eutrophication—The Threat to Clear,
    Clean Water 94

Connection
Language Arts 30
Social Studies 70
Language Arts 103
Social Studies 127
Visual Arts 158

EXPLORING

Visual exploration of concepts

The Experiments of Redi and Pasteur 20
How Viruses Multiply 52
Protozoans 82
Plant Adaptations 114
A Leaf 145
The Life Cycle of a Gymnosperm 154
The Life Cycle of an Angiosperm 159

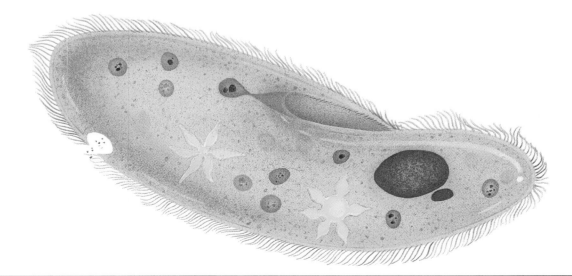

Disease Detective Solves Mystery

Focus on Public Health

This four-page feature introduces the process of scientific inquiry by involving students in a high-interest, magazine-like feature about a working scientist, physician Cindy Friedman. Using Dr. Friedman's investigation of the source of a salmonella outbreak, the article focuses on persistence, reasoning, and questioning as key elements of scientific inquiry.

Bacteria are presented in Chapter 2, Sections 2-2 and 2-3 of this book. However, students need not have any previous knowledge of that chapter's content to understand and appreciate this article.

Scientific Inquiry

◆ Before students read the article, let them read the title, examine the pictures, and read the captions on their own. Then ask: **What questions came into your mind as you looked at these pictures?** (Students might suggest questions such as "How did the Colorado Health Department know that the children were sick?"; "Why did they suspect reptiles?"; and "Do all reptiles carry salmonella?".) Point out to students that just as they had questions about what they were seeing, scientists too have questions about what they observe.

DISEASE DETECTIVE SOLVES MYSTERY

The Colorado Health Department had a problem.

Seven children had become sick with diarrhea, stomach cramps, fever, and vomiting.

Within days, another 43 people had the same symptoms.

Tests indicated that they all had become infected with salmonella. Salmonella are bacteria that are usually transmitted through foods such as contaminated meat or eggs.

How did these children become infected with salmonella? To find the answer, Colorado health officials called in Dr. Cindy Friedman. Dr. Friedman works at the Centers for Disease Control and Prevention (CDC), a United States government agency that tracks down and studies the transmission of diseases throughout the world.

Cindy Friedman studies outbreaks of diseases in groups of people rather than in individuals. Her specialty is infectious diseases, illnesses that spread from person to person. She has investigated outbreaks of disease in such places as rural Bolivia in South America, Cape Verde Islands off the coast of Africa, and a Vermont farm.

Dr. Cindy Friedman is a physician and investigator in the Foodborne and Diarrheal Diseases Branch of the Centers for Disease Control and Prevention (CDC). The youngest of three sisters, Dr. Friedman is originally from Brooklyn, New York. In her spare time she enjoys horseback riding.

Background

Facts and Figures The Centers for Disease Control and Prevention (CDC) is an agency of the United States Public Health Service. Scientists at CDC perform research to determine how diseases originate and to find ways to control them. The CDC also provides information and training to public health workers. Although CDC is based in Atlanta, Georgia, the agency also conducts international programs.

Salmonella is a type of bacteria commonly found in poultry and eggs. One kind of salmonella causes gastroenteritis. People with this type of food poisoning experience abdominal pain, fever, nausea, vomiting, and diarrhea. There are several things people can do to avoid becoming infected, such as cooking chicken and eggs thoroughly and cleaning cooking surfaces after preparing raw chicken.

An Interview With Dr. Cindy Friedman

Q *How did you get started in science?*

A When I was young, we always had pets around the house and a lot of books about medicine and science. I wanted to be a veterinarian. In college I decided that I loved animals but didn't want to practice medicine on them. I'd rather keep them as a hobby and devote my career to human medicine.

Q *How did you come to specialize in infectious diseases?*

A Out of all the subjects I studied in medical school, I liked microbiology the best—learning about different viruses and bacteria. Then, when I did my medical training in New Jersey, we had a lot of patients from Latin America. So I saw quite a few tropical and exotic diseases, which further heightened my interest.

Q *What do you enjoy about your job?*

A I really like being able to help more than one patient at a time. We do this by figuring out the risk factors for a disease and how to prevent people from getting it. Sometimes the answer is complicated, like adding chlorine to the water. Sometimes it's simple measures, like washing your hands or cooking your food thoroughly.

Q *What clues did you have in the Colorado case?*

A At first, state investigators thought the bacteria came from some contaminated food. But when they questioned the children, they couldn't identify one place where they had all eaten.

Q *How did you find out what experiences the children had in common?*

A The investigators did a second set of interviews and learned that the children had all visited the zoo the week before they got sick. They didn't eat the same food at the zoo. But they all went to a special exhibit at the reptile house.

How did the children get infected?

Did the salmonella come from infected food?

What common place had the children visited?

A ◆ 11

◆ Explain that public health is the science of preventing disease through organized community efforts.
◆ Encourage students to tell what they already know about salmonella. Ask students who have ever had food poisoning to describe how they felt. Ask students how they deduced what food had caused their food poisoning.
◆ Ask students to describe other outbreaks of disease they recall that affected many people. (*Answers may vary from the Black Plague to an outbreak of head lice.*)
◆ Encourage interested students to find out more about salmonella and ways to avoid being infected by it. Have students make a list of foods that may carry the bacterium. Ask students to share their findings with the class.
◆ Ask: **Why is it important that doctors in the United States be familiar with the causes of tropical and exotic diseases?** (*Answers may vary. Sample: Tourists may bring these diseases to the United States.*)
◆ Ask: **Why was it important for the investigators to find out how the children became infected?** (*Answers may vary. Samples: To keep other people from getting sick, to satisfy their curiosity, to learn something new about salmonella, and to prevent future outbreaks.*)
◆ If students seem particularly interested in the salmonella outbreak, share the information in Background below. Students with pet reptiles may be particularly concerned. Also suggest that they consult library books to learn more about how scientists track down the cause of disease outbreaks. (See Further Reading, page 13.)

Background

When scientists at CDC examined the Komodo dragon enclosure, they found that touching the wooden barrier was the most likely cause of the infection outbreak. The type of salmonella involved in this outbreak had an unusual appearance. For this reason, scientists could be fairly certain that the bacteria that infected the people came from the reptile display.

The people who became infected were unusually ill. Some victims were hospitalized, and some were still sick nearly a month later.

Only one of the four lizards was infected with the salmonella. The scientists were not able to determine how it became infected. They examined the lizard's food—rats—but found no trace of salmonella there.

◆ Ask: **Why did the scientists suspect the reptile exhibit?** (*They knew that reptiles can carry salmonella.*)

◆ Challenge interested students to find out more about Komodo dragons. Ask students to find out how large the lizard on p. 12 could be. Invite students to share their findings with the class.

◆ Ask students to think of some event they attended a week ago. Ask them: **Could you recall where you stood, what you touched, and what you ate and drank?** (*Most students would probably not be able to remember.*) The answers to such questions are exactly the kind of information that scientists such as Dr. Friedman would need to track down a disease. Discuss with students why this could make the job of a "disease detective" challenging.

◆ Ask: **Exactly how did all the infected children become infected with the bacteria?** (*By touching a wooden barrier on which the bacteria were growing.*) Lead students to recognize that any object, such as a barrier, a doorknob, or a stair rail that many people touch every day is likely to be contaminated with some kind of bacteria. Help students recognize that because many bacteria are spread through touching, hand-washing is an effective way to prevent infection.

◆ Have students use a dictionary or encyclopedia to find out what Dr. Friedman meant by the term *culture.* Because *culture* has several different meanings, students will need to look for the meaning that makes the most sense in context.

Q *Did you think the exhibit might be a new clue?*

A Yes. It was a clue because reptiles frequently carry the salmonella bacteria without becoming ill. In the special exhibit, there were four baby Komodo dragons, meat-eating lizards from the island of Komodo in Indonesia. They were displayed in a pen filled with mulch, surrounded by a wooden barrier about two feet high. We tested the Komodo dragons and found that one of them had salmonella bacteria. But it wasn't a petting exhibit, so I couldn't understand how the children got infected.

Q *How did you gather new data?*

A I questioned the children who became ill and compared their answers with those of children who didn't become ill. I asked about their behavior at the exhibit—where they stood, what they touched, and whether they had anything to eat or drink there. I also asked all the children if they washed their hands after visiting the exhibit. Those who did destroyed the bacteria. It was only the children who didn't wash their hands who became ill.

Q *How did you figure out the source of contamination?*

A I found that anyone who touched the wooden barrier was much more likely to have gotten sick. Children would go up to the barrier and put their hands on it. Then some of them would put their hands in their mouth or would eat without washing their hands first. Those were the children who became infected with salmonella.

Could reptiles provide the clue?

Why did some children get infected and not others?

The Komodo dragon is the largest lizard species in existence. Found on Komodo Island in Indonesia, it is nearly extinct.

Background

The CDC warns that salmonella can be found in the feces of pets, especially those with diarrhea. Reptiles are particularly likely to be infected with salmonella, even if they appear healthy. People should always wash their hands after handling reptiles. The CDC also advises that households with small children and infants should not have reptiles (including turtles) as pets. The CDC suggests that reptile owners keep their reptiles separated from each other so that they cannot spread salmonella between them.

People who have no exposure to reptiles can catch salmonella from contaminated foods. Undercooked meat, poultry, and eggs are especially likely to contain salmonella. Any hands, kitchen utensils, and work surfaces that come in contact with raw meat should be washed with soap and warm water as soon as possible.

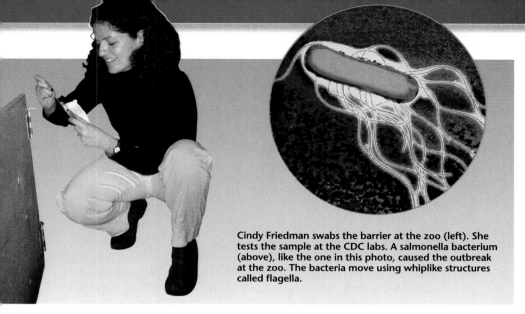

Cindy Friedman swabs the barrier at the zoo (left). She tests the sample at the CDC labs. A salmonella bacterium (above), like the one in this photo, caused the outbreak at the zoo. The bacteria move using whiplike structures called flagella.

Q *How did you test your hypothesis?*

A We took cultures—swabs from the top of the barrier where the children put their hands. When we tested those cultures in the lab, we found salmonella bacteria.

Q *What did you conclude about the bacteria on the barrier?*

A The infected Komodo dragon left its droppings in the mulch and the animals walked in it. Then they would stand on their hind legs, bracing themselves by putting their front paws on top of the barrier.

Q *What recommendations did you make?*

A We didn't want to tell zoos not to have reptile exhibits, because they're a good thing. And children should be able to get close to the animals. But at this particular exhibit, the outbreak could have been prevented with a double barrier system, so that the reptiles and the children couldn't

touch the same barrier. And hand-washing is really important. Zoos should have signs instructing people to wash their hands after going to that kind of exhibit. In homes and schools with pet reptiles, hand-washing is important, too.

Q *What's it like being a disease detective?*

A It's more the old-fashioned idea of medicine. What I do is examine the patients and listen to the stories they tell—where they've traveled, what they ate, and what they were exposed to. Then I try to figure out what caused their illness.

How can the zoo prevent future infections?

In Your Journal

Review the scientific process that Dr. Friedman used to solve the case of salmonella infections. What makes her a disease detective? Write a paragraph or two about the skills and character traits that Cindy Friedman needs to track down the source of an infectious disease.

A ◆ 13

◆ Challenge students to brainstorm some ways the zoo could set up the exhibit while protecting the visitors. *(Samples: Raise the barrier so the lizards can't lean on it; replace the wooden barrier with a glass window; build a second barrier so the lizards and visitors can't be in contact with the same barrier; wash the barrier on a regular basis; distribute alcohol wipes at the exhibit.)*

◆ Students who have pet reptiles may wish to learn more about what precautions they should take to avoid infection. Challenge interested students to make a poster or brochure for reptile owners that describes ways that owners can protect themselves from infection.

In Your Journal Have students make a concept map showing all the possible causes of the outbreak and how the scientists narrowed down the options by asking questions. Ask: **If you knew nothing about salmonella but you had to track down the source of an outbreak, what would you do first?** *(Learn all I could about what salmonella is and the conditions and environments in which it grows)* Extend the discussion by asking: **What kind of person do you think would make a good disease investigator?** *(Student answers will vary. Samples: curious, logical, persistent, detailed)*

Introducing From Bacteria to Plants

Have students look through the table of contents and the book to find the parts that relate most closely to this article. *(Chapter 2, Viruses and Bacteria, particularly Section 2-2, Bacteria, and Section 2-3, Integrating Health: Viruses, Bacteria, and Your Health.)* Ask: **Besides bacteria, what else is this book about?** *(viruses, protists, fungi, and plants)* **What kinds of things do you think you will be learning about?** *(Accept all responses without comments.)*

READING STRATEGIES

Further Reading

◆ Preston, Richard. *The Hot Zone.* Anchor Books, 1995.
◆ Garrett, Laurie. *The Coming Plague: Newly Emerging Diseases in a World Out of Balance.* Penguin USA, 1995.
◆ Regis, Edward. *Virus Ground Zero: Stalking the Killer Viruses With the Centers for Disease Control.* Pocket Books, 1996.
◆ Radetsky, Peter. *The Invisible Invaders: Viruses and the Scientists Who Pursue Them.* Little Brown and Company, 1995.

Living Things

Sections	Time	Student Edition Activities		Other Activities
CHAPTER PROJECT 1 **Mystery Object** p. 15	Ongoing (2 weeks)	Check Your Progress, pp. 23, 27, 42 Wrap Up, p. 45	TE	Chapter 1 Project Notes, pp. 14–15
1 **What Is Life?** pp. 16–24 ◆ List the characteristics all living things share. ◆ Identify what all living things need to survive.	4–5 periods/ $2\frac{1}{2}$ blocks	**Discover** Is It Living or Nonliving?, p. 16 **Try This** React!, p. 18 **Sharpen Your Skills** Designing an Experiment, p. 22 **Skills Lab: Controlling Variable** Please Pass the Bread!, p. 24	TE TE TE	Demonstration, p. 17 Building Inquiry Skills: Applying Concepts, p. 18 Integrating Chemistry, p. 22
2 **INTEGRATING EARTH SCIENCE** **The Origin of Life** pp. 25–27 ◆ Compare the atmosphere of early Earth with today's atmosphere. ◆ State how scientists hypothesize that life arose on early Earth.	$1\frac{1}{2}$ periods/ 1 block	**Discover** How Can the Composition of Air Change?, p. 25	TE	Including All Students, p. 26
3 **Classifying Organisms** pp. 28–39 ◆ Explain why scientists organize living things into groups. ◆ Explain the relationship between classification and evolution. ◆ Describe early classification systems, including that of Linneaus. ◆ Name the seven levels of classification used by scientists.	6 periods/ 3 blocks	**Discover** Can You Organize a Junk Drawer?, p. 28 **Sharpen Your Skills** Observing, p. 32 **Real-World Lab: You Be The Detective** Living Mysteries, pp. 38–39	TE TE ISLM	Inquiry Challenge, p. 29 Inquiry Challenge, p. 31 A–1, "Developing a Classification System for Seeds"
4 **The Six Kingdoms** pp. 40–42 ◆ Name and describe the six kingdoms into which all organisms are grouped.	$1\frac{1}{2}$ periods/ 1 block	**Discover** Which Organism Goes Where?, p. 40	TE TE	Real-Life Learning, p. 41 Demonstration, p. 42
Study Guide/Chapter Review pp. 43–45	1 period/ $\frac{1}{2}$ block		ISAB	Provides teaching and review of all inquiry skills

 For Standard or Block Schedule The Resource Pro® CD-ROM gives you maximum flexibility for planning your instruction for any type of schedule. Resource Pro® contains Planning Express®, an advanced scheduling program, as well as the entire contents of the Teaching Resources and the Computer Test Bank.

CHAPTER PLANNING GUIDE

Program Resources	Assessment Strategies	Media and Technology
TR Chapter 1 Project Teacher Notes, pp. 8–9 **TR** Chapter 1 Project Overview and Worksheets, pp. 10–13 **TR** Chapter 1 Project Scoring Rubric, p. 14	**SE** Performance Assessment: Chapter 1 Project Wrap Up, p. 45 **TE** Performance Assessment: Chapter 1 Project Wrap-Up, p. 45 **TE** Check Your Progress, pp. 23, 27, 42 **TR** Chapter 1 Project Scoring Rubric, p. 14	🌐 Science Explorer Internet Site
TR 1-1 Lesson Plan, p. 15 **TR** 1-1 Section Summary, p. 16 **TR** 1-1 Review and Reinforce, p. 17 **TR** 1-1 Enrich, p. 18 **TR** Chapter 1 Skills Lab, pp. 31–32	**SE** Section 1 Review, p. 23 **SE** Analyze and Conclude, p. 24 **TE** Ongoing Assessment, pp. 17, 19, 21 **TE** Performance Assessment, p. 23 **TR** 1-1 Review and Reinforce, p. 17	💿 Exploring Life Science Videodisc, Unit 1 Side 2, "It's Alive!" 🎧 Audiotapes: English-Spanish Summary 1-1 📽 Transparency 1, "Exploring Redi's Experiment" 📽 Transparency 2, "Exploring Pasteur's Experiment" 💽 Interactive Student Tutorial CD-ROM, A-1
TR 1-2 Lesson Plan, p. 19 **TR** 1-2 Section Summary, p. 20 **TR** 1-2 Review and Reinforce, p. 21 **TR** 1-2 Enrich, p. 22	**SE** Section 2 Review, p. 27 **TE** Performance Assessment, p. 27 **TR** 1-2 Review and Reinforce, p. 21	💿 Exploring Life Science Videodisc, Unit 1 Side 2, "Where Did It Come From?" 💿 Exploring Earth Science Videodisc, Unit 2 Side 2, "Air Today Gone Tomorrow" 🎧 Audiotapes: English-Spanish Summary 1-2 💽 Interactive Student Tutorial CD-ROM, A-1
TR 1-3 Lesson Plan, p. 23 **TR** 1-3 Section Summary, p. 24 **TR** 1-3 Review and Reinforce, p. 25 **TR** 1-3 Enrich, p. 26 **TR** Chapter 1 Real-World Lab, pp. 33–35 **SES** Book E, *Environmental Science*, Chapter 2	**SE** Section 3 Review, p. 37 **SE** Analyze and Conclude, p. 39 **TE** Ongoing Assessment, pp. 29, 31, 33, 35 **TE** Performance Assessment, p. 37 **TR** 1-3 Review and Reinforce, p. 25	💿 Exploring Life Science Videodisc, Unit 2 Side 2, "*Pantera leo?*" 🎧 Audiotapes: English-Spanish Summary 1-3 📽 Transparency 3, "Seven Levels of Classification" 💽 Interactive Student Tutorial CD-ROM, A-1
TR 1-4 Lesson Plan, p. 27 **TR** 1-4 Section Summary, p. 28 **TR** 1-4 Review and Reinforce, p. 29 **TR** 1-4 Enrich, p. 30 **SES** Book K, *Chemical Building Blocks*, Chapter 3	**SE** Section 4 Review, p. 42 **TE** Ongoing Assessment, p. 41 **TE** Performance Assessment, p. 42 **TR** 1-4 Review and Reinforce, p. 29	🎧 Audiotapes: English-Spanish Summary 1-4 💽 Interactive Student Tutorial CD-ROM, A-1
TR Chapter 1 Performance Assessment, pp. 156–158 **TR** Chapter 1 Test, pp. 159–162 **ISAB** Provides teaching and review of all inquiry skills	**SE** Chapter Review, pp. 43–45 **TR** Chapter 1 Performance Assessment pp. 156–158 **TR** Chapter 1 Test, pp. 159–162 **CTB** Test A–1	💾 Computer Test Bank, Test A-1 💽 Interactive Student Tutorial CD-ROM, A-1

Key: **SE** Student Edition   **TE** Teacher's Edition   **TR** Teaching Resources
     CTB Computer Test Bank   **SES** Science Explorer Series Text   **ISLM** Integrated Science Laboratory Manual
     ISAB Inquiry Skills Activity Book   **PTA** Product Testing Activities by *Consumer Reports*   **IES** Interdisciplinary Explorations Series

Meeting the National Science Education Standards and AAAS Benchmarks

National Science Education Standards	Benchmarks for Science Literacy	Unifying Themes
Science as Inquiry (Content Standard A) ◆ **Identify questions that can be answered through scientific investigations** Students develop a list of characteristics shared by living things. (*Chapter Project*) ◆ **Design and conduct a scientific investigation** Students devise a system for determining if an object is alive. (*Chapter Project*) ◆ **Communicate scientific procedures and explanations** Students report on the results of the investigation of the mystery object. (*Chapter Project*) **Life Science** (Content Standard C) ◆ **Reproduction and Heredity** Reproduction is a fundamental characteristic of living things. (*Section 1*) **History and Nature of Science** (Content Standard G) ◆ **History of science** Redi and Pasteur established that life comes from life. Miller and Urey demonstrated that conditions in Earth's early atmosphere could have produced complex organic molecules. The observations of Charles Darwin established that living things evolve. (*Sections 1–3*)	**1B Scientific Inquiry** Redi and Pasteur established that life comes from life. Miller and Urey demonstrated that conditions in Earth's early atmosphere could have produced organic molecules. Charles Darwin established that living things evolve. (*Sections 1–3*) **5A Diversity of Life** Organisms share common characteristics allowing them to be placed together in groups. Differences between organisms establish different groups. (*Sections 3–4; Real-World Lab; Chapter Project*) **5C Cells** All living things are made of cells. (*Section 1*) **5 Flow of Matter and Energy** All living things require energy. The energy is used to grow and reproduce. Different kinds of organisms obtain energy in different ways. (*Section 1*) **5F Evolution of Life** Early forms of life are responsible for altering Earth's atmosphere. Charles Darwin made observations that became the basis for understanding that living things evolve. (*Section 2*) **12D Communication Skills** Students interpret pictures of lizard behavior and transfer the information to data tables. (*Skills Lab*)	◆ **Energy** All living things must have energy to survive. Different organisms obtain energy in different ways. (*Section 1*) ◆ **Evolution** Life has evolved over time. Modern classification systems are based on evolutionary history. (*Sections 2, 3*) ◆ **Patterns of Change** The composition of air changed as a result of the presence of living organisms. (*Section 2*) ◆ **Scale and Structure** Classification groups form a hierarchy in which the largest groups are the most general and the smallest are the most specific. The smallest classification group (species) refers to just one kind of organism. (*Section 3, Real-World Lab, Chapter Project*) ◆ **Unity and Diversity** Different organisms in each classification group share important characteristics. Differences between organisms are used as a means of classifying them into different groups. (*Section 3, Real-World Lab, Chapter Project*) ◆ **Stability** Binomial nomenclature gives every organism a name that can be understood by everyone, regardless of individual differences. (*Section 4*)

Media and Technology

Exploring Life Science Videodisc

◆ **Section 1** "It's Alive!" illustrates the common characteristics of all living things: movement, metabolism, growth and development, response, and reproduction.

◆ **Section 2** "Where Did It Come From?" describes Stanley Miller's 1953 experiment in which electricity and a mixture of gases are utilized to produce the building blocks of life.

◆ **Section 3** "*Pantera leo?*" describes the modern classification system using the lion as an example.

Exploring Earth Science Videodisc

◆ **Section 2** "Air Today Gone Tomorrow" examines the composition of the atmosphere and how it has changed since the content of Earth's original atmosphere was first identified.

Interactive Student Tutorial CD-ROM

◆ **Chapter Review** Interactive questions help students to self-assess their mastery of key chapter concepts.

Student Edition Connection Strategies

◆ **Section 1** Integrating Chemistry, p. 22
◆ **Section 2** Integrating Earth Science, p. 25
◆ **Section 3** Integrating Earth Science, p. 29
  Language Arts Connection, p. 30

USING THE INTERNET

www.science-explorer.phschool.com

Visit the Science Explorer Internet site to find an up-to-date activity for Chapter 1 of *From Bacteria to Plants*.

ACTIVITY	Time (minutes)	Materials Quantities for one work group	Skills
Section 1			
Discover, p. 16	10	**Nonconsumable** wind-up toys	Forming Operational Definitions
Try This, p. 18	10	**Consumable** lemon slices **Nonconsumable** small mirrors	Classifying
Sharpen your Skills, p. 22	30	**Consumable** thin potato slices, paper towel **Nonconsumable** hair dryers, balance	Predicting
Skills Lab, p. 24	20 min first day, 5 min per day for the next 5 days or so	**Consumable** paper plates, bread without preservatives, sealable plastic bags, tap water, packing tape **Nonconsumable** plastic dropper	Controlling Variables
Section 2			
Discover, p. 25	10	**Nonconsumable** two covered plastic jars; one containing a plant and the other an animal	Inferring
Section 3			
Discover, p. 28	15	**Nonconsumable** items such as scotch tape, pencils, rubber bands, stamps, markers, erasers, rulers, envelopes, paper clips, paper	Classifying
Sharpen your Skills, p. 32	10	**Consumable** No special materials are required.	Observing
Real-World Lab, pp. 38–39	30	**Consumable** paper **Nonconsumable** pencil	Observing, Inferring, Classifying
Section 4			
Discover, p. 40	15	**Nonconsumable** mushroom, small green plant, a worm or insect, sea animal such as an urchin, anemone, or cultivated coral	Classifying

A list of all materials required for the Student Edition activities can be found on pages T14–T15. You can order Materials Kits by calling 1-800-828-7777 or by accessing the Science Explorer Internet site at **www.science-explorer.phschool.com.**

CHAPTER PROJECT 1

Mystery Object

It can be difficult to determine whether some objects are alive or not. This project allows students to observe the characteristics that make living things different from nonliving things.

Purpose In this project, students observe an object to determine whether it is alive. Students also develop strategies for distinguishing between living and nonliving objects.

Skills Focus After completing the Chapter 1 Project, students will be able to
◆ brainstorm about the characteristics of life;
◆ observe characteristics of objects to infer whether they are alive;
◆ carry out tests for signs of life;
◆ classify living organisms into kingdoms;
◆ communicate their findings about their mystery object to the class.

Project Time Line This project requires about two weeks. Some living things, such as small insects and larvae, will show obvious signs of life at first glance. Other objects, such as seeds, brine-shrimp eggs, or plants, may take a week or so to reveal signs of life. During the first two days, students should observe their objects and record their observations. Allow at least three days for students to carry out their tests for life characteristics. Remind them to include data tables as well as drawings in their project notebooks. Finally, give students time to analyze their data, classify their objects, and plan their presentations.

Possible Materials Provide students with living and nonliving objects, and instructions on their care.
◆ Living "mystery objects" may include: brine shrimp; slime mold; bread mold; insect larvae; goldfish; plants; yeast (add one spoonful of baker's yeast and sugar to 250 mL warm water; observe under microscope); and seeds (soak lentil seeds in water overnight then wrap in wet paper towel; place towel in plastic bag and store in dark; observe daily).
◆ Nonliving "mystery objects" may include: pebbles; vermiculite; lead shot (looks like seeds); artificial plants

CHAPTER 1 Living Things

WHAT'S AHEAD

SECTION 1 What Is Life?
Discover Is It Living or Nonliving?
Try This React!
Sharpen Your Skills Designing an Experiment
Skills Lab Please Pass the Bread!

SECTION 2 *Integrating Earth Science* The Origin of Life
Discover How Can the Composition of Air Change?

SECTION 3 Classifying Organisms
Discover Can You Organize a Junk Drawer?
Sharpen Your Skills Observing
Real-World Lab Living Mysteries

14 ◆ A

(look real but do not grow or have a cellular structure); soluble salts in a saturated solution (crystal gardens appear to grow); hair (cellular structure, but no longer living); and toys with microchips (can have complex responses).
◆ Plastic petri dishes and paper towels are useful for germinating seeds. BTB solution (bromthymol blue) can be used to test for the presence of carbon dioxide in water environments.

◆ Provide equipment such as a microscope, glass slides and cover slips, scissors, plastic dropper, hand lens, and a ruler. Show students how to use a microscope and make thin cross-sections.

Mystery Object

Suppose that you visited a location like the one in this scene. Imagine yourself standing perfectly still, all your senses alert to the things around you. You wonder which of the things around you are alive. The newt clearly is, but what about the rest? Is the pink thing alive? Are the other things living or nonliving?

In this chapter, you will learn that it is not always easy to determine whether something is alive. This is because living things share some characteristics with nonliving things. To explore this idea firsthand, you will be given a mystery object to observe. How can you determine if your object is a living thing? What signs of life will you look for?

Your Goal To study an object for several days to determine whether or not it is alive.

To complete this project successfully, you must
- care for your object following your teacher's instructions
- observe your object each day, and record your data
- determine whether your object is alive, and if so, which kingdom it belongs in
- follow the safety guidelines in Appendix A

Get Started With a few classmates, brainstorm a list of characteristics that living things share. Can you think of any nonliving things that share some of these characteristics? Which characteristics on your list can help you conclude whether or not your mystery object is alive?

Check Your Progress You'll be working on this project as you study this chapter. To keep your project on track, look for Check Your Progress boxes at the following points.
Section 1 Review, page 23: Carry out your tests.
Section 2 Review, page 27: Record your observations daily.
Section 4 Review, page 42: Classify the object as living or nonliving.

Wrap Up At the end of the chapter (page 45), you will display your object and present evidence for whether or not it is alive. Be prepared to answer questions from your classmates.

Both the beautiful pink coral fungus and the newt sitting beside it are alive.

A ◆ 15

Safety

CAUTION: Glass and sharp objects can cause injury. Handle with care.

Program Resources

- **Teaching Resources** Chapter 1 Project Teacher's Notes, pp. 8–9; Chapter 1 Project Overview and Worksheets, pp. 10–13; Chapter 1 Project Scoring Rubric, p. 14

Launching the Project Bring a few living organisms, such as a plant, a snail, and a fish, into the classroom to show students. Ask: **What characteristics do these objects have in common?** *(They grow; they respond to changes in the environment.)* Talk about the distinguishing characteristics that scientists use to classify the objects as living. Ask: **What tests could you design that would help you observe the characteristics of these living organisms?** *(Measure size over a period of time.)* Discuss how scientists develop and test hypotheses. Allow students to read the description of the project in their text and in the Chapter 1 Project Overview on pages 10–11 in the Teaching Resources. Pass out copies of the Chapter 1 Project Worksheets on pages 12–13 for students to review. Tell students that all tests must be approved so that living organisms are not injured.

Performance Assessment

The Chapter 1 Project Scoring Rubric on page 14 will help you evaluate how well students complete the Chapter 1 Project. Students will be assessed on
- the detail of their observations;
- how well they design tests to determine whether their object is alive, and if it is alive, if they identify which kingdom it belongs to;
- the accuracy and organization of their testing and documentation, including how well they follow directions for the care of their objects;
- whether they draw appropriate conclusions from their tests and present their results to the class in a clear and organized manner.

By sharing the Chapter 1 Project Scoring Rubric with students at the beginning of the project, you will make it clear to them what they are expected to do.

Objectives

After completing the lesson, students will be able to
◆ list the characteristics all living things share;
◆ identify what all living things need to survive.

Key Terms organism, cell, unicellular, multicellular, development, stimulus, response, reproduce, spontaneous generation, controlled experiment, variable, autotroph, heterotroph, homeostasis

1 Engage/Explore

Activating Prior Knowledge

Ask students to describe the most unusual living thing they have seen. Ask: **What did it look like? Where did it live? What was so unusual about it?** Write the heading *Living Things* on the board and list the organisms as students identify them. Have students describe whether they thought the organism was a plant, animal, or other form of life such as a mushroom.

DISCOVER

Skills Focus forming operational definitions
Materials *wind-up toys*
Time 10 minutes
Tips Do not wind toys too tightly. Urge students to think of all living things, not just animals, as they make their lists.
Expected Outcome Students could say that because the toy moves it is alive, or because the toy does not eat, grow, or reproduce, it is not alive.
Think It Over Students should conclude that growth is shared by all living things, while characteristics such as sleeping or talking are not.

SECTION
1 What Is Life?

DISCOVER .... ACTIVITY

Is It Living or Nonliving?

1. Your teacher will give you and a partner a wind-up toy.
2. With your partner, decide who will find evidence that the toy is alive and who will find evidence that the toy is not alive.
3. Observe the wind-up toy. Record the characteristics of the toy that support your position about whether or not the toy is alive.
4. Share your lists of living and nonliving characteristics with your classmates.

Think It Over
Forming Operational Definitions Based on what you learned from the activity, create a list of characteristics that living things share.

GUIDE FOR READING

◆ What characteristics do all living things share?
◆ What do living things need to survive?

Reading Tip As you read, use the headings to make an outline of the characteristics and needs of living things.

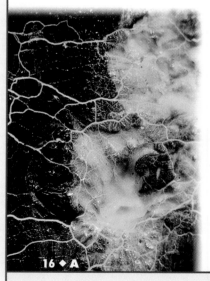

Looking like the slimy creatures that star in horror movies, the "blobs" appeared in towns near Dallas, Texas, in the summer of 1973. Jellylike masses, like the ones in Figure 1, overran yards and porches all over the towns. The glistening blobs oozed slowly along the ground. Terrified homeowners didn't know what the blobs were. Some people thought that they were life forms from another planet. People around Dallas were worried until biologists, scientists who study living things, put their minds at ease. The blobs were slime molds—living things usually found on damp, decaying material on a forest floor. The unusually wet weather around Dallas that year provided ideal conditions for the slime molds to grow in people's yards.

The Characteristics of Living Things

If you were asked to name some living things, or **organisms,** you might name yourself, a pet, and maybe some insects or plants. But you would probably not mention a moss growing in a shady spot, the mildew on bathroom tiles, or the slime molds that oozed across the lawns in towns near Dallas. But all of these things are also organisms that share six important characteristics

Figure 1 Slime molds similar to these grew in yards and porches in towns near Dallas, Texas, one summer.

READING STRATEGIES

Reading Tip Remind students that making an outline helps readers organize information so they remember key points and important details. As a guide for students, begin outlining the first main topic on the board. Complete the outline for this heading as a class. Then have students work independently to complete the rest of the outline.

I. The Characteristics of Living Things
  A. Cellular organization
    1. basic unit of structure and function
    2. unicellular or multicellular

Vocabulary Write the following pairs of key terms on the board: *unicellular/multicellular, stimulus/response, autotroph/heterotroph.* Invite volunteers to discuss how they relate to each other.

◀ Animal cells

◀ Plant cells

Figure 2 Like all living things, the butterfly and the leaf are made of cells. Although the cells of different organisms are not identical, they share important characteristics. *Making Generalizations In what ways are cells similar?*

with all other living things. **All living things have a cellular organization, contain similar chemicals, use energy, grow and develop, respond to their surroundings, and reproduce.**

Cellular Organization All organisms are made of small building blocks called cells. A **cell** is the basic unit of structure and function in an organism. The smallest cells are so tiny that you could fit over a million of them on the period at the end of this sentence. To see most cells, you need a microscope—a tool that uses lenses, like those in eyeglasses, to magnify small objects.

Organisms may be composed of only one cell or of many cells. **Unicellular,** or single-celled organisms, include bacteria (bak TEER ee uh), the most numerous organisms on Earth. A bacterial cell carries out all of the functions necessary for the organism to stay alive. **Multicellular** organisms are composed of many cells. The cells of many multicellular organisms are specialized to do certain tasks. For example, you are made of trillions of cells. Specialized cells in your body, such as muscle and nerve cells, work together to keep you alive. Nerve cells carry messages from your surroundings to your brain. Other nerve cells then carry messages to your muscle cells, making your body move.

The Chemicals of Life The cells of all living things are composed of chemicals. The most abundant chemical in cells is water. Other chemicals called carbohydrates (kahr boh HY drayt) are a cell's energy source. Two other chemicals, proteins (PROH teenz) and lipids (LIP idz), are the building materials of cells, much like wood and bricks are the building materials of houses. Finally, nucleic (noo KLEE ik) acids are the genetic material—the chemical instructions that direct the cell's activities.

2 Facilitate

The Characteristics of Living Things

Using The Visuals: Figure 2

Make sure students understand that the images in the circles are magnified many times. Have students describe differences between the plant and animal cells in the figure. (*Animal cells—rounded, have dark spots in the centers; plant cells—rectangular, have green structures inside them*) Point out that plant and animal cells have more similarities than differences. **learning modality: visual**

Demonstration

Materials *charcoal, piece of chalk, nail, small sack of fertilizer, bottle of carbonated water*
Time 10 minutes

ACTIVITY

Ask if students have heard that all the chemicals in a human body cost only a few dollars. Show the materials, explaining that in simple forms the chemicals would not cost much to buy. Challenge students to identify the chemicals in each item: charcoal (*carbon*); chalk (*calcium*); nail (*iron*); fertilizer (*phosphorus, nitrogen, and potassium*); carbonated water (*carbon dioxide and water*). Explain that the human body can convert these nonliving chemicals into complex arrangements of molecules such as carbohydrates, proteins, lipids, and nucleic acids, which help the body function and provide its structure. **learning modality: verbal**

Program Resources

◆ **Teaching Resources** 1-1 Lesson Plan, p. 15; 1-1 Section Summary, p. 16

Media and Technology

 Audiotapes English-Spanish Summary 1-1

Answers to Self-Assessment

Caption Question

Figure 2 Cells are the basic building blocks of animal and plant tissues. They are composed of complex chemicals and can perform tasks necessary to life.

Ongoing Assessment

Skills Check Have each student choose one living thing and explain how he or she knows it is alive.

The Characteristics of Living Things, continued

Skills Focus classifying
Materials *small mirrors, lemon slices*
Time 10 minutes
Tips Ask: **What does a dog do when it sees a big, juicy steak?** *(Sample: wags tail, acts excited, salivate)* Ask: **Which is the stimulus and which is the response?** *(Stimulus is the steak; response is tail wagging, acting excited, salivating.)* Remind students not to taste the lemon slices.
Expected Outcome clapping hands—sudden motion close to eyes/eyes blink; covering eyes, then uncover—change in light intensity/pupil contracts; lemon—smell/mouth puckers
Extend Challenge students to list at least 5 other stimulus / response actions demonstrated by plants or animals. *(Samples: feel pain—yelp or howl; see a predator—run away; feel heat—pull away; light source—plant stem turns toward)* **learning modality: kinesthetic**

Building Inquiry Skills: Applying Concepts

Materials *crystal "gardens"*

Tips Crystals exhibit growth similar to that of living systems. Inexpensive crystal "gardens" are available from toy stores, novelty shops, and scientific-supply houses. Allow students to construct the gardens and observe crystal growth for a few days. After crystals form, have students list the characteristics of living things, then state whether the crystals have each characteristic. Ask: **Based on your observations, do you think the crystals are alive?** After class discussion, have students write short paragraphs to support their conclusions. **learning modality: logical/mathematical**

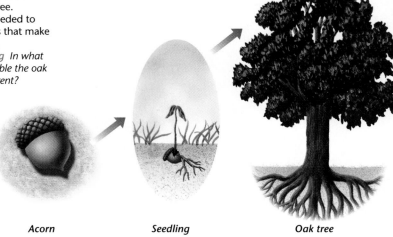

Figure 3 Over time, a tiny acorn develops into a giant oak tree. A great deal of energy is needed to produce the trillions of cells that make up the body of an oak tree. *Comparing and Contrasting In what way does the seedling resemble the oak tree? In what ways is it different?*

Acorn   *Seedling*   *Oak tree*

React!

In this activity, you will test your responses to three different stimuli.

1. Have a partner clap his or her hands together about six inches in front of your face. Describe how you react.

2. Look at one of your eyes in a mirror. Cover the eye with your hand for a minute. While looking in the mirror, remove your hand. Observe how the size of your pupil changes.

3. Bring a slice of lemon close to your nose and mouth. Describe what happens.

Classifying For each action performed, name the stimulus and the response.

Energy Use The cells of organisms use energy to do what living things must do, such as grow and repair injured parts. An organism's cells are always hard at work. For example, as you read this paragraph, not only are your eye and brain cells busy, but most of your other cells are working, too. The cells of your stomach and intestine are digesting food. Your blood cells are moving chemicals around your body. If you've hurt yourself, some of your cells are repairing the damage.

Growth and Development Another characteristic of living things is that they grow and develop. Growth is the process of becoming larger. **Development** is the process of change that occurs during an organism's life to produce a more complex organism. To grow and develop, organisms use energy to create new cells. Look at Figure 3 to see how an acorn develops as it grows into an oak tree.

You may argue that some nonliving things grow and change as they age. For example, a pickup truck rusts as it ages. Icicles grow longer as more water freezes on their tips. But pickup trucks and icicles do not use energy to change and grow. They also don't become more complex over time.

Response to Surroundings If you've ever seen a plant in a sunny window, you may have observed that the plant's stems have bent so that the leaves face the sun. Like a plant bending toward the light, all organisms react to changes in their environment. A change in an organism's surroundings that causes the organism to react is called a **stimulus** (plural *stimuli*). Stimuli include changes in temperature, light, sound, and other factors.

Background

Facts and Figures Many organisms have interesting responses to stimuli. For example:
◆ When a Newfoundland dog sees a struggling swimmer, it responds by jumping in the water, swimming to the person, and pulling them to safety.
◆ Chameleons change color in response to the temperature and brightness of their environment, as well as in response to emotional stimuli such as fright.

Media and Technology

Exploring Life Science Videodisc
Unit 1, Side 2, "It's Alive!"

Chapter 3

An organism reacts to a stimulus with a **response**—an action or change in behavior. For example, has someone ever leapt out at you from behind a door? If so, it's likely that you jumped or screamed. Your friend's sudden motion was the stimulus that caused your startled response. Nonliving things, such as rocks, do not react to stimuli as living things do.

Reproduction Another characteristic of organisms is the ability to **reproduce,** or produce offspring that are similar to the parents. Robins lay eggs that develop into young robins that closely resemble their parents. Sunflowers produce seeds that develop into sunflower plants, which in turn make more seeds. Bacteria produce other bacteria exactly like themselves.

☑ *Checkpoint* *How do growth and development differ?*

Life Comes From Life

Today, when people observe young plants in a garden or see a litter of puppies, they know that these new organisms are the result of reproduction. Four hundred years ago, however, people believed that life could appear suddenly from nonliving material. For example, when people saw flies swarming around decaying meat, they concluded that flies could arise from rotting meat. When frogs appeared in muddy puddles after heavy rains, people concluded that frogs could sprout from the mud in ponds. The mistaken idea that living things arise from nonliving sources is called **spontaneous generation.**

It took hundreds of years of experiments to convince people that spontaneous generation does not occur. One scientist who did some of these experiments was an Italian doctor, Francesco Redi. In the mid-1600s, Redi designed a controlled experiment to show that flies do not spontaneously arise from decaying meat. In a **controlled experiment**, a scientist carries out two tests that are identical in every respect except for one factor. The one factor that the scientist changes is called the **variable.** The scientist can conclude that any differences in the results of the two tests must be due to the variable.

Even after Redi's work, many people continued to believe that spontaneous generation occurred in bacteria. In the mid-1800s,

Figure 4 All organisms respond to changes in their surroundings. This willow ptarmigan's feathers have turned white in response to its snowy surroundings. This Alaskan bird's plumage will remain white until spring.

To help students better understand the experiments which helped disprove spontaneous generation, tell students they will work in groups to design illustrated posters of Redi and Pasteur's experiments. Divide students into groups. Have them read over the experiments and choose one to illustrate. Suggest they brainstorm how they will present the experiments, perhaps sketching a couple of ideas before they decide on a final model. The illustrations should show all aspects of the experiment, and each of the steps should be labeled or explained. Posters can range from flowcharts to illustrated stories, such as in a comic book format. Tell students to include the scientists' reasoning and conclusions, and a title for the poster. Each of the students in the group should work on producing the poster, such as drawing or coloring the illustrations, or writing captions. They can present their posters as a group to their classmates. Posters can be displayed in the classroom and in the school hall.
learning modality: visual

Answers to Self-Assessment

Caption Question
Figure 3 The seedling and the tree are both made of cells which contain complex chemicals; use energy, grow and develop; respond to their environment, and are capable of reproduction. Both have stems, roots, and leaves; and are plants. They differ in their size and in the number of their cells.

☑ *Checkpoint*
Growth is the process of becoming larger. Development is a process of change that produces a more complex organism.

Ongoing Assessment

Oral Presentation Have students give brief presentations to the class on the topic *How to Design a Controlled Experiment.* Each student should design a different experiment. Encourage students to use visuals in their presentations.

Life Comes From Life,
continued

Language Arts Connection

Some students may have problems distinguishing the variable in an experiment. Write the prefix *vari* on the chalkboard and point out that it means "diverse" or "having different aspects or characteristics." Pair students and have them look up words that begin with *vari*, including *variable*, *variable star*, *variation*, and *vary*. Suggest that students find synonyms that will help them identify the variable in an experiment. They should discuss the meanings quietly among themselves. Call on students to share their synonyms and definitions with the class. After the class discussion, students should write in their journals what is meant by the variable in an experiment. **limited English proficiency**

The Needs of Living Things

Addressing Naive Conceptions

Students may be confused by the statement that plants make their own food because they are familiar with products marketed as "plant food." Show students the label from a plant-food package. Most of these products contain forms of nitrogen, phosphorus, and potassium. Tell students that these chemicals are not actually food because they are not an energy source, but nutrients that plants need to convert sunlight, water, and carbon dioxide into food. **learning modality: verbal**

the French chemist Louis Pasteur designed some controlled experiments that finally disproved spontaneous generation. The controlled experiments of Francesco Redi and Louis Pasteur helped to convince people that living things do not arise from nonliving material. Look at *Exploring the Experiments of Redi and Pasteur* to learn more about the experiments they performed.

☑ *Checkpoint* *What is a controlled experiment?*

The Needs of Living Things

Imagine yourself biking through a park on a warm spring day. As you ride by a tree, you see a squirrel running up the tree trunk. Although it may seem that squirrels and trees do not have the

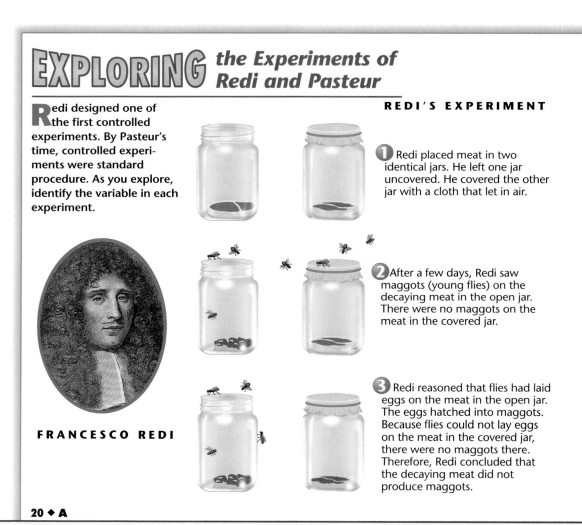

EXPLORING the Experiments of Redi and Pasteur

Redi designed one of the first controlled experiments. By Pasteur's time, controlled experiments were standard procedure. As you explore, identify the variable in each experiment.

FRANCESCO REDI

REDI'S EXPERIMENT

1 Redi placed meat in two identical jars. He left one jar uncovered. He covered the other jar with a cloth that let in air.

2 After a few days, Redi saw maggots (young flies) on the decaying meat in the open jar. There were no maggots on the meat in the covered jar.

3 Redi reasoned that flies had laid eggs on the meat in the open jar. The eggs hatched into maggots. Because flies could not lay eggs on the meat in the covered jar, there were no maggots there. Therefore, Redi concluded that the decaying meat did not produce maggots.

20 ◆ A

Background

History of Science In 1651, an English physician, William Harvey, published a book describing his studies of reproduction. Harvey speculated that insects, worms, and frogs arise from seeds or eggs. Redi had read Harvey's book, so it may have inspired his experiments.

In 1860, the French Academy of Sciences offered a prize to anyone who could "throw new light" on spontaneous generation, and Pasteur responded. He had shown that

organisms in air caused fermentation in milk and alcohol, and decided to investigate whether the organisms were always in the air or arose by spontaneous generation. Pasteur's conclusion that microorganisms develop from other microorganisms in the air was supported in 1876 by another Englishman, physicist John Tyndall. Tyndall was able to show that pure air did not contribute to the production of organisms as regular air did.

same basic needs as you, they do. All organisms need four things to stay alive. **Living things must satisfy their basic needs for energy, water, living space, and stable internal conditions.**

Energy You read earlier that organisms need a source of energy to live. They use food as their energy source. Organisms differ in the ways they obtain their energy. Some organisms, such as plants, capture the sun's energy and use it along with carbon dioxide, a gas found in Earth's atmosphere, and water to make their own food. Organisms that make their own food are called **autotrophs** (AW tuh trawfs). *Auto-* means "self" and *-troph* means "feeder." Autotrophs use the food they make as an energy source to carry out their life functions.

PASTEUR'S EXPERIMENT

1 In one experiment, Pasteur put clear broth into two flasks with curved necks. The necks would let in oxygen but keep out bacteria from the air. Pasteur boiled the broth in one flask to kill any bacteria in the broth. He did not boil the broth in the other flask.

2 In a few days, the unboiled broth became cloudy, showing that new bacteria were growing. The boiled broth remained clear. Pasteur concluded that bacteria do not spontaneously arise from the broth. New bacteria appeared only when living bacteria were already present.

LOUIS PASTEUR

Later, Pasteur took the curve-necked flask containing the broth that had remained clear and broke its long neck. Bacteria from the air could now enter the flask. In a few days, the broth became cloudy. This evidence confirmed Pasteur's conclusion that new bacteria appear only when they are produced by existing bacteria.

Chapter 1 **A ◆ 21**

Answers to Self-Assessment

✓ Checkpoint

A controlled experiment involves performing at least two tests that are identical in every respect except for one factor called a variable.

EXPLORING
The Experiments of Redi and Pasteur

After students have read about the experiments of Redi and Pasteur, lead students in a discussion of controlled experiments. Draw a compare/contrast table on the chalkboard. Ask: **In Redi's experiment, what factors were identical in each test?** *(Both had meat in a jar and both were exposed to air.)* Invite a volunteer to fill in the compare/contrast table. Ask: **How did the tests differ?** *(Redi covered one of the jars with a cloth.)* Write the answer in the compare/contrast table. Ask: **What factor is the variable?** *(The cloth covering the jar so that flies could not reach the meat. If necessary, remind students that the cloth still allowed the meat to be exposed to air.)* Challenge students to make either a compare/contrast table or a Venn diagram for Pasteur's experiment. When students have finished, ask: **What is the variable in Pasteur's experiment?** *(The presence of bacteria in broth as a result of the broth's exposure to air)*

Extend Encourage the class to role-play an encounter between the scientists and people who have a strong belief in spontaneous generation. Have two students act as Redi and Pasteur and explain their arguments in answer to questions posed by the class. **learning modality: verbal**

 Students can save their Venn diagrams or compare/contrast tables in their portfolios.

Ongoing Assessment

Writing Ask students to explain how we now know that spontaneous generation does not take place.

Sharpen your *Skills*

Designing an Experiment

Materials *thin potato slices, hair dryers, balance, paper towel*

Time 30 minutes

Before class, slice the potatoes thin *(but not too thin or they will blow away)*. Keep slices in a container of cold water to keep them hydrated. Remind students to thoroughly dry potato slices.

Expected Outcome Students should use the balance to find the mass of the wet potato slice, then use the hairdryer to dry the potato. Students next find the mass of the dry potato slice, then subtract to find the mass of the water lost. Slices should be placed on a paper towel on a tray or other flat surface and turned frequently. Students should calculate the water content to be about 40%.

Extend Have students test other fruits and vegetables such as apples, bell peppers, or carrots. They should predict the moisture content before they begin.

learning modality: kinesthetic

Integrating Chemistry

Materials *2 small beakers, 60 mL water, 60 mL vegetable oil, salt, sugar, wooden stirrers*

Time 10 minutes

Half the class should try to dissolve 10 g salt in a beaker of water and in a beaker of oil. The other half should try to dissolve 10 g sugar in the water and oil. Remind students not to taste the materials, and make sure they clean up all spills immediately. Encourage students to compare results. *(The water dissolves both salt and sugar. The oil does not dissolve salt.)* Tell students that salt and sugar are both necessary to sustain human life. Ask: **Why is water and not oil the liquid that fills your cells?** *(Oil doesn't dissolve chemicals such as salt.)* **learning modality: kinesthetic**

Sharpen your *Skills*

Designing an Experiment

Your teacher will give you a slice of potato. Predict what percentage of the potato's mass is water. Then come up with a plan to test your prediction. For materials, you will be given a hairdryer and a balance. Obtain your teacher's approval before carrying out your plan. How does your result compare with your prediction?

Figure 5 All organisms need a source of energy to live. **A.** *Volvox* is an autotroph that lives in fresh water, where it uses the sun's energy to make its own food. **B.** This American lobster, a heterotroph, is feeding on a herring it has caught. *Applying Concepts How do heterotrophs depend on autotrophs for energy?*

Organisms that cannot make their own food are called **heterotrophs** (HET uh roh trawfs). *Hetero-* means "other." A heterotroph's energy source is also the sun—but in an indirect way. Heterotrophs either eat autotrophs and obtain the energy in the autotroph's stored food, or they consume other heterotrophs that eat autotrophs. Animals, mushrooms, and slime molds are examples of heterotrophs.

Water All living things need water to survive—in fact, most organisms can live for only a few days without water. Organisms need water to do things such as obtain chemicals from their surroundings, break down food, grow, move substances within their bodies, and reproduce.

One important property of water that is vital to living things is its ability to dissolve more chemicals than any other substance on Earth. In your body, for example, water makes up 92 percent of the liquid part of your blood. The oxygen and food that your cells need dissolve in the blood and are transported throughout your body. Carbon dioxide and other waste also dissolve in the blood. Your body's cells also provide a watery environment in which chemicals are dissolved. In a sense, you can think of yourself as a person-shaped sack of water in which other substances are dissolved. Fortunately, your body contains some substances that do not dissolve in water, and so you hold your shape.

Background

History of Science The concept of homeostasis was developed by a French scientist, Claude Bernard. Bernard was born in 1813, the son of an unsuccessful vineyard owner, and his family could not afford to give him a formal science education. After an attempt at writing plays, he enrolled in the Faculty of Medicine in Paris. He eventually became a research assistant, then a deputy, for a famous physiologist. His experiments led Bernard to understand the role of the pancreas in digestion and the role of glycogen in liver function. He showed that glycogen served as storage for carbohydrates, which could be broken down when needed. Bernard's discoveries illustrate homeostasis, how the body maintains a stable internal environment despite changes in the external environment.

Living Space All organisms need a place to live—a place to get food and water and find shelter. Because there is a limited amount of living space on Earth, some organisms may compete for space. Plants, for example, occupy a fixed living space. Above the ground, their branches and leaves compete for living space with those of other plants. Below ground, their roots compete for water and minerals. Unlike plants, organisms such as animals move around. They may either share living space with others or compete for living space.

Stable Internal Conditions Because conditions in their surroundings can change significantly, organisms must be able to keep the conditions inside their bodies constant. The maintenance of stable internal conditions despite changes in the surroundings is called **homeostasis** (hoh mee oh STAY sis). You know that when you are healthy your body temperature stays constant despite temperature changes in your surroundings. Your body's regulation of temperature is an example of homeostasis.

Other organisms have different mechanisms for maintaining homeostasis. For example, imagine that you are a barnacle attached to a rock at the edge of the ocean. At high tide, the ocean water covers you. At low tide, however, your watery surroundings disappear, and you are exposed to hours of sun and wind. Without a way to keep water in your cells, you'd die. Fortunately, a barnacle can close up its hard outer plates, trapping a bubble of water inside. In this way, the barnacle can keep its body moist until the next high tide.

Figure 6 A tree trunk provides these mushrooms with food, water, and shelter.

Section 1 Review

1. Name six characteristics that you have in common with a tree.
2. List the four things that all organisms need to stay alive.
3. How did Pasteur's experiment show that bacteria do not arise spontaneously in broth?
4. **Thinking Critically Applying Concepts** You see a crowd of gulls fighting over an object on the wet sand at the ocean's edge. You investigate. The object is a vase-shaped, pink blob about as round as a dinner plate. How will you decide if it is a living thing?

Check Your Progress
CHAPTER PROJECT 1

At this point, you should be ready to carry out your tests for signs of life following your teacher's directions. Before you start, examine your mystery object carefully, and record your observations. Also, decide whether you need to revise the list of life characteristics you prepared earlier. (*Hint:* Do not be fooled by the object's appearance— some organisms appear dead during a certain stage of their life.)

Section 1 Review Answers

1. Cellular organization, similar chemicals, use energy, grow and develop, respond to surroundings, and can reproduce.
2. A source of energy, water, living space, and stable internal conditions
3. By heating the broth in one flask, Pasteur killed the bacteria in the broth. No bacteria grew in the heated broth until the broth was exposed to bacteria in the air. Unheated broth was the control.
4. Students might suggest changing a condition in the environment to see if the object responds, examining a sample under the microscope to see if it contains cells, or observing it for a period of time. Accept all answers that describe testing the object to determine whether it has the characteristics of living things.

Check Your Progress
CHAPTER PROJECT 1

Make sure students are caring for their objects according to your instructions. As you review plans, discuss with students any plans that require deviation from the care instructions. Plans should test for different characteristics and predict how students expect a living thing to respond to each test. Work with students to revise any plans that do not meet your approval.

Program Resources

◆ **Teaching Resources** 1-1 Review and Reinforce, p. 17; 1-1 Enrich, p. 18

Media and Technology

 Interactive Student Tutorial CD-ROM A-1

Answers to Self-Assessment

Caption Question

Figure 5 Heterotrophs cannot produce their own food, so they obtain their energy from the food they eat. They either eat autotrophs and directly consume their stored energy, or they eat other heterotrophs that eat autotrophs.

Performance Assessment

Writing Have students invent a living thing that meets all the criteria outlined in this section. Students should describe their creature and may draw a picture of it.

Portfolio Students can save their descriptions and drawings in their portfolios.

A ◆ 23

Please Pass the Bread!

Preparing for Inquiry

Key Concept Bread mold needs water to grow.

Skills Objective Students will be able to
- control variables to determine the effect of different factors;
- draw conclusions about how various factors affect the growth of bread mold.

Time 20 minutes first day; 5 minutes per day for the next 5 days or so

Advance Planning The day before, obtain bread without preservatives.

Guiding Inquiry

Troubleshooting the Experiment
- Tell students to handle the moist bread gently. Show them how to slide the bread off the side of the plate into a bag.
- Students can draw the bread with a grid containing squares of equal size. A 5 × 5 grid contains 25 squares, so each represents 4% of the slice. They can use this drawing to estimate the mold growth.

Expected Outcome
Mold should grow on the moistened bread. Little or no mold should grow on the unmoistened bread.

Analyze and Conclude
1. Mold grows faster with moisture, darkness, and warmth.
2. The variable was moisture. Answers for the manipulated variable in the second experiment will vary.
3. The mold needed water, food (bread), and a place to grow (a dark, warm space).
4. Controlling variables means keeping all conditions the same except the one that the experimenter purposely changes. If variables are not controlled, experimenters cannot be sure which variable caused a specific change.

Extending the Inquiry
Students' designs will vary but should take account of the fact that bread mold spores are in the air.

Please Pass the Bread!

In this lab, you will control variables in an investigation into the needs of living things.

Problem
What factors are necessary for bread molds to grow?

Materials
paper plates	tap water
plastic dropper	packing tape
bread without preservatives	
sealable plastic bags	

Procedure

1. Brainstorm with others to predict which factors might affect the growth of bread mold. Record your ideas.
2. To test the effect of moisture on bread mold growth, place two slices of bread of the same size and thickness on separate, clean plates.
3. Add drops of tap water to one bread slice until the whole slice is moist. Keep the other slice dry. Expose both slices to the air for 1 hour.
4. Put each slice into its own sealable bag. Press the outside of each bag to remove the air. Seal the bags. Then use packing tape to seal the bags again. Store the bags in a warm, dark place.
5. Copy the data table into your notebook.
6. Every day for at least 5 days, briefly remove the sealed bags from their storage place. Record whether any mold has grown. Estimate the area of the bread where mold is present. **CAUTION:** *Do not unseal the bags. At the end of the experiment, give the sealed bags to your teacher.*
7. Choose another factor that may affect mold growth, such as temperature or the amount of light. Set up an experiment to test the factor you choose. Remember to keep all conditions the same except for the one you are testing.

Analyze and Conclude
1. What conclusions can you draw from each of your experiments?
2. What was the variable in the first experiment? In the second experiment?
3. What basic needs of living things were demonstrated in this lab? Explain.
4. **Think About It** What is meant by "controlling variables"? Why is it necessary to control variables in an experiment?

Design an Experiment
Suppose that you lived in Redi's time. A friend tells you that living things such as molds just suddenly appear on bread. Design an experiment that might convince your friend that the new mold comes from existing mold.

DATA TABLE

	Moistened Bread Slice		Unmoistened Bread Slice	
	Mold Present?	Area with Mold	Mold Present?	Area with Mold
Day 1				
Day 2				

Sample Data Table

	Moistened Bread Slice		Unmoistened Bread Slice	
	Mold Present?	Area with Mold	Mold Present?	Area with Mold
Day 1	No		No	
Day 2	No		No	

Safety
Do not open sealed bags. Released mold spores could aggravate allergies, asthma, or other medical problems.

Program Resources
- **Teaching Resources** Chapter 1 Skills Lab, pp. 31–32
- **Inquiry Skills Activity Book** Provides teaching and review of all inquiry skills

SECTION 2 The Origin of Life

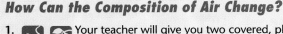
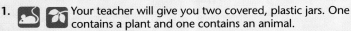

DISCOVER .... ACTIVITY

How Can the Composition of Air Change?

1.  Your teacher will give you two covered, plastic jars. One contains a plant and one contains an animal.

2. Observe the organisms in each jar. Talk with a partner about how you think each organism affects the composition of the air in its jar.

3. Write a prediction about how the amount of oxygen in each jar would change over time if left undisturbed.

4. Return the jars to your teacher.

Think It Over
Inferring Scientists hypothesize that Earth's early atmosphere was different from today's atmosphere. What role might early organisms have played in bringing about those changes?

You stare out the window of your time machine. You have traveled back to Earth as it was 3.6 billion years ago. The landscape is rugged, with bare, jagged rocks and little soil. You search for a hint of green, but there is none. You see only blacks, browns, and grays. Lightning flashes all around you. You hear the rumble of thunder, howling winds, and waves pounding the shore.

You neither see nor hear any living things. However, you know that this is the time period when scientists think that early life forms arose on Earth. You decide to explore. To be safe, you put on your oxygen mask. Stepping outside, you wonder what kinds of organisms could ever live in such a place.

Earth's Early Atmosphere

You were smart to put on your oxygen mask before exploring early Earth. Scientists think that early Earth had a different atmosphere than it has today. **Nitrogen, water vapor, carbon dioxide, and methane were probably the most abundant gases in Earth's atmosphere 3.6 billion years ago. Although all these gases are still found in the atmosphere today, the major gases are nitrogen and oxygen.** You, like most of today's organisms, could not have lived on Earth 3.6 billion years ago, because there was no oxygen in the air. However, scientists think that life forms appeared on Earth at that time.

> ### GUIDE FOR READING
>
> ◆ How was the atmosphere of early Earth different from today's atmosphere?
>
> ◆ How do scientists hypothesize that life arose on early Earth?
>
> *Reading Tip* Before you read, preview Figure 7. List some ways that you think early Earth differed from today's Earth.

Chapter 1 **A ◆ 25**

SECTION 2 The Origin of Life

Objectives
After completing the lesson, students will be able to
◆ compare the atmosphere of early Earth with today's atmosphere;
◆ state how scientists hypothesize that life arose on early Earth.

Key Term fossil

1 Engage/Explore

Activating Prior Knowledge
Mention to students that the air around us is composed of gases in varying amounts. Ask students: **What are some of the gases found in air?** *(Sample: oxygen, nitrogen, carbon dioxide, and argon)* Tell students that in this section they will discover how the composition of gases in the atmosphere has changed over time.

.... DISCOVER ....

Skills Focus inferring
Materials *two covered plastic jars; one containing a plant and the other, an animal*
Time 10 minutes
Tips Select animals such as snails, insects, or earthworms. Release animals immediately after students observe them. Students may need help to identify factors such as respiration that will change the air inside the containers.
Think It Over Because the animal consumes oxygen and the plant produces oxygen, students will suggest that early organisms either removed things from or put things back into the air so that eventually the atmospheric composition changed.

READING STRATEGIES

Reading Tip Suggest students create two-column charts with the headings *Early Earth* and *Today's Earth*. As they view Figure 7, students can list in each column of the chart information about contrasting conditions on the planet. Direct students to add to the chart as they read the section. Invite volunteers to share their charts.

Program Resources

◆ **Teaching Resources** 1-2 Lesson Plan, p. 19; 1-2 Section Summary, p. 20

Media and Technology

 Audiotapes English-Spanish Summary 1-2

2 Facilitate

Earth's Early Atmosphere

Building Inquiry Skills: Comparing and Contrasting

Ask students to explain why scientists propose that early life forms might be like some anaerobic bacteria that live in extreme habitats. Ask: **What do these specialized bacteria have in common with early life forms?** *(They don't need oxygen, they are unicellular, they can live in extreme environments.)* Point out that scientists use fossils to support their hypotheses that the two life forms share characteristics. **learning modality: visual**

Life's Chemicals

Building Inquiry Skills: Organizing Information

Have students make flowcharts to describe Miller and Urey's experiment. Ask: **Why did they make sure there was no oxygen in the flask?** *(Because there was no oxygen in Earth's early atmosphere)* Ask students to speculate about the role of the electric current in the experiment. *(Sample: It adds energy.)* **learning modality: verbal**

The First Cells

Including All Students

Materials *clay, prepared plaster of Paris, almond, peanut, walnut and pecan shells* **Time** 40 minutes

ACTIVITY

Students who are visually challenged can examine fossil models by touch. Give student pairs one of each kind of shell. Have them make impressions of the shells in clay and compare them and the shells. Students should then fill their impressions with plaster to make casts. When the plaster dries, have them remove the clay and compare the casts with the shells. Tell students that impressions and casts are two types of fossils. **learning modality: kinesthetic**

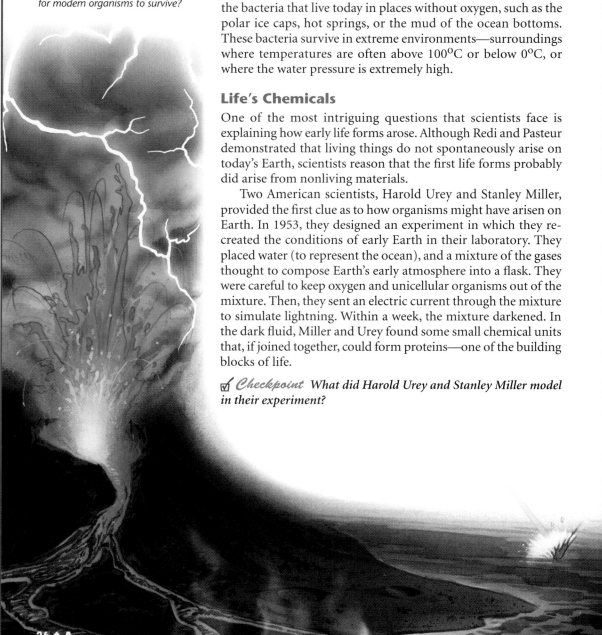

Figure 7 The atmosphere of early Earth had little oxygen. There were frequent volcanic eruptions, earthquakes, and violent weather. *Inferring What conditions on early Earth would have made it impossible for modern organisms to survive?*

26 ◆ A

No one can ever be sure what the first life forms were like, but scientists have formed hypotheses about them. First, early life forms did not need oxygen to survive. Second, they were probably unicellular organisms. Third, they probably lived in the oceans. Many scientists think that the first organisms resembled the bacteria that live today in places without oxygen, such as the polar ice caps, hot springs, or the mud of the ocean bottoms. These bacteria survive in extreme environments—surroundings where temperatures are often above 100°C or below 0°C, or where the water pressure is extremely high.

Life's Chemicals

One of the most intriguing questions that scientists face is explaining how early life forms arose. Although Redi and Pasteur demonstrated that living things do not spontaneously arise on today's Earth, scientists reason that the first life forms probably did arise from nonliving materials.

Two American scientists, Harold Urey and Stanley Miller, provided the first clue as to how organisms might have arisen on Earth. In 1953, they designed an experiment in which they re-created the conditions of early Earth in their laboratory. They placed water (to represent the ocean), and a mixture of the gases thought to compose Earth's early atmosphere into a flask. They were careful to keep oxygen and unicellular organisms out of the mixture. Then, they sent an electric current through the mixture to simulate lightning. Within a week, the mixture darkened. In the dark fluid, Miller and Urey found some small chemical units that, if joined together, could form proteins—one of the building blocks of life.

Checkpoint *What did Harold Urey and Stanley Miller model in their experiment?*

Background

Facts and Figures Some scientists have proposed that organic building blocks came from space. Two scientists, Jeffrey Bada and Luann Becker, studied the site of an ancient meteoroid crash in Ontario. They discovered a large quantity of buckyballs. The buckyballs contained helium, which is rare on Earth but plentiful in space. If the buckyballs came from outer space without burning up, other organic molecules could, too.

Media and Technology

 Exploring Earth Science Videodisc
Unit 2, Side 2, "Air Today Gone Tomorrow"

Chapter 2

 Exploring Life Science Videodisc
Unit 4, Side 2, "Where Did It Come From?"

Chapter 1

The First Cells

In experiments similar to Miller and Urey's, other scientists succeeded in producing chemical units that make up carbohydrates and nucleic acids. **From the results of these experiments, scientists hypothesized that the small chemical units of life formed gradually over millions of years in Earth's waters.** Some of these units joined to form the large chemical building blocks that are found in cells. Eventually, some of these large chemicals accumulated and became the forerunners of the first cells.

These hypotheses are consistent with evidence from fossils. **Fossils** are traces of ancient organisms that have been preserved in rock or other substances. The fossils in Figure 8 are of bacteria-like organisms that were determined to be between 3.4 and 3.5 billion years old. Scientists think that these ancient cells may be evidence of Earth's earliest life forms.

The first cells could not have needed oxygen to survive. They probably were heterotrophs that used the chemicals in their surroundings for energy. As they grew and reproduced, their numbers increased. In turn, the amount of chemicals available to them decreased. At some point, some of the cells may have developed the ability to make their own food. These early ancestors of today's autotrophs had an important effect on the atmosphere. As they made their own food, they produced oxygen as a waste product. As the autotrophs thrived, oxygen accumulated in Earth's atmosphere. Over millions of years, the amount of oxygen increased to its current level.

No one will ever know for certain how life first appeared on Earth. However, scientists will continue to ask questions, construct models, and look for both experimental and fossil evidence about the origin of life on Earth.

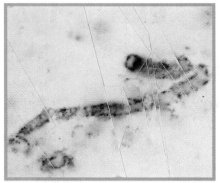

Figure 8 This fossil of bacteria-like cells was found in western Australia. It is the oldest fossil known—about 3.5 billion years old.

Section 2 Review

1. Explain why you could not have survived in the atmosphere of early Earth.
2. Describe how scientists think that life could have arisen on Earth.
3. Describe Urey and Miller's experiment.
4. **Thinking Critically** *Inferring* How is the existence of organisms in hot springs today consistent with the scientific hypothesis of how life forms arose on Earth?

Check Your Progress — CHAPTER PROJECT 1
Observe your object at least once a day. Record your observations in a data table. Draw accurate diagrams. *(Hint: Measuring provides important information. Take measurements of your object regularly. If you cannot measure it directly, make estimates.)*

Answers to Self-Assessment

Caption Question

Figure 7 Earth lacked oxygen.

✓ *Checkpoint*

Urey and Miller's experiment modeled conditions thought to exist on early Earth.

3 Assess

Section 2 Review Answers

1. There was no oxygen in the atmosphere of early Earth and humans need oxygen to survive.
2. Small chemical units of life formed in Earth's waters over millions of years. Some of these units joined to form large chemical building blocks found in cells today. Some of these large chemicals accumulated to form the forerunners of cells.
3. They placed water and a mixture of gases thought to be present in Earth's early atmosphere in a sealed container and sent an electric current through the mixture over time. After a week, the mixture darkened because it contained chemicals that can form proteins.
4. The fact that organisms can live in such extreme conditions suggests that life forms could have formed under the extreme conditions in Earth's early atmosphere.

Check Your Progress — CHAPTER PROJECT 1
Make sure students spend time making observations of their object. If students seem bored because their object is not doing anything, encourage them to consider whether this inactivity proves that the object is not alive, or whether they should revise their methods of observation. For example, encourage students to explain how they could be sure that the object is not breathing or growing.

Performance Assessment

Writing Have students write paragraphs describing how scientists asked questions, used models, and interpreted experimental data to test their hypotheses about how life began on Earth.

SECTION 3 Classifying Organisms

Objectives

After completing the lesson, students will be able to

◆ explain why scientists organize living things into groups;

◆ explain the relationship between classification and evolution;

◆ describe early classification systems, including that of Linnaeus;

◆ name the seven levels of classification used by scientists.

Key Terms classification, taxonomy, binomial nomenclature, genus, species, evolution, taxonomic key

1 Engage/Explore

Activating Prior Knowledge

Ask students: **How do libraries organize their books?** *(First by whether they are fiction or nonfiction, then by subject matter, then in alphabetical order by author's last name, first name, and finally title)* Discuss with students how difficult it would be to find a book in the library without some sort of organizing system.

•••••••• DISCOVER ••••••••

Skills Focus classifying
Materials *items such as scotch tape, pencils, rubber bands, stamps, markers, erasers, rulers, envelopes, paper clips, paper*
Time 15 minutes
Tips Avoid using sharp objects. Stress that items in a set must share at least one common trait.
Expected Outcome A variety of classification systems may be proposed. For example, students may group by function (items you write with) or by shape (round).
Think It Over Each grouping system will have strengths and weaknesses. Criteria for usefulness will vary. Possibilities include systems that emphasize similar functions or systems that allow objects to be found quickly.

DISCOVER ·······················ACTIVITY···

Can You Organize a Junk Drawer?

1. Your teacher will give you some items that you might find in the junk drawer of a desk. Your job is to organize the items.

2. Examine the objects and decide on three groups into which you can sort them.

3. Place each object into one of the groups based on how the item's features match the characteristics of the group.

4. Compare your grouping system with those of your classmates.

Think It Over
Classifying Explain which grouping system seemed most useful.

GUIDE FOR READING

◆ Why do scientists organize living things into groups?

◆ What is the relationship between classification and evolution?

Reading Tip Before you read, make a list of the boldfaced vocabulary terms. As you read, write the meaning of each term in your own words.

Suppose you had only ten minutes to run into a supermarket to get what you need—milk and tomatoes. Could you do it? In most supermarkets this would be an easy task. First, you might go to the dairy aisle and find the milk. Then you'd go to the produce aisle and find the tomatoes. Finally, you'd pay for the items and leave the store.

Now imagine shopping for these same items in a market where the shelves were organized in a random manner. To find what you need, you'd have to search through boxes of cereal, cans of tuna, bins of apples, and much more. You could be there for a long time!

Why Do Scientists Classify?

Just as shopping can be a problem in a disorganized store, finding information about one of the millions of kinds of organisms can also be a problem. Today, scientists have identified at least 2.5 million kinds of organisms on Earth. This number includes all forms of life, from plants and animals to bacteria. It is important for biologists to have all these living things organized.

People organize a lot of things into groups. For example, if a friend asks you what kind of music you like, you might say that you like country or rap music. Although you may not know it, you have grouped the music you like. **Classification** is the process of grouping things based on their similarities.

READING STRATEGIES

Reading Tip Have students write the vocabulary words on the fronts of index cards and their definitions on the backs. Students can work in pairs to quiz each other and practice pronouncing the words.

Study and Comprehension Before students read the section, have them write the seven main section headings on one or more sheets of paper, leaving enough space between each heading to write at least three sentences. Then instruct students to read the information under each section heading and summarize it before reading the next section. Remind students that summarizing involves identifying the main idea of a passage and restating it accurately and concisely in their own words.

Biologists use classification to organize living things into groups so that the organisms are easier to study. The scientific study of how living things are classified is called **taxonomy** (tak SAHN uh mee). Taxonomy is useful because once an organism is classified, a scientist knows a lot about that organism. For example, if you know that crows are classified as birds, you know that crows have wings, feathers, and a beak.

 INTEGRATING EARTH SCIENCE Biologists aren't the only scientists who classify things. For example, geologists—scientists who study the structure and history of Earth—classify rocks. Geologists separate rocks into three groups according to how they formed. By classifying rocks in this way, geologists can make sense of the variety of rocks on Earth.

Early Classification Systems

The first scientist to develop a classification system for organisms was the Greek scholar Aristotle. In the fourth century B.C., Aristotle observed many animals. He recorded each animal's appearance, behavior, and movement. Then he divided animals into three groups: those that fly, those that swim, and those that walk, crawl, or run.

Aristotle could see that even though organisms in a group moved in a similar way, they were different in many other ways. So he used their differences to divide each group into subgroups—smaller groups of organisms that shared other similarities.

Aristotle's method of using careful observations as the basis for classification and his idea of creating subgroups are still used today. However, organisms are no longer classified into large groups on the basis of how they move or where they live.

☑ *Checkpoint* *What were the three major groups of animals in Aristotle's system of classification?*

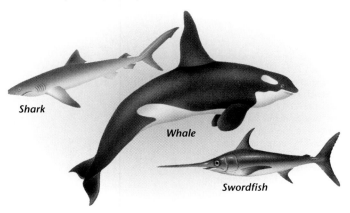

Shark

Whale

Swordfish

Figure 9 Aristotle would have classified this shark, whale, and swordfish together. However, he would have separated them into subgroups because they differ from each other in many ways. *Classifying List two differences that would place these animals into separate subgroups.*

Answers to Self-Assessment

Caption Question

Figure 9 Answers will vary but might include gills or lungs and horizontal or vertical caudal fins.

☑ *Checkpoint*

Animals that fly; those that swim; and those that crawl, walk, or run

2 Facilitate

Why Do Scientists Classify?

Integrating Earth Science

Although rocks are classified into three groups, they change over time through the rock cycle. Igneous rocks form from molten rock found deep inside Earth. Ask students: **How does knowing the relationships between the different types of rocks help geologists?** *(They can study rocks to determine the geological history of an area.)* Students can learn more about geological history by examining rock layers along a highway cut. **learning modality: verbal**

Inquiry Challenge

Materials *igneous, metamorphic, and sedimentary rocks; three labeled boxes* **Time** 20 minutes

ACTIVITY

Display a specimen of each rock type in front of a labeled box. Discuss the characteristics of each kind of rock. Pass out rocks to small groups of students so that every group has one of each kind to examine and classify. Have groups classify their rocks. **limited English proficiency**

Early Classification Systems

Building Inquiry Skills: Thinking Critically

Challenge students to think of some examples of animals that Aristotle would have classified in the same group but that today's scientists classify in very different groups. *(Sample: ostrich, cheetah, and lizard)* **learning modality: verbal**

Ongoing Assessment

Writing Have students describe the difference between classification and taxonomy.

The Classification System of Linnaeus

Language Arts
CONNECTION

Ask students to consider the term *binomial nomenclature. Bi* translates as "two" or "twice" while *nomen* means "name." Ask: **How does English provide hints about the meanings of Latin terms?** *(Sample: In the term "Viola missouriensis," English helps identify Missouri as a location of the plant.)*

In Your Journal Provide biology textbooks and classification books along with dictionaries and encyclopedias. *(*Musca domestica: *housefly;* Hirudo medicinalis: *medicinal leech. Students may recognize these English words in the Latin terms: domestic, medicine.)* **learning modality: verbal**

Building Inquiry Skills: Applying Concepts

Write these scientific names on the board: *Perognathus californicus, Perognathus nelsoni, Perognathus spinatus.* Explain that all three animals are North American pocket mice. Challenge students to see how much information they can infer about these animals just from their names. *(They are from the same genus. Each is a different species, so mating among them would not produce fertile offspring. Students may also infer that* nelsoni *was discovered by someone named Nelson,* californicus *is found in California, or* spinatus *has prickly fur.)* **learning modality: logical/mathematical**

Language Arts
CONNECTION

What's In a Name?

You don't have to know Latin to understand the meaning of a scientific name. Just hearing the name *Ursus horribilis* should tell you that you don't want to meet that organism up close. *Ursus horribilis* is commonly known as a grizzly bear. The Latin word *ursus* means "bear" and *horribilis* means "horrible or feared."

A species name describes an organism like an adjective describes the noun it modifies. Some names describe a specific trait; others tell who discovered the organism. For example, *Pheidole fullerae* is the name of a species of ants discovered by an office worker named Fuller. Other names tell you where the organism was discovered or where it lives. Guess where you'd find the plant *Viola missouriensis.*

In Your Journal

Look in dictionaries or other reference books to find the meaning of these species names: *Musca domestica, Hirudo medicinalis,* and *Cornus florida.* Then try to identify English words that are derived from the Latin terms.

The Classification System of Linnaeus

In the 1750s, a Swedish scientist named Carolus Linnaeus expanded on Aristotle's ideas of classification. Like Aristotle, Linnaeus used observations as the basis of his system. He wrote descriptions of organisms from his observations, and placed organisms in groups based on their observable features.

Linnaeus also used his observations to devise a naming system for organisms. In Linnaeus's naming system, called **binomial nomenclature** (by NOH mee ul NOH men klay chur), each organism is given a two-part name.

The first part of an organism's scientific name is its genus. A **genus** (JEE nus) (plural *genera*) is a classification grouping that contains similar, closely related organisms. For example, pumas, ocelots, and house cats are all classified in the genus *Felis.* Organisms that are classified in the genus *Felis* share characteristics such as sharp, retractable claws and behaviors such as hunting other animals.

The second part of an organism's scientific name is its species name. A **species** (SPEE sheez) is a group of similar organisms that can mate and produce fertile offspring in nature. A species name sets one species in a genus apart from another. The species name often describes a distinctive feature of an organism, such as where it lives or its color. For example, the scientific name for many pumas, or mountain lions, is *Felis concolor. Concolor* means "the same color" in Latin. The scientific name for some ocelots is *Felis pardalis.* The word *pardalis* means "spotted like a panther" in Latin. The scientific name for house cats is *Felis domesticus.* The species name *domesticus* means "of the house" in Latin.

Figure 10 These animals belong to the genus *Felis.* The species names of the animals distinguish them from each other. **A.** This puma's coat is one color, which is indicated by its species name *concolor.* **B.** This ocelot has a spotted coat, which is described by its species name *pardalis.* **C.** The species name of this kitten is *domesticus,* which indicates that it is a house cat.

Background

Facts and Figures Latin was originally spoken by small groups that lived near the Tiber River in Italy. As the power and territory of the Roman Empire spread, so did the Latin language. The spoken language of various parts of the Empire developed into the modern Romance languages, which include French, Italian, Spanish, Portuguese, and Romanian.

The name *Romance* comes from an old French form of the Latin word *Romanticus.* This word was used in the Middle Ages to refer to a popular form of Latin speech, rather than the form used by the church. By the end of the twentieth century, more than 1 billion people spoke a Romance language.

Romance languages share a high proportion of basic vocabulary and many grammatical forms with the language of the Roman empire.

Linnaeus's system might remind you of the way you are named because you, also, have a two-part name made up of your first name and your family name. Your two-part name distinguishes you from others. In a similar way, binomial nomenclature ensures that a combination of two names distinguishes one kind of organism from another. Together, a genus and a species name identify one kind of organism.

Notice that both the genus and species names are Latin words. Linnaeus used Latin words in his naming system because Latin was the language that scientists communicated in during that time. Notice also that a complete scientific name is written in italics. The genus is capitalized while the species name begins with a small letter.

Binomial nomenclature makes it easy for scientists to communicate about an organism because everyone uses the same name for the same organism. Look at the organism in Figure 11. This photograph shows one type of pine tree that grows in the southern United States. People call this tree by any one of a number of common names: loblolly pine, longstraw pine, or Indian pine. Fortunately, this tree has only one scientific name, *Pinus taeda*.

✓ *Checkpoint* **Which part of a scientific name is like your first name? Your family name?**

Figure 11 Although there are many common names for this tree, it has only one scientific name.
Making Generalizations What is the advantage of having scientific names for organisms?

Materials *index cards or small pieces of paper, tape, markers*
Time 15 minutes

Ask: **What would happen if scientists used only one word to name organisms?** *(They might run out of names, and they would not be able to express relationships between similar organisms.)* Point out that numbers are often used to classify objects. Challenge small groups of students to use the numbers from 0 to 9 to classify objects in the classroom by genus and species. Have students write each digit on ten pieces of paper. A typical system includes assigning one number for the genus and a second number for the species. Allow students to tape the labels onto the objects to identify the genus and species. Challenge groups to identify the system used by other groups. *(A sample system would place all furniture with legs in a genus, with individual species such as tables, desks, and chairs.)* Ask: **How many different species names could you have?** *(100)* Encourage students to think of ways to increase the number of names they could have. *(By using more than one digit for each name.)* **learning modality: logical/mathematical**

Ongoing Assessment

Skills Check Tell students that the scientific name for dogs is *Canis familiaris*. Call on students to identify the parts of the name. (Canis *is the* genus; familiaris *is the species.*) List the following binomial names on the board and have students identify the genus and species and then describe the animal by comparing it to an animal of the same genus from p. 30: *Felis onca, Ursus arctos, Canis latrans.*

Media and Technology

Exploring Life Science Videodisc
Unit 2, Side 2,
"*Pantera leo?*"

Chapter 1

Answers to Self-Assessment

Caption Question

Figure 11 Using scientific names makes it easy for scientists to communicate about organisms, because everyone uses the same name for the same organism.

✓ *Checkpoint*

Genus name —family name; species name —given name.

Sharpen your Skills

Observing

Time 10 minutes

Tips If students have difficulty finding common traits of animals at the kingdom level, ask: **Are these animals unicellular or multicellular?** *(multicellular)* **Are they autotrophs or heterotrophs?** *(heterotrophs)* Next, have students compare and contrast the birds pictured at the class and genus levels. Point out that structural adaptations for movement and obtaining food are often used in assigning classification. If students need more help, question them about adaptations that help birds fly, eat, and perch on branches. Guide students to compare the pictures and focus on the specific traits that owls exhibit.

Expected Outcome The closer to the species level, the longer the list of shared characteristics. *(Kingdom: multicellular heterotrophs; Class: multicellular heterotrophs with wings, feathers, a beak, feet made to grip; Genus: multicellular heterotrophs with wings, feathers, feet made to grip, similar body shape, tufts of feathers, hooked beak, flat, round face, forward facing eyes, and talons)*

Extend Challenge students to describe some shared characteristics of humans. *(Samples: multicellular heterotroph, walks on two legs, has hair, opposable thumb, stands upright)* **learning modality: visual**

Sharpen your Skills

Observing ACTIVITY

Test your observational skills using Figure 12. Look carefully at the organisms pictured together at the kingdom level. Make a list of the characteristics that the organisms share. Then make two more lists of shared characteristics—one for the organisms at the class level and the other for those at the genus level. How does the number of characteristics on your lists change at each level?

Levels of Classification

The classification system that scientists use today is based on the contributions of Aristotle and Linnaeus. But today's classification system uses a series of seven levels to classify organisms. To help you understand the levels in classification, imagine a room filled with everybody who lives in your state. First, all of the people who live in your *town* raise their hands. Then, those who live in your *neighborhood* raise their hands. Then, those who live on your *street* raise their hands. Finally, those who live in your *house* raise their hands. Each time, fewer people raise their hands. But you'd be in all of the groups. The most general group you belong to is the state. The most specific group is the house. The more levels you share with others, the more you have in common with them.

The Seven Levels of Classification Modern biologists classify organisms into the seven levels shown in Figure 12. Of course, organisms are not grouped by where they live but rather by their shared characteristics. First an organism is placed in a broad group, which in turn is divided into more specific groups.

A kingdom is the broadest level of organization. Within a kingdom, there are phyla (FY luh) (singular *phylum*). Within each phylum are classes. Each class is divided into orders. Each order contains families, and each family contains at least one genus. Finally, within a genus, there are species. The more classification levels that two organisms share, the more characteristics they have in common.

Classifying an Owl Take a closer look at Figure 12 to see how the levels of classification apply to the great horned owl, a member of the animal kingdom. Look at the top row of the figure. As you can see, a wide variety of organisms also belong to the animal kingdom. Now, look at the phylum, class, and order levels. Notice that as you move down the levels in the figure, there are fewer kinds of organisms in each group. More importantly, the organisms in each group have more in common with each other. For example, the class Aves includes all birds, while the order Strigiformes only includes owls. Different owls have more in common with each other than they do with other birds.

☑ *Checkpoint* List the seven levels of classification from the broadest to the most specific.

Background

Facts and Figures The name *horned owl* can refer to any owl in the genus *Bubo*, but usually relates to the great horned owl (*Bubo virginianis*) of the Americas. The great horned owl ranges from the Arctic to the Strait of Magellan at the tip of South America. It is adapted to deserts and forests, and migrates only when food is scarce.

Great horned owls can be more than 60 cm long and weigh as much as 2 kilos. The female can have a wingspan of 200 cm. These owls are often called "tigers of the sky," because they are so large and aggressive. They have been known to evict eagles from their nests. Although great horned owls prefer prey like rabbits, they are one of the few predators that prey on skunks.

Kingdom Animalia

Phylum Chordata

Class Aves

Order Strigiformes

Family Strygidae

Genus *Bubo*

Species *Bubo virginianus*

Figure 12 Scientists use seven levels to classify organisms such as the great horned owl. Notice that, as you move down the levels, the number of organisms decreases. The organisms at lower levels share more characteristics with each other. *Interpreting Diagrams How many levels do a robin and the great horned owl share?*

Materials *posterboard or other heavyweight paper, pen, ruler, colored pencils, glue, scissors, nature magazines, dictionaries*
Time 50 minutes

Of the animals shown in Figure 12, have students find one that is most closely related to their pets or their friends' pets. Ask: **On which levels of Figure 12 would you find house cats?** *(Kingdom Animalia and Phylum Chordata)* Direct students to create model classification charts for their pets similar to the one shown in Figure 12 for the owl. Provide students with lists of the class, order, and family of several common pets, and encourage them to find the scientific name and determine the genus and species. Students should write the names and draw or glue pictures of several appropriate animals on the first five levels. Some students might like to attach pictures of their pets at the species level. **learning modality: visual**

 Students can save their classification charts in their portfolios.

Answers to Self-Assessment

Caption Question

Figure 12 The robin and the great horned owl share three levels: kingdom, phylum, and class.

☑ *Checkpoint*

kingdom, phylum, class, order, family, genus, species

Ongoing Assessment

Skills Check Ask students to tell you which classification level will always have the greatest number of organisms and which level will always have the smallest number and why. *(Kingdom, species; because kingdom contains all organisms in that category and species is a specific organism)*

Evolution and Classification

Building Inquiry Skills: Applying Concepts

Have students predict and sketch the types of beaks birds would need to eat burrowing insects, mice, sunflower seeds, and fruit. Students should label their sketches according to the food the bird could eat. Suggest students use the birds shown in Figures 12 and 13 to help them. For example, an owl has a hooked beak and eats flesh. The bird in Figure 13B is an insect eater. Figure 13C shows a bird that eats large seeds, and Figure 13A shows a bird that eats fruit. The robin's beak is adapted to eating a variety of foods such as insects, worms, and berries. **limited English proficiency**

 Students can save their sketches in their portfolios.

Social Studies Connection

Use a globe or map to show students the location of the Galapagos Islands. The Galapagos are volcanic islands of geologically recent origin. Among the unique creatures found only on the Galapagos Islands are the giant land tortoises, which are thought to live longer than any other animal. These tortoises once lived in other places but are now extinct everywhere except the Islands. Forty percent of the plants and most of the birds in the Galapagos are found only on the Islands, although scientists think they originated in South America. Ask students: **Why do you think the plants and animals on the Galapagos are so different from similar animals in South America?** *(The animals on the island are isolated from those in South America and live in different environments. Thus, they evolved differently.)* **learning modality: verbal**

Figure 13 These three species of finches that live on the Galapagos Islands may have arisen from a single species. Notice the differences in these birds' appearances, especially their beaks. **A.** This cactus finch uses its pointed beak to pierce the outer covering of cactus plants. **B.** The warbler finch uses its needlelike beak to trap insects. **C.** The large-billed ground finch cracks open large seeds with its strong, wide beak.

Evolution and Classification

At the time that Linnaeus developed his classification system, people thought that species never change. They could see that some organisms were similar. They thought that these organisms had always been similar, yet distinct from each other. In 1859, a British naturalist named Charles Darwin published a theory about how species can change over time. Darwin's theory has had a major impact on how species are classified.

Darwin collected much of the data for his theory on the Galapagos Islands off the western coast of South America. As he studied the islands' finches, he observed that some species of finches were similar to each other but different from finches living in South America. Darwin hypothesized that some members of a single species of finch flew from South America to the islands. Once on the islands, the species changed little by little over a long time until it was very different from the species remaining in South America. In this way, two groups of a single species can accumulate enough differences over a long time to become two separate species. This process by which species gradually change over time is called **evolution**.

☑ *Checkpoint* **Who first proposed the theory of evolution?**

Classification Today

The theory of evolution changed the way biologists think about classification. Today, scientists understand that certain organisms are similar because they share a common ancestor. For example, Darwin hypothesized that the finches that lived on the Galapagos Islands shared a common ancestor with the finches that live in South America. When organisms share a

---

History of Science When people think of evolution and natural selection, they usually think of Charles Darwin. However, it was another Englishman, Alfred Russel Wallace, who first introduced both terms.

In 1848, Wallace went on an expedition to the Amazon. Most of the items he collected were lost on his return voyage when his ship sank. However, in 1854–62 he traveled to the Malay Archipelago to gather more evidence to support his theory of evolution. In early 1858, he wrote, "There suddenly flashed before me the idea of the survival of the fittest."

Although Wallace came up with the idea of evolution through natural selection first, Darwin developed the theory further, provided more evidence, and was mainly responsible for the acceptance of the theory.

common ancestor, they share an evolutionary history. Today's system of classification considers the history of a species when classifying the species. **Species with similar evolutionary histories are classified more closely together.**

How do scientists get information about the evolutionary history of a species? One way is by studying fossils. Scientists compare the body structures as well as the chemical makeup of fossils to each other and to modern organisms. This information adds to their knowledge of evolutionary relationships among organisms.

Scientists also obtain clues about the evolutionary history of a species by comparing the body structures of living organisms. For example, look at the organisms in Figure 14. Notice that the bones in the flipper of a whale are similar to the bones in the wing of a bat and in the arm of a human. This similarity indicates that whales, bats, and humans have a similar evolutionary history.

Additional information about evolutionary history can be learned by comparing the early development of different organisms. Humans and rabbits, for example, go through similar stages in their early development before birth. The similarity provides evidence that humans and rabbits may share some evolutionary history.

Figure 14 Compare the bones in the limbs of the bat, whale, and human. Although a bone may differ in size and shape, it is in a similar location in each of the limbs.
Inferring What do the bones in the limbs suggest about the animals' evolutionary history?

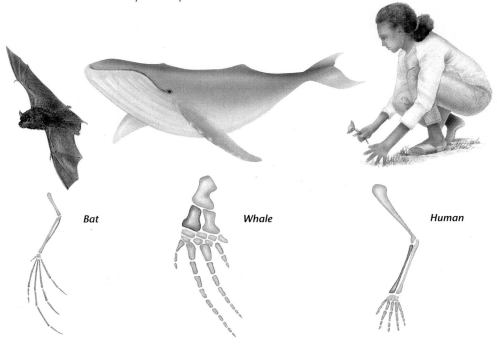

Bat   Whale   Human

Using the Visuals: Figure 14

If students have difficulty seeing the similarities among the forelimbs, focus their attention on the long upper bone (humerus) of the human arm first. Encourage students to find the bones in similar locations in the other animals. Ask: **How does this bone compare to the bone in the same location in the bat? The whale?** *(Bat: wider at the shoulder and narrower at the elbow; whale: proportionately much shorter and heavier)* This questioning strategy may be applied to the lower arm bones (radius and ulna), the wrist bones (carpels), hand (metacarpals) and fingers (phalanges). **learning modality: visual**

Program Resources

Integrated Science Laboratory Manual A–1, *"Developing a Classification System for Seeds"*

Answers to Self-Assessment

Caption Question

Figure 14 The similarity suggests that these animals have a similar evolutionary history.

☑ *Checkpoint*
Charles Darwin

Ongoing Assessment

Writing Have students write short paragraphs explaining how scientists learn about the evolutionary history of a species. *(They compare the structure and chemical makeup of fossils to each other and modern organisms, compare modern body structures, compare development before birth, and compare chemical makeup of cells.)*

Using the Classification System

Using the Visuals: Figure 16
Have students work in groups. Have them use the taxonomic key to draw a picture of each organism listed. When students have drawn all the organisms, have groups compare their drawings for each type. The reporter from each group should explain how the group used the key to determine what features each should have. Ask: **What other information did you need to draw your pictures but could not find in the taxonomic key?** (*Answers will vary, but some students may want to know what color the organisms are, what kind of legs they have, or where their eyes are located.*)
Ask students: **Are the characteristics that are not mentioned in the key necessary to identify an organism? Explain.** (*No, the information in the key is enough to identify it even if the key does not describe everything about it.*)
cooperative learning

Figure 15 Scientists analyze the chemical makeup of an organism's cells to learn about its evolutionary history. By comparing the chemicals in the cells of weasels, top, and skunks, bottom, scientists learned that these organisms are not as closely related as once thought.

Today, scientists rely primarily on information about the chemical makeup of cells to determine evolutionary history. The more closely two species are related, the more similar the chemicals that make up their cells. The skunk and weasel had been classified in the same family for 150 years. Recently, however, scientists compared some nucleic acids from the cells of skunks and weasels. Surprisingly, they found many differences, suggesting that these organisms are not as closely related as they had thought. Some scientists propose changing the classification of skunks. They suggest removing skunks from the family Mustelidae, which contains members of the weasel family. They want to reclassify skunks into a family called Mephitidae, which means "noxious gas" in Latin.

☑ *Checkpoint* *How do scientists use fossils to learn about the evolutionary history of organisms?*

Using the Classification System

You may be wondering why you should care about taxonomy. Suppose you wake up and feel something tickling your ankle. You fling back the covers and stare at a tiny creature crouching in the sheets by your right foot. Although it's only the size of a small melon seed, you don't like the looks of its two claws waving at you. Then, in a flash, it's gone—darting off under the safety of your covers.

How could you learn the identity of the organism that tickled you awake? One way to identify the organism would be to use a field guide. Field guides are books with illustrations that highlight differences between similar-looking organisms.

Another tool you could use to identify the organism is called a taxonomic key. A **taxonomic key** is a series of paired statements that describe the physical characteristics of different organisms.

Background
Integrating Science Using what is commonly known as DNA testing, scientists can also test the nucleic acids in cells to find relationships between human ancestors.

In 1918, the Russian royal family, including Tsar Nicholas II and his wife Alexandra, were executed by soldiers of the Russian revolution. The bodies were buried in a mass grave, which was discovered in 1989. The bodies were exhumed, and scientists assembled five female and four male skeletons. To identify the bodies, scientists tested DNA taken from the skeletons and compared it to DNA donated by the Duke of Edinburgh, grand-nephew of the Empress Alexandra. This allowed the researchers to conclude that the bodies actually belonged to the royal family.

All the bodies found in the grave were buried on July 17, 1998 in St. Petersburg, Russia.

Taxonomic Key

Step 1		
1a. Has 8 legs		Go to Step 2.
1b. Has more than 8 legs		Go to Step 3.
Step 2		
2a. Has one oval-shaped body region		Go to Step 4.
2b. Has two body regions		Go to Step 5.
Step 3		
3a. Has one pair of legs on each body segment		Centipede
3b. Has two pairs of legs on each body segment		Millipede
Step 4		
4a. Is less than 1 millimeter long		Mite
4b. Is more than 1 millimeter long		Tick
Step 5		
5a. Has clawlike pincers		Go to Step 6.
5b. Has no clawlike pincers		Spider
Step 6		
6a. Has a long tail with a stinger		Scorpion
6b. Has no tail or stinger		Pseudoscorpion

The taxonomic key in Figure 16 can help you identify the organism in your bed. To use the key, start by reading the two paired statements numbered 1a and 1b. Notice that the two statements are opposites. Decide which of the statements applies to the organism. Follow the direction at the end of that statement. For example, if the organism has 8 legs, follow the direction at the end of statement 1a, which says "Go to Step 2." Continue this process until you learn the organism's identity.

Figure 16 A taxonomic key is a series of paired statements that describe the physical characteristics of different organisms. There are six pairs of statements in this key. *Drawing Conclusions What is the identity of the organism shown in the picture?*

 Section 3 Review

1. Why is it important for biologists to classify organisms into groups?
2. How is an organism's evolutionary history related to the way in which it is classified?
3. Explain Linnaeus's contribution to modern taxonomy.
4. **Thinking Critically Applying Concepts** Create a taxonomic key that could help identify a piece of fruit as either an apple, an orange, a strawberry, or a banana.

Science at Home

With a family member, go on a "classification hunt" in the kitchen. Look in your cabinets, refrigerator, and drawers to discover what classification systems your family uses to organize items. Discuss the advantages of organizing items in your kitchen in the way that you do. Then explain to your family member the importance of classification in biology.

Program Resources

◆ **Teaching Resources** 1-3 Review and Reinforce, p. 25; 1-3 Enrich, p. 26

Media and Technology

 Interactive Student Tutorial CD-ROM A-1

Answers to Self-Assessment

Caption Question

Figure 16 A pseudoscorpion

☑ *Checkpoint*

Scientists compare the body structures and chemical makeup of fossils to each other and to modern organisms.

3 Assess

Section 3 Review Answers

1. Scientists classify living things into groups because it makes it easier for the scientists to study them.
2. An organism's evolutionary history determines how it is classified.
3. Linnaeus devised the naming system, binomial nomenclature, which classifies organisms into genus and species.
4. Sample taxonomic key:

Step 1	
1a. Red fruit	Go to Step 2.
1b. Fruit not red	Go to Step 3.
Step 2	
2a. Fruit has smooth skin with seeds inside	Apple
2b. Fruit has little seeds scattered over the skin	Strawberry
Step 3	
3a. Yellow, elongated fruit	Banana
3b. Orange, round fruit	Orange

Science at Home

Remind students to identify the criteria used to classify kitchen objects in their houses. Families may have organized items by size, by function, or by location of use. Ask students whether their family members agreed with their classification systems.

Performance Assessment

Skills Check Write this list on the board: *bed, dining table, recliner, dresser, sofa, cabinet, bookshelf.* Instruct students to create a seven-level classification system that includes all of these items. *(Sample: Kingdom Furniture, Phylum Household Furniture, Class Legged, Order Seats, Family Individual, Genus Chair, Species Recliner)*

A ◆ 37

Classifying

Living Mysteries

Preparing for Inquiry

Key Concept Taxonomic keys can be used to classify organisms.

Skills Objectives Students will be able to
- observe and identify characteristics of mammals;
- classify organisms into one of five mammalian orders using a taxonomic key.

Time 30 minutes

Guiding Inquiry

Invitation
Encourage students to list characteristics that all mammals share. Students may suggest live birth, milk from mammary glands, and hair covering body. Other characteristics include three ear bones, differentiated teeth, and a diaphragm for breathing.

Introducing the Procedure
- Suggest students try out the taxonomic key on page 37 to become familiar with how keys are used.

Troubleshooting the Experiment
Students may wonder why some mammals, such as bats, are not represented in the key. Explain that there are more than 15 orders of mammals. Only five are represented here.

Expected Outcome
Each of the five organisms will be classified in one of the five orders.

You Be the Detective

Living Mysteries

In this lab, you will discover how some familiar mammals are classified.

Problem

How does a taxonomic key help you classify living things?

Skills Focus

observing, inferring, classifying

Materials

pencil   paper

Procedure

1. Observe the five organisms labeled A through E. All of these organisms belong to the class known as mammals, a group that includes you and many of the animals that are most familiar to you. Each of these mammals belongs to a different order of mammals.
2. Examine the paired statements in the taxonomic key for mammals. Begin at Step 1 to identify the order to which the mammal in photograph A belongs. Because the animal in photograph A does not have five digits or hands with flexible thumbs, go to Step 2. Keep following the key until you identify this mammal's order.
3. Use the key to identify the order to which the mammals in photographs B through E belong.

Taxonomic Key for Mammals

Step 1		
1a.	Have five digits on all limbs, and hands with flexible thumbs	Primates (includes monkeys, chimpanzees, and humans)
1b.	Do not have five digits on all limbs, and hands with flexible thumbs	Go to Step 2.
Step 2		
2a.	Have limbs with claws or nails, not hooves	Go to Step 3.
2b.	Have limbs with hooves, not claws or nails	Go to Step 4.
Step 3		
3a.	Have long muscular trunks	Proboscidea (includes all types of elephants)
3b.	Have sharp teeth for biting and tearing flesh	Carnivora (includes lions, bears, and raccoons)
Step 4		
4a.	Have limbs with an even number of hooved toes	Artiodactyla (includes antelopes, sheep and cows)
4b.	Have limbs with an odd number of hooved toes	Perissodactyla (includes horses and rhinoceroses)

Analyze and Conclude

1. For each organism in the photographs, name the order of mammals to which it belongs.
2. Why is it important that the pair of statements at Step 1 be opposites?
3. Could you use this taxonomic key to classify animals that are not mammals? Explain.
4. Could you use this key to classify different types of carnivores, such as foxes, skunks, and walruses? Explain.

5. **Think About It** Based on your answers to questions 3 and 4, what can you infer about the limits of specific taxonomic keys?

More to Explore

Try making a taxonomic key to sort four or five everyday objects such as writing implements or shoes. Try out your key on a partner to test it. Make any necessary changes. Then, exchange keys with a classmate. Use the keys to sort the selected objects.

Program Resources

◆ **Teaching Resources** Chapter 1 Real-World Lab, pp. 33–35

Analyze and Conclude

1. A: Artiodactyla; B: Carnivora; C: Primates; D: Perissodactyla; E: Proboscidea
2. The opposite statements are written so that the organisms being classified match one choice or the other. This situation leads the user either to a correct classification or to the next step in the process. Each pair of statements is written to cover all possible choices.
3. No. The key is designed only for classifying the five groups of mammals into appropriate orders.
4. No. The key is not designed to classify animals within each order of mammals.
5. Any taxonomic key is designed to classify a specific group of organisms. The key does not work for organisms outside that group. Also, the key cannot be used to classify members of the group into smaller categories.

Extending the Inquiry

More to Explore Students can demonstrate the process of making a key by role-playing someone thinking aloud while considering various routes to take in sequencing the key. Encourage students to remark why one route might be easier or harder for the writer and/or the user of the key.

Objectives

After completing the lesson, students will be able to

◆ name and describe the six kingdoms into which all organisms are grouped.

Key Terms prokaryotes, nucleus, eukaryotes

1 Engage/Explore

Activating Prior Knowledge

Ask students: **How many different kinds of movies are there?** Encourage students to list different genres of movies. Write appropriate suggestions on the board. (*Sample: action, mystery, comedy, romance, western, foreign*) Invite students to consider how using these categories helps them describe and compare movies.

DISCOVER

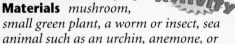

Skills Focus classifying
Materials *mushroom, small green plant, a worm or insect, sea animal such as an urchin, anemone, or cultivated coral*
Time 15 minutes
Tips Cultivated coral and sea animals can be purchased at tropical fish stores. Caution students to be careful handling the animals and to wash their hands immediately after the activity.
Expected Outcome Students may place all the organisms in the same kingdom. Biologists classify the sea animal and the worm or insect in the same kingdom.
Think It Over Defining characteristics will vary but are likely to focus on movement. Discuss features biologists use to classify living things such as cell type, food-making ability, and number of cells.

SECTION 4 The Six Kingdoms

DISCOVER ··· ACTIVITY

Which Organism Goes Where?

1. Your teacher will give you some organisms to observe. Two of the organisms are classified in the same kingdom.

2. Observe the organisms. Decide which organisms might belong in the same kingdom. Write the reasons for your decision. Wash your hands after handling the organisms.

3. Discuss your decision and reasoning with your classmates.

Think It Over
Forming Operational Definitions What characteristics do you think define the kingdom into which you placed the two organisms?

GUIDE FOR READING

◆ What are the six kingdoms into which all organisms are grouped?

Reading Tip Before you read the section, make a list of the headings. As you read, list the characteristics of organisms in each kingdom.

When Linnaeus developed his system of classification, there were two kingdoms: plant and animal. But, the use of the microscope led to the discovery of new organisms and the identification of differences among cells. A two-kingdom system was no longer useful. **Today, the system of classification includes six kingdoms: archaebacteria, eubacteria, protists, fungi, plants, and animals.** Organisms are placed into kingdoms based on their type of cells, their ability to make food, and the number of cells in their bodies.

Archaebacteria

In 1983, scientists took a water sample from a spot deep in the Pacific Ocean where hot gases and molten rock boiled into the ocean from Earth's interior. To their surprise, they discovered unicellular organisms in the sample. Today, scientists classify these organisms in a kingdom called Archaebacteria (ahr kee bak TEER ee uh), which means "ancient bacteria."

Archaebacteria can be either autotrophic or heterotrophic. Some live on the ocean floor, some in salty water, and some in hot springs. Don't be alarmed, but some even live in your intestines.

Figure 17 Heat-loving archaebacteria thrive in this hot spring in Yellowstone National Park.

40 ◆ A

READING STRATEGIES

Reading Tip Provide each student with six note cards. Instruct students to write a kingdom name on one side of each card. As students read the section, have them list, on the opposite side of each card, the characteristics of organisms in the kingdom. Then have partners take turns using their sets of note cards as flashcards for testing their knowledge about the six kingdoms.

Study and Comprehension Have students work in small groups to prepare a compare/contrast table that shows similarities and differences among organisms in the six kingdoms. Suggest that students write these column headings: *Kingdom, Cell Type, Ability to Make Food, Number of Cells, Examples.* Have students list the kingdoms in the first column and fill in information from their reading for the remaining columns.

Archaebacteria are **prokaryotes** (proh KAR ee ohtz), organisms whose cells lack a nucleus. A **nucleus** (NOO klee us) (plural *nuclei*) is a dense area in a cell that contains nucleic acids—the chemical instructions that direct the cell's activities. In prokaryotes, nucleic acids are not contained within a nucleus.

Eubacteria

What do the bacteria that produce yogurt have in common with the bacteria that give you strep throat? They both belong to the kingdom known as Eubacteria (yoo bak TEER ee uh). Like archaebacteria, eubacteria are unicellular prokaryotes. And like archaebacteria, some eubacteria are autotrophs while others are heterotrophs. Eubacteria are classified in their own kingdom, however, because their chemical makeup is different from that of archaebacteria.

Unlike some eubacteria, such as those that cause strep throat, most eubacteria are helpful. Some produce vitamins, some produce foods like yogurt, and some recycle essential chemicals, such as nitrogen.

☑ *Checkpoint* How are eubacteria similar to archaebacteria? How do they differ?

Protists

Slime molds, like the ones that frightened people near Dallas, are protists (PROH tists). The protist kingdom is sometimes called the "odds and ends" kingdom because its members are so different from one another. For example, some protists are autotrophs, while others are heterotrophs. Also, although most protists are unicellular, some, such as the organisms that are commonly called seaweeds, are multicellular.

You may be wondering why those protists that are unicellular are not classified in one of the kingdoms of bacteria. It is because, unlike bacteria, protists are **eukaryotes** (yoo KAR ee ohtz)—organisms with cells that contain nuclei.

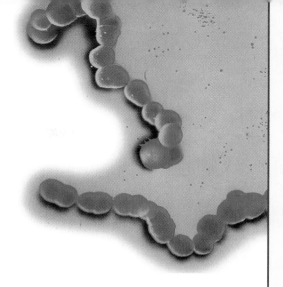

Figure 18 Most eubacteria are helpful. However, these eubacteria are *Streptococci*, which can give you strep throat! *Classifying What characteristics do eubacteria share?*

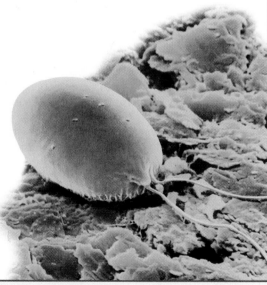

Figure 19 The protist kingdom contains diverse organisms. This unicellular green protist, which lives in fresh water, is called *Chlamydomonas*.

Program Resources

◆ **Teaching Resources** 1-4 Lesson Plan, p. 27; 1-4 Section Summary, p. 28

Media and Technology

🎧 **Audiotapes** English-Spanish Summary 1-4

Answers to Self-Assessment

Caption Question

Figure 18 Eubacteria are unicellular prokaryotes that are either autotrophs or heterotrophs.

☑ *Checkpoint*

Both are unicellular prokaryotes that are either autotrophs or heterotrophs. Their chemical makeups differ.

2 *Facilitate*

Archaebacteria

Language Arts Connection

Have students describe some characteristics of archaebacteria. Ask: **Why do you think this type of bacteria has this name?** (*The name means "ancient bacteria," and these bacteria are like the earliest life forms.*) **learning modality: verbal**

Eubacteria

Real-Life Learning

Materials *plastic bucket with dilute suspension of blue tempera and water, soap, paper towels, plastic dropcloth*
Time 30 minutes

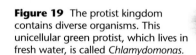

Direct students to dip their hands in the bucket of diluted tempera and let them air-dry. Then students should close their eyes and wash their hands without looking. Students should see if they have removed all the "bacteria." Ask: **What can you infer about washing your hands from this experiment?** (*If blue stain remains on their hands, they have not removed all the bacteria.*) **learning modality: kinesthetic**

Protists

Cultural Diversity

Seaweed is an important source of nutrition in many Asian countries. In Japan, different varieties are used depending on the menu. For example, nori, wakame, kombu and laver are used in soups, salads, tea and sushi. **learning modality: verbal**

Ongoing Assessment

Oral Presentation Ask volunteers to describe themselves as an archaebacteria, eubacteria, or protist. Have the class guess which organism the volunteers are pretending to be.

Fungi

Real-Life Learning

Encourage students to contact local organic gardening centers to find out more about the role of fungi in decaying plants such as those used in compost. Students should prepare a list of questions before they talk to a gardener. **learning modality: verbal**

Plants

Demonstration

To help students who have difficulty ACTIVITY understanding the test explanation, soak a light green leaf in alcohol for 24 hours. Dry the leaf, place it in a glass dish, and cover it with iodine. Explain that iodine darkens when it comes in contact with starch, a type of food. Have students take turns looking at the leaf. Ask: **What can we conclude about plants from this demonstration?** *(They have starch in their leaves.)* **How did it get there?** *(The plant made it using the sun's energy, carbon dioxide, and water.)* **limited English proficiency**

Animals

Building Inquiry Skills: Classifying

Materials *prepared slides of different bacteria in plant or animal cells,* microscopes
Time 20 minutes

Demonstrate how to use a microscope, and direct students to examine the slides and sketch the cells. Then have them decide which cells are bacteria and which are plant or animal. *(Cells with a nucleus are animals or plants, those without are bacteria.)* **learning modality: visual**

Figure 20 The animal you see peeking out of this cuplike fungus is a poison arrow frog. These organisms live in the forests of Central America. *Interpreting Photographs Which organisms in the photograph are heterotrophs?*

Fungi

If you have ever seen mushrooms, you have seen fungi (FUN jy). Mushrooms, molds, and mildew are all fungi. Most fungi are multicellular eukaryotes. A few, such as yeast, are unicellular eukaryotes. Fungi are found almost everywhere on land, but only a few live in fresh water. All fungi are heterotrophs. Most fungi feed on dead or decaying organisms. The cuplike fungus you see in Figure 20 obtains its food from the parts of plants that are decaying in the soil.

Plants

Dandelions on a lawn, mosses in a forest, and tomatoes in a garden are familiar kinds of plants. Plants are all multicellular eukaryotes. In addition, plants are autotrophs that make their own food. Without plants, life on Earth would not exist. Plants feed almost all of the heterotrophs on Earth. The plant kingdom includes a variety of organisms. Some plants produce flowers, while others do not. Some plants, such as a giant sequoia tree, can grow very tall. Others, like mosses, never grow taller than a few centimeters.

Animals

A dog, a flea on the dog's ear, and a rabbit the dog chases have much in common because all are animals. All animals are multicellular eukaryotes. In addition, all animals are heterotrophs. Animals have different adaptations that allow them to locate food, capture it, eat it, and digest it. Members of the animal kingdom are found in diverse environments on Earth.

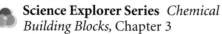

Section 4 Review

1. List the six kingdoms into which all organisms are classified.
2. Which two kingdoms include only prokaryotes?
3. Which kingdoms include only heterotrophic organisms?
4. **Thinking Critically Classifying** In a rain forest, you see an unfamiliar green organism. As you watch, an ant walks onto one of its cuplike leaves. The leaf closes and traps the ant. Do you have enough information to classify this organism? Why or why not?

Check Your Progress CHAPTER PROJECT 1
Now that you have completed your observations, analyze your data. Conclude whether your object is alive. Then review what you learned about the six kingdoms. Which kingdom does your object belong in or most resemble? *(Hint: Recall that an organism's nutrition is an important distinction among some of the kingdoms. How did your mystery object obtain its food?)*

42 ◆ A

Program Resources

 Science Explorer Series *Chemical Building Blocks*, Chapter 3
◆ **Teaching Resources** 1-4 Review and Reinforce, p. 29; 1-4 Enrich, p. 30

Media and Technology

Interactive Student Tutorial CD-ROM A-1

Answers to Self-Assessment

Caption Question

Figure 20 Both the frog and the fungus are heterotrophs.

SECTION

1 What Is Life?

Key Ideas
◆ All living things have a cellular organization, contain similar chemicals, use energy, grow and develop, respond to their surroundings, and reproduce.
◆ Organisms arise from other organisms similar to themselves.
◆ All living things must satisfy their basic needs for energy, water, living space, and stable internal conditions.

Key Terms

organism	variable
cell	autotroph
unicellular	heterotroph
multicellular	homeostasis
development	
stimulus	
response	
reproduce	
spontaneous generation	
controlled experiment	

 SECTION

2 The Origin of Life

INTEGRATING EARTH SCIENCE

Key Ideas
◆ Nitrogen, water vapor, carbon dioxide, and methane were probably the most abundant gases in Earth's atmosphere 3.6 billion years ago. Today the major gases are nitrogen and oxygen.
◆ Scientists hypothesize that over millions of years, the small chemical units of life formed in Earth's oceans. Some joined to form the large chemical building blocks found in cells.

Key Term
fossil

 SECTION

3 Classifying Organisms

Key Ideas
◆ Biologists use classification to organize living things into groups so that the organisms are easy to study.
◆ Carolus Linnaeus devised a system of naming organisms called binomial nomenclature.
◆ Today, organisms are classified into seven levels: kingdom, phylum, class, order, family, genus, and species.
◆ Species with similar evolutionary histories are classified more closely together.

Key Terms
classification
taxonomy
binomial nomenclature
genus
species
evolution
taxonomic key

SECTION

4 The Six Kingdoms

Key Ideas
◆ All organisms are grouped into six kingdoms: archaebacteria, eubacteria, protists, fungi, plants, and animals.
◆ Some characteristics used to classify organisms into kingdoms are cell structure, the way organisms obtain food, and the number of cells in organisms.

Key Terms

prokaryote	nucleus	eukaryote

USING THE INTERNET
www.science-explorer.phschool.com

CHAPTER 1 REVIEW

3 Assess

Section 4 Review Answers
1. Archaebacteria, eubacteria, protists, fungi, plants, animals
2. Archaebacteria and eubacteria
3. Fungi and animals
4. Some kingdoms can be eliminated, but there is not enough information to make a definite identification. The organism is multicellular, so it is not an archaebacteria or a eubacteria. It is green, so it may be an autotroph, but because it is trapping food, it may be a heterotroph. So it might be a plant or an animal or a multicellular protist because it is in a moist environment.

Check Your Progress CHAPTER PROJECT 1
Remind students they should be designing a display to present to the class. Provide students with guidelines to analyze their data.

Program Resources

◆ **Teaching Resources** Chapter 1 Project Scoring Rubric, p. 14; Chapter 1 Performance Assessment Teacher Notes, p. 156; Chapter Performance Assessment Student Worksheet, pp. 157–158; Chapter 1 Test, pp. 159–162

Performance Assessment

Drawing Invite students to sketch a member of each kingdom and describe the characteristics that place it in that kingdom.

 Students can save their sketches in their portfolios.

Reviewing Content:
Multiple Choice

1. b 2. c 3. c 4. a 5. b

True or False

6. true 7. heterotroph 8. true
9. Linnaeus 10. true

Checking Concepts

11. Students might point out that plants will bend toward sunlight and that plants grow, develop, and reproduce.
12. The earliest organisms to live on Earth probably lived in the oceans. They were heterotrophs and took in chemicals from the waters around them for energy.
13. A scientific name gives information about an organism's characteristics and avoids confusion about the identity of the organism.
14. Scientists compare the body structures of organisms, the early development of their embryos, and the chemical makeup of their cells. They also study fossils.
15. Fungi are heterotrophs; plants are autotrophs.
16. Students' paragraphs should discuss how the pet obtains food and water, describe the pet's living space, and mention at least one way the pet maintains homeostasis.

Thinking Visually

17. a. water b. living space c. autotrophs d. heterotrophs e. food and water

Applying Skills

18. Yes; the light is the variable.
19. Sample hypothesis: If plants do not have enough light, they will die.
20. In two weeks, the plant on the left will be dead, but the plant on the right will be healthy.
21. Sample experiment: Two plants receive the same light, but one receives one-fourth cup of water a day, and the other one-fourth cup every two days.

Reviewing Content

 For more review of key concepts, see the Interactive Student Tutorial CD-ROM.

Multiple Choice
Choose the letter of the answer that best completes each statement.

1. The idea that life could spring from nonliving matter is called
   a. development.
   b. spontaneous generation.
   c. homeostasis.
   d. evolution.

2. Which gas was not part of Earth's atmosphere 3.6 billion years ago?
   a. methane   b. nitrogen
   c. oxygen   d. water vapor

3. The science of placing organisms into groups based on shared characteristics is called
   a. development.   b. biology.
   c. taxonomy.   d. evolution.

4. A genus is divided into
   a. species.   b. phyla.
   c. families.   d. classes.

5. Which organisms have cells that do not contain nuclei?
   a. protists   b. archaebacteria
   c. plants   d. fungi

True or False
If the statement is true, write true. If it is false, change the underlined word or words to make the statement true.

6. Your first teeth fall out and are replaced by permanent teeth. This is an example of <u>development</u>.

7. When you eat salad, you are acting like an <u>autotroph</u>.

8. The first organisms on Earth were probably <u>heterotrophs</u>.

9. <u>Aristotle</u> devised a system of naming organisms that is called binomial nomenclature.

10. The process by which organisms gradually change over a long period of time is called <u>evolution</u>.

Checking Concepts

11. Your friend thinks that plants are not alive because they do not move. How would you respond to your friend?
12. Describe where Earth's early organisms lived, and how they obtained food.
13. What are the advantages of identifying an organism by its scientific name?
14. What evidence do scientists use to learn about the evolutionary history of a species?
15. What is the major difference between fungi and plants?
16. **Writing to Learn** Write a paragraph that describes how your pet, or a friend's pet, meets its needs as a living thing.

Thinking Visually

17. **Concept Map** Copy the concept map about the needs of organisms onto a separate sheet of paper. Then complete it and add a title. (For more on concept maps, see the Skills Handbook.)

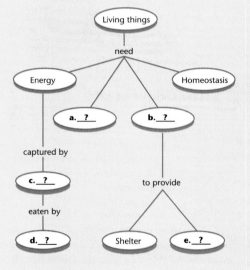

Thinking Critically

22. Although all robots use energy and some respond to their surroundings, they do not use energy to grow and develop. Living things are made out of cells and are able to reproduce themselves.
23. *Entamoeba histolytica* and *Entamoeba coli*; they are in the same genus.
24. This recipe may have worked because the grains attracted mice into the open pot. To disprove this, you could observe the pot to make sure mice did not enter, or cover the pot so air could enter, but mice could not.

Applying Skills

A student designed an experiment to test how light affects the growth of plants. Refer to the illustrations below to answer Questions 18–21.

18. **Controlling Variables** Is this a controlled experiment? If not, why not? If so, identify the variable.
19. **Developing Hypotheses** What hypothesis might this experiment be testing?
20. **Predicting** Based on what you know about plants, predict how each plant will have changed after two weeks.
21. **Designing Experiments** Design a controlled experiment to determine whether the amount of water that a plant receives affects its growth.

Thinking Critically

22. **Applying Concepts** How do you know that a robot is not alive?
23. **Classifying** Which two of the following organisms are most closely related: *Entamoeba histolytica, Escherichia coli, Entamoeba coli*? Explain your answer.
24. **Relating Cause and Effect** When people believed that spontaneous generation occurred, there was a recipe for making mice: Place a dirty shirt and a few wheat grains in an open pot; wait three weeks. List the reasons why this recipe might have worked. How could you demonstrate that spontaneous generation was not responsible for the appearance of mice?

Performance Assessment

CHAPTER PROJECT 1 Wrap Up

Present Your Project Prepare a display presenting your conclusion about your mystery object. Describe the observations that helped you to reach your conclusion. Compare your ideas with those of other students. If necessary, defend your work.

Reflect and Record Make a list of the characteristics of life that you observed in your mystery object. Which were hard to study? Explain in your journal why some characteristics were hard to investigate.

Getting Involved

In Your Community Go to a park or playground with a pad of paper and a pencil. Record the names of ten living things that you see there. Record the characteristics of life you observe for each organism. Classify each organism into a kingdom. Make a poster to display in your classroom. Your poster should include the location you studied, the common and scientific names of the organisms, their characteristics of life, and their kingdom.

Program Resources

◆ **Inquiry Skills Handbook** Provides teaching and review of all inquiry skills

---

Performance Assessment

CHAPTER PROJECT 1 Wrap Up

Present Your Project
Students' displays should be well organized and describe how students tested their hypotheses. Have each student give a brief presentation to the class describing how the results of their tests support their conclusions. Encourage students to talk about results that they found surprising.

Reflect and Record Students may have had trouble determining whether their object was alive if it was a fungus, a plant, or an animal such as coral that does not move.

Getting Involved

In Your Community Have students take a list of the characteristics of life with them. Some characteristics, such as reproduction and growth, will be difficult to observe directly but might be inferred if younger, smaller individuals of the same species are present. Students may have difficulty determining the species names for the organisms they record. Suggest they sketch the organisms to help them find the names later. Challenge students to look for members of each kingdom.

2 Viruses and Bacteria

Sections	Time	Student Edition Activities	Other Activities	
Be a Disease Detective p. 47	Ongoing (1½ weeks)	Check Your Progress, pp. 54, 73 Wrap Up, p. 77	TE	Chapter 2 Project Notes, pp. 46–47
1 Viruses pp. 48–55 ◆ Give reasons why viruses are considered to be nonliving. ◆ Describe the basic structure of a virus. ◆ Explain how viruses multiply.	4 periods/ 2 blocks	**Discover** Can You Cure a Cold?, p. 48 **Try This** Modeling a Virus, p. 51 **Skills Lab: Making Models** How Many Viruses Fit on a Pin?, p. 55	TE TE	Inquiry Challenge, p. 50 Including All Students, p. 51
2 Bacteria pp. 56–67 ◆ Describe ways in which bacteria cells are different from all other organism's cells. ◆ List positive roles that bacteria play in people's lives. ◆ Name the two kingdoms of bacteria and tell how bacteria reproduce and survive.	6 periods/ 3 blocks	**Discover** How Quickly Can Bacteria Multiply?, p. 56 **Sharpen Your Skills** Graphing, p. 59 **Try This** Bacteria for Breakfast, p. 61 **Real-World Lab: You, the Consumer** Do Disinfectants Work?, pp. 66–67	TE TE ISLM IES PTA	Building Inquiry Skills: Classifying, p. 57; Designing Experiments, p. 60; Drawing Conclusions, p. 63 Demonstration, p. 64 A-2, "Eubacteria That Dine on Vegetables" "Riddles of the Pharaohs," p. 38 "Testing Yogurt," pp. 1–8
3 *INTEGRATING HEALTH* **Viruses, Bacteria, and Your Health** pp. 68–74 ◆ Describe how infectious diseases spread from person to person. ◆ Describe some ways in which infectious diseases can be treated or prevented.	3–4 periods/ 1½ blocks	**Discover** How Do Infectious Diseases Spread?, p. 68	TE TE	Demonstrations, pp. 69, 72 Real-Life Learning, p. 70
Study Guide/Chapter Review pp. 75–77	1 period/ ½ block		ISAB	Provides teaching and review of all inquiry skills

 For Standard or Block Schedule The Resource Pro® CD-ROM gives you maximum flexibility for planning your instruction for any type of schedule. Resource Pro® contains Planning Express®, an advanced scheduling program, as well as the entire contents of the Teaching Resources and the Computer Test Bank.

CHAPTER PLANNING GUIDE

Program Resources	Assessment Strategies	Media and Technology
TR Chapter 2 Project Teacher Notes, pp. 36–37 **TR** Chapter 2 Project Overview and Worksheets, pp. 38–41 **TR** Chapter 2 Project Scoring Rubric, p. 42	**SE** Performance Assessment: Chapter 2 Project Wrap Up, p. 77 **TE** Check Your Progress, pp. 54, 73 **TE** Performance Assessment: Chapter 2 Project Wrap Up, p. 77 **TR** Chapter 2 Project Scoring Rubric, p. 42	Science Explorer Internet Site
TR 2-1 Lesson Plan, p. 43 **TR** 2-1 Section Summary, p. 44 **TR** 2-1 Review and Reinforce, p. 45 **TR** 2-1 Enrich, p. 46 **TR** Chapter 2 Skills Lab, pp. 55–56 **SES** Book C, *Cells and Heredity,* Chapter 1	**SE** Section 1 Review, p. 54 **SE** Analyze and Conclude, p. 55 **TE** Ongoing Assessment, pp. 49, 51, 53 **TE** Performance Assessment, p. 54 **TR** 2-1 Review and Reinforce, p. 45	Exploring Life Science Videodisc, Unit 2 Side 2, "On the Trail of a Disease" Audiotapes: English-Spanish Summary 2-1 Transparency 4, "How a Virus Attaches to a Host Cell" Transparency 5, "Exploring How Active Viruses Multiply" Transparency 6, "Exploring How Hidden Viruses Multiply" Interactive Student Tutorial CD-ROM, A-2
TR 2-2 Lesson Plan, p. 47 **TR** 2-2 Section Summary, p. 48 **TR** 2-2 Review and Reinforce, p. 49 **TR** 2-2 Enrich, p. 50 **TR** Chapter 2 Real-World Lab, pp. 57–59 **SES** Book H, *Earth's Waters,* Chapter 1	**SE** Section 2 Review, p. 65 **SE** Analyze and Conclude, p. 67 **TE** Ongoing Assessment, pp. 57, 59, 61, 63 **TE** Performance Assessment, p. 65 **TR** 2-2 Review and Reinforce, p. 49	Exploring Life Science Videodisc, Unit 2 Side 2, "Positive Bacteria" Audiotapes: English-Spanish Summary 2-2 Transparency 7, "The Structure of a Bacterial Cell" Interactive Student Tutorial CD-ROM, A-2
TR 2-3 Lesson Plan, p. 51 **TR** 2-3 Section Summary, p. 52 **TR** 2-3 Review and Reinforce, p. 53 **TR** 2-3 Enrich, p. 54 **SES** Book E, *Environmental Science,* Chapter 5	**SE** Section 3 Review, p. 73 **TE** Ongoing Assessment, pp. 69, 71 **TE** Performance Assessment, p. 73 **TR** 2-3 Review and Reinforce, p. 53	Exploring Life Science Videodisc, Unit 2 Side 2, "Have You Had Your Shots?" Audiotapes: English-Spanish Summary 2-3 Interactive Student Tutorial CD-ROM, A-2
TR Chapter 2 Performance Assessment, pp. 163–165 **TR** Chapter 2 Test, pp. 166–169	**SE** Chapter Review, pp. 75–77 **TR** Chapter 2 Performance Assessment, pp. 163–165 **TR** Chapter 2 Test, pp. 166–169 **CTB** Test A-2	Computer Test Bank, Test A-2 Interactive Student Tutorial CD-ROM, A-2

Key: **SE** Student Edition   **TE** Teacher's Edition   **TR** Teaching Resources
CTB Computer Test Bank   **SES** Science Explorer Series Text   **ISLM** Integrated Science Laboratory Manual
ISAB Inquiry Skills Activity Book   **PTA** Product Testing Activities by *Consumer Reports*   **IES** Interdisciplinary Explorations Series

Meeting the National Science Education Standards and AAAS Benchmarks

National Science Education Standards	Benchmarks for Science Literacy	Unifying Themes
Science as Inquiry (Content Standard A) ◆ **Use mathematics in scientific inquiry** How many viruses fit on a pin? *(Skills Lab)* ◆ **Use appropriate tools and techniques to gather, analyze, and interpret data** Students investigate how well disinfectants control the growth of bacteria. *(Real-World Lab)* **Life Science** (Content Standard C) ◆ **Diversity and adaptations of organisms** Students learn the main characteristics of viruses and how they reproduce. *(Section 1)* Students learn the main characteristics of bacteria and how they reproduce. *(Section 2)* ◆ **Populations and ecosystems** Students learn that bacteria function as decomposers of dead organic matter. *(Section 2)* ◆ **Structure and function of living systems** Students learn that the cells of bacteria are different from those of other living organisms. *(Section 2)* Students learn that disease is often the result of infection by bacteria and viruses *(Section 3)*	**1B Scientific Inquiry** Students compare the effects of two disinfectants and make inferences about which is more effective by gathering and analyzing data. *(Real-World Lab)* **1C Mathematical Inquiry** Students use models to investigate the size of viruses. *(Skills Lab)* **3C Issues in Technology** Students learn that technology has influenced the development of helpful antibiotics and study how antibiotic resistance affects society. *(Section 3, Science and Society)* **5A Diversity of Life** Positive roles that bacteria play in people's lives are presented as well as a discussion of bacteria's role as a decomposer and recycler of organic matter. *(Section 2)* **5D Interdependence of Life** The relationship between viruses and their host cells are discussed. *(Section 1)* **12D Communication** Students organize information in data tables and use the results to make inferences about the relative effectiveness of two disinfectants. *(Real-World Lab)*	◆ **Scale and Structure** Viruses are considered to be nonliving, but have genetic material necessary to reproduce. Bacteria are different in structure from other cells. *(Sections 1, 2)* ◆ **Unity and Diversity** There are many types of viruses and bacteria, but they all share basic characteristics. Bacteria and viruses are responsible for infectious disease and are transmitted by one of four different ways. *(Sections 1, 2, 3)* ◆ **Evolution** The first forms of life on Earth were similar to bacteria. *(Section 2)* ◆ **Patterns of Change** Bacteria are responsible for altering Earth's early atmosphere. *(Section 2)* ◆ **System and Interactions** Bacteria interact with their environment in many ways. Some are producers, some are decomposers, some are parasites. Early bacteria probably altered Earth's atmosphere. *(Sections 1, 2, 3)*

Media and Technology

Exploring Life Science Videodisc
◆ **Section 1** "On the Trail of a Disease" tracks an outbreak of the Ebola virus from "patient zero" and notes how the scientists attempt to protect the population.
◆ **Section 2** "Positive Bacteria" shows the positive use of bacteria in a water treatment operation and in the process of photosynthesis.
◆ **Section 3** "Have You Had Your Shots?" describes the role of vaccines and antibiotics in protecting against deadly diseases.

Interactive Student Tutorial CD-ROM
◆ **Chapter Review** Interactive questions help students to self-assess their mastery of key chapter concepts.

Student Edition Connection Strategies

◆ **Section 1** Integrating Technology, p. 54
◆ **Section 2** Integrating Earth Science, p. 59
Science & History, pp. 62–63
Integrating Environmental Science, p. 64
Integrating Technology, p. 65
◆ **Section 3** Integrating Health, p. 68
Social Studies Connection, p. 70

USING THE INTERNET

www.science-explorer.phschool.com

Visit the Science Explorer Internet site to find an
up-to-date activity for Chapter 2 of *From Bacteria to Plants.*

ACTIVITY	Time (minutes)	Materials — Quantities for one work group	Skills
Section 1			
Discover, p. 48	20	**Nonconsumable** assortment of empty containers for over-the-counter cold medications (pills and liquids), such as decongestants, pain relievers, cough medications	Inferring
Try This, p. 51	20	**Consumable** pipe cleaners, string, thread, rubber bands, construction paper, aluminum foil, straws, plastic wrap, glue, tape **Nonconsumable** paper clips, clay, scissors	Making Models
Skills Lab, p. 55	45	**Consumable** long strips of paper, tape **Nonconsumable** straight pin, pencil, scissors, calculator, meter stick	Making Models
Section 2			
Discover, p. 56	20	**Nonconsumable** paper cups; dried lima, kidney, or navy beans	Inferring
Sharpen your Skills, p. 59	20	**Consumable** graph paper **Nonconsumable** pencil	Graphing
Try This, p. 61	20	**Consumable** unpasteurized yogurt, methylene blue **Nonconsumable** plastic dropper, glass slide, cover slip, microscope, lab apron	Observing
Real-World Lab, pp. 66–67	30	**Consumable** 2 household disinfectants, transparent tape **Nonconsumable** clock, 2 plastic droppers, 3 plastic petri dishes with sterile nutrient agar, wax pencil	Observing, Inferring, Drawing Conclusions
Section 3			
Discover, p. 68	20	**Consumable** distilled water, 0.01 M sodium hydroxide solution, phenol red solution **Nonconsumable** aprons, plastic cups, eyedroppers, goggles	Predicting

A list of all materials required for the Student Edition activities can be found on pages T14–T15. You can order Materials Kits by calling 1-800-828-7777 or by accessing the Science Explorer Internet site at **www.science-explorer.phschool.com.**

Be a Disease Detective

In this chapter, students will be introduced to viruses and bacteria and their importance in human health. This project will give them an opportunity to explore how perceptions of a common childhood disease have changed between generations.

Purpose In this project, students will have the opportunity to investigate a childhood disease by doing research in a library or on the Internet as well as preparing, conducting, and analyzing the results of a survey.

Skills Focus Students will be able to
◆ ask questions so they can research a particular disease, then prepare and conduct a survey asking people about their experience and knowledge of a disease;
◆ draw conclusions concerning how the incidence of a childhood disease and people's knowledge of the disease have changed over time.

Project Time Line Before the project, check with the librarian and the school nurse to find out whether they are willing to help students during the research phase of the project. The entire project will take four weeks. During the first week, students will research a childhood disease. During the second and third weeks, students will write and conduct their surveys. In week four, students will analyze the results of their surveys and present their report to the class. Before beginning the project, see Chapter 2 Project Teacher Notes on pages 36–37 in Teaching Resources for more details on carrying out the project. Also distribute the Chapter 2 Project Overview and Worksheets and Scoring Rubric on pages 38–42 in Teaching Resources.

Suggested Shortcuts You can simplify the project by allowing students to work in pairs or small groups. Students should work together to plan their surveys and should each interview several people, making sure that the total group includes people of different ages.

Possible Materials In addition to the library and school nurse, students could talk to their doctors to research their diseases.

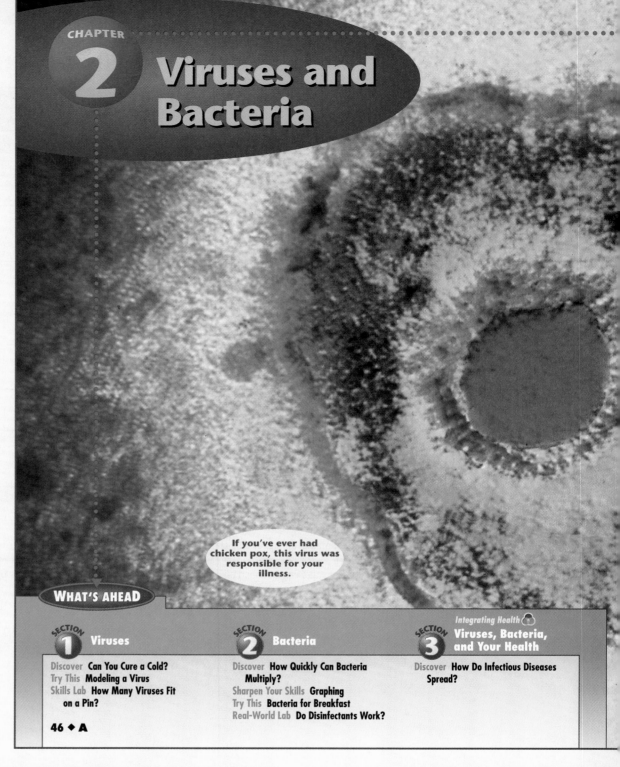

CHAPTER 2 Viruses and Bacteria

If you've ever had chicken pox, this virus was responsible for your illness.

WHAT'S AHEAD

SECTION 1 **Viruses**
Discover **Can You Cure a Cold?**
Try This **Modeling a Virus**
Skills Lab **How Many Viruses Fit on a Pin?**

46 ◆ A

SECTION 2 **Bacteria**
Discover **How Quickly Can Bacteria Multiply?**
Sharpen Your Skills **Graphing**
Try This **Bacteria for Breakfast**
Real-World Lab **Do Disinfectants Work?**

Integrating Health
SECTION 3 **Viruses, Bacteria, and Your Health**
Discover **How Do Infectious Diseases Spread?**

Launching the Project To introduce the project and to stimulate student interest, ask: **What vaccinations did you have when you were younger?** *(Sample: diphtheria, tetanus, pertussis [whooping cough], influenza, polio, measles, mumps, rubella)* Ask students: **What are the symptoms of these diseases?** *(Students may have difficulty describing the symptoms because these diseases are quite rare, due in part to the use of vaccines.)* Tell students that the vaccinations for these diseases were introduced after 1920. Also discuss the chickenpox *(Varicella)* vaccine, which was introduced in the United States in 1995. Some students in your class may have had chicken pox and will be able to describe the symptoms accurately. Ask: **Do you think students ten years from now will be able to describe the symptoms of chicken pox?** *(Probably not, since few will have had the disease growing up.)*

Be a Disease Detective

The virus pictured on this page may look harmless, but it's not. If you've ever had chicken pox, you've experienced it firsthand. Soon after the virus enters your body, red blotches appear on your skin, and you begin to itch. The chicken pox virus as well as many other viruses and bacteria cause diseases that pass from person to person. In this chapter, you will learn about viruses and bacteria, and how they affect other living things.

Not too long ago, catching certain viral and bacterial "childhood diseases" was a routine part of growing up. Those diseases included chicken pox, mumps, and pertussis (whooping cough), as well as others. In this project, you will select one childhood disease to investigate. You'll then survey people of all ages to learn who has had the disease. You'll also find out what people of different generations know about the disease.

Your Goal To survey people of different ages to find out what they know about a childhood disease.

To complete this project successfully, you must
◆ select and research one disease to learn more about it
◆ prepare a questionnaire to survey people about their knowledge and experience with the disease
◆ question a total of 30 people in different age groups, and report any patterns that you find

Get Started With several classmates, make a list of childhood diseases. Choose one disease for your survey. Do some research to find out more about the disease. Also write down the steps involved in carrying out a survey. What questions will you need to ask? How will you select the people for your survey? Draft your questionnaire.

Check Your Progress You'll be working on this project as you study this chapter. To keep your project on track, look for Check Your Progress boxes at the following points.
Section 1 Review, page 54: Write your questionnaire, and identify the people to survey.
Section 3 Review, page 73: Analyze your survey results and look for patterns.

Wrap Up At the end of the chapter (page 77), you will present your survey results to your classmates.

A ◆ 47

Program Resources

◆ **Teaching Resources** Chapter 2 Project Teacher's Notes, pp. 36–37; Chapter 2 Project Overview and Worksheets, pp. 38–41; Chapter 2 Project Scoring Rubric, p. 42

Performance Assessment

The Chapter 2 Project Scoring Rubric on page 42 of Teaching Resources will help you evaluate how well students complete the Chapter 2 Project. Students will be assessed on
◆ the thoroughness of their research on the disease;
◆ how well-organized, complete, and informative the survey is and whether it is given to 30 individuals of different ages;
◆ the clarity, thoroughness, and organization of their survey analysis and written reports;
◆ their presentations and how well they use their results to explain a change in the occurrence of, or the knowledge about, the disease.
By sharing the Chapter 2 Project Scoring Rubric with students at the beginning of the project, you will make it clear to them what they are expected to do.

Objectives

After completing the lesson, students will be able to

◆ give reasons why viruses are considered to be nonliving;

◆ describe the basic structure of a virus;

◆ explain how viruses multiply.

Key Terms virus, host, parasite, bacteriophage

1 Engage/Explore

Activating Prior Knowledge

Invite students to name diseases they are familiar with. List the diseases on the board. Tell students that viruses are the cause of some diseases. Encourage them to identify any diseases on the list that they know are caused by viruses. *(Sample: cold, flu, smallpox, measles, mumps, polio)*

DISCOVER

Skills Focus inferring
Materials *assortment of empty containers for over-the-counter cold medications (pills and liquids), such as decongestants, pain relievers, cough medications*
Time 20 minutes
Tips Have students list some symptoms of colds. Guide students to read the labels critically. The labels generally specify the active ingredients, those ingredients that actually have an effect on the body. Guide students to associate the active ingredients with the product's claims.
Think It Over Students should conclude that none of the products can cure colds, although they can relieve cold symptoms.

SECTION
1 Viruses

DISCOVER · ACTIVITY

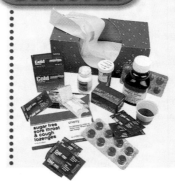

Can You Cure a Cold?

1. Look at the cold medications that your teacher displays. You may have used some of these products when you had a cold.

2. Read the ingredient labels on the products. Read the product claims.

3. Decide which medication you would use if you had a cold. Record the reasons for your choice of product.

Think It Over
Inferring Do medications cure colds? Explain your answer.

GUIDE FOR READING

◆ Why are viruses considered to be nonliving?

◆ What is the basic structure of a virus?

◆ How do viruses multiply?

Reading Tip As you read, use the headings to outline information about the characteristics of viruses.

It is a dark and quiet night. An enemy spy slips silently across the border. Invisible to the guards, the spy creeps cautiously along the edge of the road, heading toward the command center. Undetected, the spy sneaks by the center's security system and reaches the door. Breaking into the control room, the spy takes command of the central computer. The enemy is in control.

Moments later the command center's defenses finally activate. Depending on the enemy's strength and cunning, the defenses may squash the invasion before much damage is done. Otherwise the enemy will win and take over the territory.

What Is a Virus?

Although this spy story may read like a movie script, it describes events that can occur in your body. The spy acts very much like a virus invading an organism. A **virus** is a small, nonliving particle that invades and then reproduces inside a living cell.

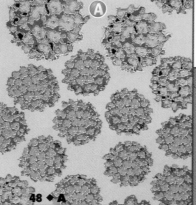

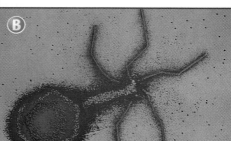

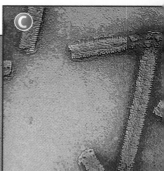

48 ◆ A

READING STRATEGIES

Reading Tip Before students read, remind them that an outline is one way to organize main ideas and details in order to remember key points about a selection. Write the following outline guide on the board and review each item. Encourage students to use the guide while they read to outline information about the characteristics of viruses.

I. First Main Idea
  A. First supporting idea or fact
    1. detail or example
    2. detail or example
  B. Second supporting idea or fact
II. Second Main Idea (outline will continue)

Vocabulary Tell students that the word *virus* is from a Latin word meaning *"slimy liquid."* Suggest they research to find what language the word *bacteriophage* comes from.

Biologists consider viruses to be nonliving because viruses are not cells. Viruses do not use energy to grow or to respond to their surroundings. Viruses also cannot make food, take in food, or produce wastes.

The only way in which viruses are like organisms is in their ability to multiply. But, although viruses can multiply, they do so differently than organisms. Viruses can only multiply when they are inside a living cell. The organism that a virus enters and multiplies inside is called a host. A **host** is a living thing that provides a source of energy for a virus or an organism. Organisms that live on or in a host and cause harm to the host are called **parasites** (PA ruh syts). Almost all viruses act like parasites because they destroy the cells in which they multiply.

No organisms are safe from viruses. Viruses can infect the organisms of all six kingdoms—archaebacteria, eubacteria, protists, fungi, plants, and animals. Each virus, however, can enter, or infect, only a few types of cells in a few specific species. For example, most cold viruses only infect cells in the nose and throat of humans. The tobacco mosaic virus only infects the leaf cells of tobacco plants.

☑ *Checkpoint* *When you have a cold, are you the host or the parasite?*

Naming Viruses

Because viruses are not alive, scientists do not use binomial nomenclature to name them. Instead, scientists may name a virus, such as the polio virus, after the disease it causes. Other viruses are named for the organisms they infect, as is the case with the tomato mosaic virus, which infects tomato plants. Scientists named the Ebola virus after the place in Africa where it was first found. And scientists sometimes name viruses after people. The Epstein-Barr virus, for example, was named for the two scientists who first identified the virus that causes the disease known as infectious mononucleosis.

Figure 1 Viruses are tiny nonliving particles that invade and reproduce inside living cells. Viruses can infect the organisms of all six kingdoms. **A.** Papilloma viruses cause warts to form on human skin. **B.** This virus, called a bacteriophage, infects bacteria. **C.** Tobacco mosaic viruses infect tobacco plants. **D.** The rabies virus infects nerve cells in certain animals. **E.** The blue circles in this photo are viruses that cause German measles in humans.

 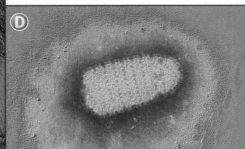 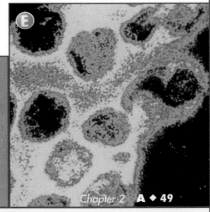

Program Resources

◆ **Teaching Resources** 2-1 Lesson Plan, p. 43; 2-1 Section Summary, p. 44

Media and Technology

 Audiotapes English-Spanish Summary 2-1

Answers to Self-Assessment

☑ *Checkpoint*
You are the host because you provide cells in which the cold viruses can multiply.

2 *Facilitate*

What Is a Virus?

Using the Visuals: Figure 1
Point out that the viruses in these photos are magnified many thousands of times. Invite students to read the captions carefully and compare and contrast the appearance of the different viruses. *(Students may notice that each virus has a distinct shape or some kind of organization. Viruses can infect organisms of all six kingdoms.)* **learning modality: visual**

Naming Viruses

Building Inquiry Skills: Comparing and Contrasting
Ask students to recall why scientists use binomial nomenclature to name living organisms. *(It allows scientists to make sure they all use the same name to refer to a specific species.)* Challenge students to compare this with the methods used for naming viruses. Ask: **What can you tell about a virus from its name?** *(Sometimes you can tell where it was discovered, what kind of organism it infects, or what disease it causes.)* Encourage students to speculate about problems with how viruses are named. **learning modality: verbal**

Ongoing Assessment

Writing Have students write two sentences explaining why viruses must invade cells in order to multiply.

The Shapes and Sizes of Viruses

Using the Visuals: Figure 2
As students compare the sizes of the viruses and the bacterial cell, explain that the bacteria are much smaller than most body cells. Encourage students to speculate on how having so many different sizes and shapes could influence how viruses affect the bodies of their hosts. (*Students might say that it is hard for the body to fight them because they are so different.*) **learning modality: visual**

Structure of Viruses

Inquiry Challenge
Materials *construction paper in different colors, scissors, glue, posterboard*

Time 30 minutes
Tips To help students who have difficulty grasping the meaning of the text, before class, cut out four large circles to represent four different types of cells. Use scissors to notch the edges of the circles so that each circle has a distinct pattern. Divide the class into four groups and give each group one cell model. Challenge groups to create model viruses to attach to their type of cell. Tell students to imagine that they are trying to make a puzzle piece that will fit into the cell. Encourage students to refer to the viruses shown in Figure 1 for inspiration. You may want to challenge each student in the group to make at least one model virus, so that groups can develop the greatest variety of viruses that can attach to one type of cell. When students have completed their models, each group can make a poster showing the cell and the viruses. Ask: **If each virus can only attach to one kind of cell, does that mean that each cell can only be attacked by one kind of virus?** (*No, viruses of different sizes with different structures can attach to the same type of cell.*) **limited English proficiency**

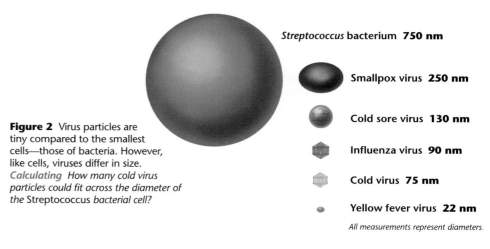

Figure 2 Virus particles are tiny compared to the smallest cells—those of bacteria. However, like cells, viruses differ in size. *Calculating How many cold virus particles could fit across the diameter of the* Streptococcus *bacterial cell?*

Streptococcus bacterium **750 nm**

Smallpox virus **250 nm**

Cold sore virus **130 nm**

Influenza virus **90 nm**

Cold virus **75 nm**

Yellow fever virus **22 nm**

All measurements represent diameters.

The Shapes and Sizes of Viruses

As you can see from the photographs in Figure 1, viruses vary widely in shape. Some viruses are round, while some others are rod-shaped. Other viruses have bricklike, threadlike, or bulletlike shapes. There are even some viruses, such as the bacteriophage in Figure 1B, that have complex, robotlike shapes. A **bacteriophage** (bak TEER ee oh fayj) is a virus that infects bacteria. In fact, its name means "bacteria eater."

Just as viruses vary in shape, they also vary in size. Viruses are smaller than cells and cannot be seen with the microscopes you use in school. Viruses are so small that they are measured in units called nanometers (nm). One nanometer is one billionth of a meter (m). The smallest viruses, such as yellow fever viruses, are about 22 nanometers in diameter. The largest viruses, such as smallpox viruses, are about 250 nanometers in diameter. Most viruses measure between 50 and 60 nanometers in diameter. The smallest cells, those of bacteria, are much larger than the average virus, as you can see in Figure 2.

Structure of Viruses

Although the viruses in Figure 1 may look very different, they all have a similar structure. **All viruses have two basic parts: an outer coat that protects the virus and an inner core made of genetic material.** A virus's genetic material contains the instructions for making new viruses. Figure 3 shows the basic structure of a virus. The structure might remind you of a chocolate-covered candy. The outer coat of a virus is like the chocolate on the outside of a candy. The inner core is like the gooey filling inside the candy.

Genetic material

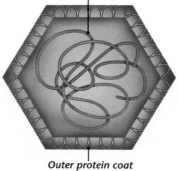

Outer protein coat

Figure 3 All viruses have a similar structure. They have an outer coat made of protein and an inner core that contains genetic material.

Background

Facts and Figures Scientists can now use a virus's ability to get inside cells as a way to alleviate the symptoms of disease. In one instance, scientists studying the painful and disabling disease, rheumatoid arthritis, discovered that its symptoms were caused by a high level of a substance called interleukin-1(IL-1). Scientists isolated a gene that programs the manufacture of a substance that blocks IL-1. But the problem was how to get the gene into the cells around the affected joint. The vector (gene-delivery vehicle) they decided to use was a replication-defective virus. This is a virus that still has the biological mechanism for injecting genetic material into a cell, but cannot reproduce itself in tissues. When the technique was tested on rabbits with arthritic knee joints, the rabbit's symptoms were much reduced.

The coat of a virus plays an important role during the invasion of a host cell. This coat is made of proteins. Each virus contains unique proteins in its coat. The shape of the proteins allows the virus's coat to attach to, or lock onto, certain cells in the host. Like keys, a virus's proteins only fit into certain "locks," or proteins, on the surface of a host's cells. Figure 4 shows how the lock-and-key action works. Because this action is highly specific, a certain virus will attach to only one or a few types of cells. For example, the human immunodeficiency virus, or HIV, can only attach to one kind of human white blood cell. This blood cell is the one with proteins on its surface that complement, or "fit", those on the virus.

☑ *Checkpoint* *Why does a virus only invade a specific kind of cell?*

How Viruses Multiply

After a virus attaches to a cell, it enters the cell. **Once inside, a virus's genetic material takes over the cell's functions. The genetic material directs the cell to produce the virus's proteins and genetic material. These proteins and genetic material are then assembled into new viruses.** Some viruses take over the cell's functions immediately. Other viruses wait for a while.

Active Viruses After entering a cell, an active virus immediately goes into action. The virus's genetic material takes over the cell's functions, and the cell quickly begins to produce the virus's proteins and genetic material. Then these parts assemble into new viruses. Like a photocopy machine left in the "on" position, the invaded cell makes copy after copy of new viruses. When it

Modeling a Virus

In this activity you will make a model of a bacteriophage.

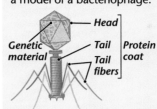

Head
Genetic material
Tail
Tail fibers
Protein coat

1. Sketch the bacteriophage above in your notebook.
2. Decide what materials you will use to model the virus.
3. Build your model.

Making Models Label your model. On each label, state the role that the part plays in infecting a host cell.

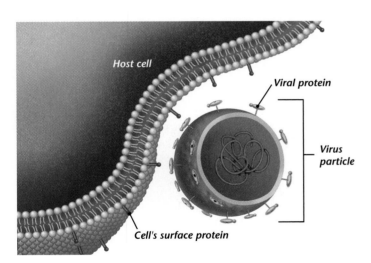

Host cell
Viral protein
Virus particle
Cell's surface protein

Figure 4 The shape of the proteins in a virus's coat determines what type of cell the virus will infect. The proteins fit together with the cell's proteins in the same way that a key fits a lock. Once attached, the virus can inject its genetic material into the cell.

Answers to Self-Assessment

Caption Question

Figure 2 About ten

☑ *Checkpoint*

A virus only invades a specific kind of cell because its coat has unique proteins that attach only to proteins of a particular host cell.

Skills Focus making models

Materials *model-making materials such as pipe cleaners, string, thread, rubber bands, paper clips, construction paper, aluminum foil, straws, plastic wrap, clay, glue, tape, scissors*

Time 20 minutes

Tips Encourage students to make a second sketch after they have decided what materials to use, showing the model they are going to build.

Expected Outcome Students should label the outer protein coat, the genetic material, the tail, and the tail fibers.

Extend Challenge students to model what happens when a bacteriophage attacks a bacterial cell. **learning modality: kinesthetic**

Including All Students

Some students may have difficulty understanding the structure of a virus. Distribute a peanut in the shell to each student. CAUTION: *Some students may be allergic to peanuts.* Ask: **How is the structure of a virus similar to a peanut?** *(The shell is like the protein coat; the nut is like the genetic material.)* **learning modality: visual**

How Viruses Multiply

Building Inquiry Skills: Comparing and Contrasting

Have students compare and contrast the operation of a photocopier stuck in the "on" position with the operation of an active virus that has invaded a host cell. *(The photocopier will make copies until it runs out of paper. The virus will make copies until the cell bursts. The photocopies do not infect other copy machines. The new viruses go on to attack other cells.)* **learning modality: logical/ mathematical**

Ongoing Assessment

Drawing Have students draw a flowchart illustrating the steps a virus uses to invade a cell.

How Viruses Multiply, continued

EXPLORING
How Viruses Multiply

Have students work in cooperative groups. While volunteers read aloud the descriptions of the active virus, have each group create a flowchart that shows each step and its result. Repeat the process for the hidden virus. Have a reporter from each group present that group's flowchart to the class. Ask: **At what stage in the flowchart do the cycles of the two viruses begin to differ?** (*In Stage 3*) **What does the active virus do at that point?** (*Its host cell begins to produce the virus's proteins and genetic material.*) **What does the hidden virus do before it becomes active?** (*Its genetic material becomes part of the host's genetic material.*)
cooperative learning

Building Inquiry Skills: Communicating

Challenge students to apply the concept of how viruses multiply by writing a creative story about a hidden or active virus that invades a human body cell. Students should take the virus through each step in its cycle, explaining what happens and the effect on the host cell.
learning modality: verbal

is full of new viruses, the host cell bursts open and releases the new viruses. In *Exploring How Viruses Multiply*, you can follow how an active virus multiplies.

Hidden Viruses Some viruses function differently than active viruses after entering a cell—at least for a while. The genetic material of these viruses enters a host cell. Then, instead of going into action like an active virus does, the virus's genetic material becomes part of the cell's genetic material. The virus does not appear to affect the cell's functions. The virus's genetic material may stay in this inactive state for a long time. Then, for reasons that scientists do not yet fully understand, the virus's genetic material suddenly becomes active. It takes over the cell's

EXPLORING How Viruses Multiply

Active viruses enter cells and immediately begin to multiply, leading to the quick death of the invaded cells. Other viruses "hide" for a while inside the host cells before they become active.

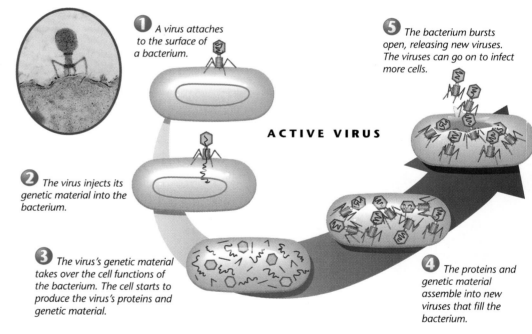

1 A virus attaches to the surface of a bacterium.

2 The virus injects its genetic material into the bacterium.

3 The virus's genetic material takes over the cell functions of the bacterium. The cell starts to produce the virus's proteins and genetic material.

4 The proteins and genetic material assemble into new viruses that fill the bacterium.

5 The bacterium bursts open, releasing new viruses. The viruses can go on to infect more cells.

ACTIVE VIRUS

Background

Facts and Figures The hidden, or latent, virus that causes cold sores is called *Herpes simplex*. Another *Herpes* virus is *cytomegalovirus*. This virus rarely causes symptoms in healthy adults. However, infants who are infected by the virus can become deaf, blind, or retarded. Adults with compromised immune systems can become infected and develop an inflammation of the retina that leads to blindness.

Another serious illness, SSPE, is caused by a measles virus that remains dormant in brain cells for many years until it is reactivated in adolescence. Scientists do not know why hidden viruses, which are present in the tissues of most adults, reactivate and cause diseases in some people, but not in others.

functions in much the same way that active viruses do. In a short time, the cell is full of new viruses, and it bursts open to release them. Look at *Exploring How Viruses Multiply* to see how a hidden virus multiplies.

The virus that causes cold sores in humans is an example of a hidden virus. The virus can remain inactive for months or years inside the nerve cells in the face. While hidden, the virus causes no symptoms. When it becomes active, the virus causes a swollen, painful sore to form near the mouth. Strong sunlight and stress are two factors that scientists believe may activate a cold sore virus. After an active period, the virus once again "hides" in the nerve cells until it becomes active once again.

✓ *Checkpoint* **Give one example of a hidden virus.**

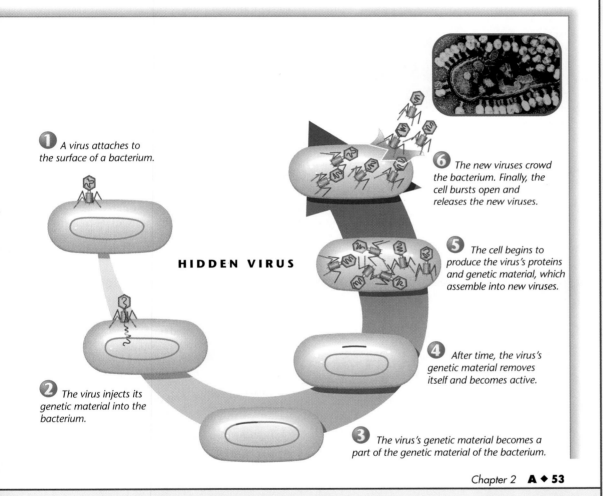

1 A virus attaches to the surface of a bacterium.

HIDDEN VIRUS

2 The virus injects its genetic material into the bacterium.

3 The virus's genetic material becomes a part of the genetic material of the bacterium.

4 After time, the virus's genetic material removes itself and becomes active.

5 The cell begins to produce the virus's proteins and genetic material, which assemble into new viruses.

6 The new viruses crowd the bacterium. Finally, the cell bursts open and releases the new viruses.

Answers to Self-Assessment

✓ *Checkpoint*
The virus that causes cold sores

Social Studies Connection

Tell students that descriptions of viral diseases date to the tenth century B.C., but the concept of viruses was not proposed until the 1890s, when two different researchers proposed an infectious agent so small that it would pass through a filter that would not allow the passage of bacteria. Viruses could not be examined in detail until the 1940s. In 1952, Alfred Hershey and Martha Chase demonstrated how viruses multiply. Ask: **Why do you think it took so long for scientists to study viruses?** *(Because viruses are so small, scientists could not isolate them until powerful microscopes and other equipment were invented.)* **learning modality: verbal**

Real-Life Learning

Computer viruses are quite different from biological viruses. Invite a computer science instructor or software programmer to talk to the class about computer viruses. Before the visit, explain to students that when a computer virus enters a computer via a disk, the computer may infect all other disks with which it comes into contact by copying the virus onto them. Encourage students to develop a list of questions about computer viruses before the visit. Help students come up with questions that will help them understand the difference between computer viruses and viruses that invade cells. **learning modality: verbal**

Ongoing Assessment

Skills Check Have students make a poster illustrating the differences between what happens when an active virus attaches to a cell and what happens when a hidden virus attaches to a cell, with accompanying explanations on the poster.

A ◆ 53

Viruses and the Living World

Integrating Technology

One method for introducing new genetic material into defective cells was developed by researchers searching for a way to treat rheumatoid arthritis. They chose to use a virus that was replication-defective (could not reproduce, even inside a cell). Ask students to discuss why researchers would want to use a virus in gene therapy that could not reproduce itself. **learning modality: logical/mathematical**

3 Assess

Section 1 Review Answers

1. Viruses are not cells, and they do not respond to their surroundings or use energy to grow.
2. Viruses have an outer protein coat surrounding a core of genetic material.
3. An active virus takes over the host's genetic material and uses it to make new viruses. A hidden virus is incorporated into the host's genetic material, but seems to have no effect on the cell. At any time, the hidden virus can become active and multiply.
4. Viruses could not have existed without organisms, because they need host cells to reproduce.

Check Your Progress
CHAPTER PROJECT 2

Make sure students' survey questions will elicit relevant information. Encourage them to ask questions requiring yes/no or numerical answers. For other questions, students should devise a tally system to record the most common responses. Encourage students to test and revise the questions.

Performance Assessment

Oral Presentation Have students choose either an active virus or a hidden virus, then prepare a lesson on that virus to give to younger students.

Figure 5 The beautiful striped pattern on this Rembrandt tulip was originally caused by the tulip mosaic virus.

Viruses and the Living World

If you've ever had a cold sore or been sick with a cold or flu, you know that viruses can cause disease in organisms. Some diseases, such as colds, are mild—people are sick for a short time but soon recover. Other diseases, such as acquired immunodeficiency syndrome, or AIDS, can cause death.

Viruses also cause diseases in organisms other than humans. For example, the rice dwarf virus stunts the growth of rice plants, resulting in lower yields of this food crop. Alfalfa mosaic disease kills alfalfa plants, an important food source for horses, cattle, and other farm animals. House pets, such as dogs and cats, can get a deadly viral disease called distemper. Dogs, foxes, and raccoons are a few of the animals that rabies viruses can infect. If a rabid animal bites a person, it can transmit rabies to the person.

INTEGRATING TECHNOLOGY By now you might be thinking that viruses do no good. But the news about viruses isn't all bad. Scientists are putting viruses to use in a new technique called gene therapy. In gene therapy, scientists take advantage of a virus's ability to get inside a host cell. They add important genetic material to a virus and then use the virus as a "messenger service" to deliver the genetic material to cells that need it. Scientists have used gene therapy on people with disorders such as cystic fibrosis (SIS tik fy BRO sis). People with cystic fibrosis do not have the genetic material they need to keep their lungs functioning properly. Gene therapy shows some promise to become a medical treatment for cystic fibrosis and other disorders.

Section 1 Review

1. Explain why biologists consider viruses to be nonliving.
2. Describe the basic structure of a virus.
3. Compare the two ways that viruses can multiply.
4. **Thinking Critically Inferring** Scientists hypothesize that viruses could not have existed on Earth before organisms, such as bacteria, appeared. Use what you know about viruses to support this hypothesis.

Check Your Progress
CHAPTER PROJECT 2

By now, you should have a draft of the questions you will ask in your survey. Have your teacher review your questions. Then begin your survey. (*Hint:* Design the questionnaire so that you can easily record and tally the responses. Test your survey on a few people you know to make sure the questions are clear.)

Program Resources

◆ **Teaching Resources** 2-1 Review and Reinforce, p. 45; 2-1 Enrich, p. 46

Media and Technology

 Interactive Student Tutorial CD-ROM A-2

How Many Viruses Fit on a Pin?

In this lab, you will make models to help you investigate the size of viruses.

Problem

How many viruses could fit on the head of a pin?

Materials

straight pin
pencil
scissors
calculator (optional)
long strips of paper
meter stick
tape

Procedure ✂

1. Examine the head of a straight pin. Write a prediction about the number of viruses that could fit on the pinhead. **CAUTION:** *Avoid pushing the pin against anyone's skin.*

2. Assume that the pinhead has a diameter of about 1 mm. If the pinhead were enlarged 10,000 times, its diameter would measure 10 m. Create a model of the pinhead by cutting and taping together narrow strips of paper to make a strip that is 10 m long. The strip of paper represents the diameter of the enlarged pinhead.

3. Lay the 10-m strip of paper on the floor of your classroom or in the hall. Imagine creating a large circle that had the strip as its diameter. The circle would be the pinhead at the enlarged size. Calculate the area of the enlarged pinhead using this formula:

$$\text{Area} = \pi \times \text{radius}^2$$

Remember that you can find the radius by dividing the diameter by 2.

4. A virus particle may measure 200 nm on each side (1 nm equals a billionth of a meter). If the virus were enlarged 10,000 times, each side would measure 0.002 m. Cut out a square 0.002 m by 0.002 m to serve as a model for a virus. *(Hint:* 0.002 m = 2 mm)

5. Next, find the area in meters of one virus particle at the enlarged size. Remember that the area of a square equals side × side.

6. Now divide the area of the pinhead that you calculated in Step 3 by the area of one virus particle to find out how many viruses could fit on the pinhead.

7. Exchange your work with a partner, and check each other's calculations. Make any corrections that are necessary.

Analyze and Conclude

1. Approximately how many viruses can fit on the head of a pin?
2. How did your calculation compare with your prediction? If the two numbers were very different, explain why they were different.
3. What did you learn about the size of viruses by magnifying both the viruses and pinheads to 10,000 times their actual size?
4. **Think About It** Why do scientists sometimes make and use enlarged models of very small things such as viruses?

More to Explore

Think of another everyday object that you could use to model some other facts about viruses, such as their shapes or how they infect cells. Describe your model and explain why the object would be a good choice.

How Many Viruses Fit on a Pin?

Preparing for Inquiry

Key Concept To help appreciate the small size of viruses, people often compare them to other known objects.

Skills Objective Students will be able to
◆ make models to illustrate the size of a virus relative to the head of a pin;
◆ calculate the number of viruses that could fit on the head of a pin.

Time 45 minutes

Alternative Materials To make the 10-m strip, obtain long rolls of paper such as adding machine tape.

Guiding Inquiry

Invitation

Point out that referring to how many items fit on a pinhead often occurs when discussing things that are very small or very numerous.

Introducing the Procedure

◆ Review the idea of scale.
◆ Review metric measurements, if necessary.

Troubleshooting the Experiment

◆ Remind students that there are often different ways to solve specific calculation problems. Match up students using similar methods, then let different groups share their strategies with the class.

Expected Outcome

Area of the enlarged pinhead: $\pi \times \text{radius}^2 = 3.1 \times 25 = 77.5$ m²; area of enlarged virus: $0.002 \times 0.002 = 0.000004$ m²; could fit $77.5/0.000004 = 19{,}375{,}000$ viruses on pinhead

Analyze and Conclude

1. About 20 million
2. Students should explain whether their predictions were based on reasoning or whether they "just guessed."
3. Although the magnified pinhead became very large, the magnified virus size was still quite small.

Safety

Remind students not to push the pin against anyone's skin. Caution students not to lose any of the pins.

Program Resources

◆ **Teaching Resources** Chapter 2 Skills Lab, pp. 55–56

4. The enlarged models help them to understand details of structure.

Extending the Inquiry

More to Explore Encourage students to explain how they chose their models. Ask students to compare their models to what they know about viruses to determine the strengths and weaknesses of the model.

Objectives

After completing the lesson, students will be able to
◆ describe ways in which bacteria cells are different from all other organisms' cells;
◆ list positive roles that bacteria play in people's lives;
◆ name the two kingdoms of bacteria and tell how bacteria reproduce and survive.

Key Terms cytoplasm, ribosome, flagellum, binary fission, asexual reproduction, sexual reproduction, conjugation, respiration, endospore, decomposer

1 Engage/Explore

Activating Prior Knowledge

Display samples of yogurt and Swiss cheese. Ask students what these foods have in common, then record their responses on the board. Tell students that these products are all produced with the help of certain kinds of bacteria. Ask: **What other foods can you think of that might be prepared with the aid of bacteria?** (Sample: Buttermilk, sauerkraut, sour cream)

········ DISCOVER ········

Materials paper cups; dried lima, kidney, or navy beans

Time 20 minutes

Tips Remind students to calculate the elapsed time based on the fact that it takes 20 minutes for bacteria to divide.

Expected Outcome Cup 1–1 bean; Cup 2–2 beans; Cup 3–4 beans; Cup 4–8 beans; Cup 5–16 beans; Cup 6–32 beans; Cup 7–64 beans; Cup 8–128 beans. There are 128 cells in the eighth generation. Two hours and twenty minutes have passed since there was only 1 bacterium.

Think It Over Students will probably infer that the numbers increase rapidly because each bacterium can double every 20 minutes.

SECTION
2 Bacteria

DISCOVER ·······················ACTIVITY···

How Quickly Can Bacteria Multiply?

1. Your teacher will give you some beans and paper cups. Number the cups 1 through 8. Each bean will represent a bacterial cell.

2. Put one bean into cup 1 to represent the first generation of bacteria. Approximately every 20 minutes, a bacterial cell reproduces by dividing into two cells. Put two beans into cup 2 to represent the second generation of bacteria.

3. Calculate how many bacterial cells there would be in the third generation if each cell in cup 2 divided into two cells. Place the correct number of beans in cup 3.

4. Repeat Step 3 five more times. All the cups should now contain beans. How many cells are in the eighth generation? How much time has elapsed since the first generation?

Think It Over
Inferring Based on this activity, explain why the number of bacteria can increase rapidly in a short period of time.

GUIDE FOR READING

◆ How are the cells of bacteria different from those of all other organisms?

◆ What positive roles do bacteria play in people's lives?

Reading Tip Before you read, make a list of the boldfaced vocabulary words in the section. Predict the meaning of each word. As you read, check your predictions.

You may not know it, but seconds after you were born, tiny organisms surrounded and invaded your body. Today, millions of these organisms coat your skin. As you read this page, they swarm inside your nose, throat, and mouth. In fact, there are more of these organisms living in your mouth than there are people who are living on Earth. You don't see or feel these organisms because they are very small. But you cannot escape them. They are found nearly everywhere on Earth—in soil, rocks, Arctic ice, volcanoes, and in all living things. These organisms are bacteria.

The Bacterial Cell

Although there are many bacteria on Earth, they were not discovered until the late 1600s. A Dutch businessman named Anton van Leeuwenhoek (LAY vuhn hook) found them by accident. Leeuwenhoek had a rather unusual hobby—making microscopes. One day, while he was using one of his microscopes to look at scrapings from his teeth, he saw some tiny organisms in the sample. However, because his microscopes were not very powerful, Leeuwenhoek could not see any details inside these tiny organisms.

◀ **Bacteria on the surface of a human tooth**

56 ◆ A

READING STRATEGIES

Reading Tip Suggest that students create charts with the headings *Word, What I Think It Means*, and *What It Means* on which to record boldface words and make their predictions. Remind students to study the parts of each word and to think of words they already know that have the same word roots or parts.

Study and Comprehension As students read, remind them of these strategies for breaking down information:
◆ Read the title, headings, subheadings, and captions to get an overview.
◆ Read one section of text at a time, line by line. Reread parts you did not understand fully.
◆ Jot down unfamiliar words. Try to determine their meanings or look up the words in a dictionary.

If Leeuwenhoek had owned one of the high-powered microscopes in use today, he would have seen the single-celled organisms that are known as bacteria in detail. As you learned in Chapter 1, the cells of bacteria differ from the cells of other organisms in many ways. **Bacteria are prokaryotes. The genetic material in their cells is not contained in a nucleus.** In addition to lacking a nucleus, the cells of prokaryotes also lack many other structures that are found in the cells of eukaryotes. However, regardless of the structure of their cells, prokaryotes accomplish all tasks necessary for life. That is, each bacterial cell uses energy, grows and develops, responds to its surroundings, and reproduces.

Cell Shapes If you were to look at bacterial cells under a microscope, you would notice that bacterial cells have one of three basic shapes: spherical, rodlike, or spiral shaped. The shape of a bacterial cell helps scientists identify the type of bacteria. For example, bacteria that cause strep throat are spherical. Figure 6 shows the different shapes of bacterial cells.

Cell Structures The shape of a bacterial cell is determined by the chemical makeup of its outermost structure—the cell wall. Cell walls surround most bacterial cells. A bacterium's rigid cell wall helps to protect the cell.

Inside the cell wall is the cell membrane, which controls what materials pass into and out of the cell. The region inside the cell membrane, called the **cytoplasm** (SY toh plaz um), contains a gel-like material. Tiny structures called ribosomes are located in the cytoplasm. **Ribosomes** (RY buh sohmz) are chemical factories where proteins are produced. The cell's genetic material, which looks like a thick, tangled string, is also located in the cytoplasm. If you could untangle the genetic material, you would see that it forms a circular shape. The genetic material contains the instructions for all the cell's functions, such as how to produce proteins on the ribosomes.

Figure 6 Bacteria have three basic shapes. **A.** Like the bacteria that cause strep throat, these *Staphylococcus aureus* bacteria are spherical. They represent over 30 percent of the bacteria that live on your skin. **B.** *Escherichia coli* bacteria have rodlike shapes. These bacteria are found in your intestines. **C.** *Borrelia burgdorferi* bacteria, which cause Lyme disease, are spiral-shaped.

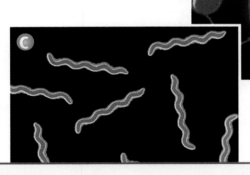

Chapter 2 **A ◆ 57**

Program Resources

◆ **Teaching Resources** 2-2 Lesson Plan, p. 47; 2-2 Section Summary, p. 48

Media and Technology

🎧 **Audiotapes** English-Spanish Summary 2-2

2 Facilitate

The Bacterial Cell

Building Inquiry Skills: Comparing and Contrasting

Write the terms *prokaryote* and *eukaryote* on the board and invite students to recall their meanings. Challenge them to explain the differences and similarities between the two types of cells. *(Both have genetic material and reproduce by cell division. Prokaryotes do not have a nucleus or other cell structures.)* **learning modality: verbal**

Building Inquiry Skills: Classifying

Materials *light microscope, prepared slides of cocci, bacilli, and spirilla*

Time 20 minutes
Tips Provide students with the materials and tell them they are going to observe and identify the three main bacterial cell shapes. As students view the various slides, have them sketch what they observe. Have pairs of students compare sketches and classify the bacteria as rod-shaped *(bacilli)*, spherical *(cocci)*, or spiral-shaped *(spirilla)*. **learning modality: visual**

Using the Visuals: Figure 6

As students compare the bacteria shown, ask: **How many cells does each bacterium have?** *(one)* Point out to students that some of the bacteria in the picture are dividing. Remind students that bacteria are unicellular, and that each image shows several bacteria. **learning modality: visual**

Ongoing Assessment

Writing Have students write sentences explaining in their own words the function of each of these structures: cell wall, cell membrane, ribosome, cytoplasm.

Two Kingdoms of Bacteria

Addressing Naive Conceptions

Students who are accustomed to classifying organisms as plants or animals may need extra help to understand that bacteria are not animals or plants. Ask students: **What do bacteria have in common with animals?** *(They are alive, some are heterotrophs.)* **How are they different?** *(Bacteria are one-celled organisms, while animals have many cells that are highly organized.)* **learning modality: verbal**

Integrating Earth Science

Ask students: **Why do scientists think the bacteria that originally began to alter Earth's atmosphere were similar to autotrophic eubacteria?** *(To alter the atmosphere, the first organisms had to produce oxygen.)* **Why do scientists think the first life forms on Earth were similar to archaebacteria?** *(The conditions on ancient Earth may have been too extreme for ordinary bacteria to survive.)* **learning modality: verbal**

Including All Students

Students just learning English may have difficulty with the names of the two kingdoms, Archaebacteria and Eubacteria. Have students look up the definitions of the prefixes *archaeo-* *(ancient)* and *eu-* *(good* or *true).* Ask them to find other words that begin with each prefix used in the same sense *(archaeology, archaeopteryx, eukaryote, eulogy, euphony, euphoria)* Why are eubacteria called "true" bacteria? *(The chemical processes in eubacteria are similar to those of other eukaryotes.)* **learning modality: verbal**

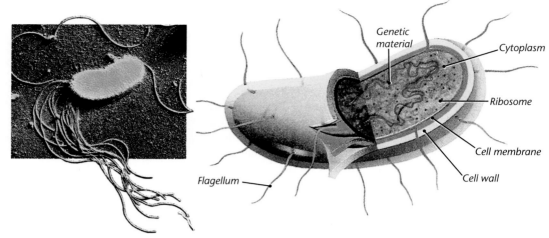

Figure 7 The diagram shows the structures found in a typical bacterial cell. *Interpreting Photographs Which structures can you locate in the photograph of the bacterium? What roles do these structures play?*

You can see the cell wall, cytoplasm, ribosomes, and genetic material in the bacterial cell in Figure 7. Another structure you see is a flagellum. A **flagellum** (fluh JEL um) (plural *flagella*) is a long, whiplike structure that extends out through the cell membrane and cell wall. Using a back and forth motion, a flagellum helps a cell to move, much as kicking your feet helps you to swim. A bacterial cell can have many flagella, one, or none. Bacteria that do not have flagella cannot move on their own. Instead, they depend on air, water currents, clothing, and other objects to carry them from one place to another.

Two Kingdoms of Bacteria

Until recently, biologists grouped all bacteria together in a single kingdom on the basis of their similar cellular structure. However, although all bacteria look similar, some differ chemically. After analyzing the chemical differences, scientists have reclassified bacteria into two separate kingdoms—Archaebacteria and Eubacteria.

Archaebacteria As you learned in Chapter 1, the word *archaebacteria* means "ancient bacteria." And these bacteria are ancient! Archaebacteria already existed on Earth for billions of years before dinosaurs appeared. Scientists think that today's archaebacteria closely resemble Earth's first life forms.

Many archaebacteria live in extreme environments. They are found in such places as hot springs, where some thrive in water that is as hot as 110°C. Others live in environments that are as acidic as lemon juice. Some archaebacteria live in salty waters, such as Utah's Great Salt Lake. Archaebacteria also live in the intestines of animals, the mud at the bottom of swamps, and in sewage. It is the bacteria that produce the foul odors that you may associate with these places.

Background

Integrating Science Because of the large number of bacteria with different characteristics, scientists have changed the classifications of bacteria several times. Although bacteria-like organisms are believed to be the earliest life forms, the evolutionary relationships among bacteria have been very difficult to study, partly because the fossil record of bacteria is difficult to analyze.

A new approach to classification of bacteria was developed in the 1980s, based on the amount of time that has passed since two organisms developed from a common ancestor. Scientists are now able to classify bacteria according to how closely they are related. Based on these studies, scientists now believe that eubacteria and archaebacteria evolved from a common ancestor.

Eubacteria Unlike archaebacteria, most eubacteria do not live in extreme environments. However, they live everywhere else. For example, millions of eubacteria live on and in your body. Eubacteria coat your skin and swarm in your nose. Don't be alarmed. Most of them are either useful or harmless to you.

 INTEGRATING EARTH SCIENCE Eubacteria help maintain some of Earth's physical conditions and thus help other organisms to survive. For example, some eubacteria are autotrophs that float near the surfaces of Earth's waters. These bacteria use the sun's energy to produce food and oxygen. Scientists think that billions of years ago autotrophic bacteria were responsible for adding oxygen to Earth's atmosphere. Today, the distant offspring of those bacteria help to keep Earth's current level of oxygen at 20 percent.

☑ *Checkpoint* *Why are archaebacteria and eubacteria placed in separate kingdoms?*

Reproduction in Bacteria

When bacteria have plenty of food, the right temperature, and other suitable conditions, they thrive and reproduce frequently. Under these ideal conditions, some bacteria can reproduce as often as once every 20 minutes. Fortunately, growing conditions for bacteria are rarely ideal. Otherwise, there would soon be no room on Earth for other organisms!

Asexual Reproduction Bacteria reproduce by **binary fission,** a process in which one cell divides to form two identical cells. Binary fission is a form of **asexual reproduction.** Asexual reproduction is a reproductive process that involves only one parent and produces offspring that are identical to the parent. In binary fission, the cell first duplicates its genetic material and then divides into two separate cells. Each new cell gets its own complete copy of the parent cell's genetic material as well as some of the parent's ribosomes and cytoplasm. Figure 8 shows a parent cell forming two new cells by binary fission.

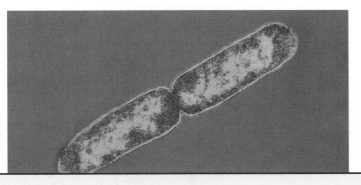

Sharpen your Skills

Graphing ACTIVITY

Suppose a bacterium reproduces by binary fission every 20 minutes. The new cells survive and reproduce at the same rate. The table below shows how many bacteria there would be each hour over a 5-hour period.

Bacterial Reproduction	
Time	Number of Bacteria
Start	1
1 hour	8
2 hours	64
3 hours	512
4 hours	4,096
5 hours	32,768

Construct a line graph using the information in the table. Plot time on the horizontal axis and the number of bacteria on the vertical axis. Then use the graph to explain why the number of bacteria increases more rapidly as time goes by.

Figure 8 Bacteria, such as this *Escherichia coli,* reproduce by binary fission. Each new cell is identical to the parent cell.

Reproduction in Bacteria

Sharpen your Skills

Graphing

Materials *graph paper and pencil*
Time 20 minutes
Tips Have students predict how their line graphs will look after they have finished plotting data.
Expected Outcome Students' graphs should show that bacterial numbers remain relatively steady for almost 3 hours. The numbers increase slightly between 3 and 4 hours, then increase sharply because the bacteria are reproducing exponentially.
Extend Challenge students to calculate the number of bacteria there would be after 24 hours. (8^{24}, *or approximately* 4.722×10^{21}) **learning modality: logical/mathematical**

Using the Visuals: Figures 8 and 9

As students study the forms of bacterial reproduction shown in both figures, ask: **What main difference can you see between conjugation and binary fission?** (*Binary fission—only one cell is involved; conjugation—two cells are involved.*) Then ask: **How does conjugation result in the production of new bacteria?** (*After conjugation, the original cells have new combinations of genetic material.*) **learning modality: visual**

Answers to Self-Assessment

Caption Question

Figure 7 Flagellum—helps the bacterium move. Cell wall—protects bacterium.

☑ *Checkpoint*

Archaebacteria can live in extreme environments; eubacteria live everywhere except in extreme conditions. The two differ chemically.

Ongoing Assessment

Skills Check Have students create Venn diagrams that compare and contrast archaebacteria and eubacteria. Students can save their diagrams in their portfolios.

Reproduction in Bacteria, continued

Building Inquiry Skills: Inferring

Allow students to form small groups and discuss the possible evolutionary advantage of different individuals or populations of bacteria exchanging genetic information. *(By exchanging genetic information, bacteria may find better combinations that will enhance survival or increase reproductive success.)* **learning modality: logical/ mathematical**

Survival Needs

Building Inquiry Skills: Designing Experiments

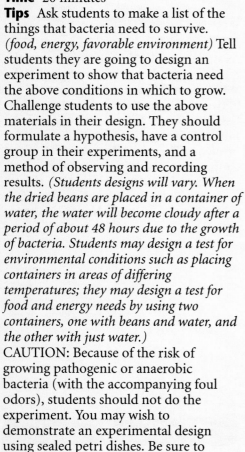

Materials *beakers, dried beans, water*
Time 20 minutes
Tips Ask students to make a list of the things that bacteria need to survive. *(food, energy, favorable environment)* Tell students they are going to design an experiment to show that bacteria need the above conditions in which to grow. Challenge students to use the above materials in their design. They should formulate a hypothesis, have a control group in their experiments, and a method of observing and recording results. *(Students designs will vary. When the dried beans are placed in a container of water, the water will become cloudy after a period of about 48 hours due to the growth of bacteria. Students may design a test for environmental conditions such as placing containers in areas of differing temperatures; they may design a test for food and energy needs by using two containers, one with beans and water, and the other with just water.)*
CAUTION: Because of the risk of growing pathogenic or anaerobic bacteria (with the accompanying foul odors), students should not do the experiment. You may wish to demonstrate an experimental design using sealed petri dishes. Be sure to follow district and state guidelines for disposing of the petri dishes.

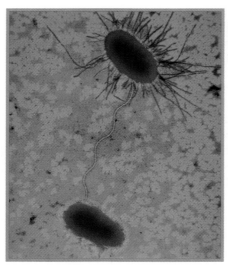

Figure 9 In conjugation, one bacterium transfers some of its genetic material into another bacterium. *Observing What structure allows the cells to transfer genetic material?*

Sexual Reproduction Some bacteria, such as the ones in Figure 9, may at times undergo a simple form of sexual reproduction called conjugation. **Sexual reproduction** involves two parents who combine their genetic material to produce a new organism, which differs from both parents. During **conjugation** (kahn juh GAY shun), one bacterium transfers some of its genetic material into another bacterial cell through a thin, threadlike bridge that joins the two cells. After the transfer, the cells separate.

Conjugation results in bacteria with new combinations of genetic material. When these bacteria divide by binary fission, the new genetic material passes to the new cells. Conjugation does not increase the number of bacteria. However, it does result in the production of new bacteria, which are genetically different than the parent cells.

Survival Needs

From the bacteria that live inside the craters of active volcanoes to those that live in the pores of your skin, all bacteria need certain things to survive. Bacteria must have a source of food, a way of breaking down the food to release the food's energy, and survival techniques when conditions in their surroundings become unfavorable.

Obtaining Food Some bacteria are autotrophs and make their own food. Autotrophic bacteria make food in one of two ways. Some autotrophic bacteria make food by capturing and using the sun's energy as plants do. Other autotrophic bacteria, such as those that live deep in the ocean, do not use the sun's energy. Instead, these bacteria use the energy from chemical substances in their environment to make their food.

Some bacteria are heterotrophs that obtain food by consuming autotrophs or other heterotrophs. Heterotrophic bacteria may consume a variety of foods—from milk and meat, which you might also eat, to the decaying leaves on a forest floor.

Respiration Like all organisms, bacteria need a constant supply of energy to carry out their functions. This energy comes from food. The process of breaking down food to release its energy is called **respiration**. Like many other organisms, most bacteria need oxygen to break down their food. But a few kinds of bacteria do not need oxygen for respiration. In fact, those bacteria die if oxygen is present in their surroundings. For them, oxygen is a poison that kills!

Background

Integrating Science The tomb of the Egyptian pharaoh Tutankhamen was discovered by the archaeologist Howard Carter in 1922. In the seven years following the discovery, eleven people, including Lord Carnarvon (who had paid for the excavation), died. Although the story of a curse was cooked up by security guards to keep away looters, others have speculated that bacteria sealed up in the tomb formed endospores and survived. Since there are few similarities between the deaths of the individuals, disease from ancient spores seems unlikely. However, it is possible for some bacterial spores to survive for a long time. *Bacillus anthracis*, the bacteria that causes anthrax, can live in the soil for many decades or longer. Archaeologists who excavate in areas where anthrax is known to have occurred must take precautions.

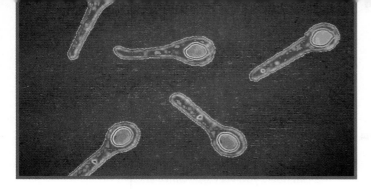

Figure 10 When conditions in the environment become unfavorable for growth, some bacteria form endospores. These endospores of *Clostridium tetani* can survive for years.

Endospore Formation Sometimes the conditions in the environment become unfavorable for the growth of bacteria. For example, food sources can disappear or wastes can poison the bacteria. Some bacteria can survive these harsh conditions by forming endospores like the ones you see in Figure 10. An **endospore** is a small, rounded, thick-walled, resting cell that forms inside a bacterial cell. It contains the cell's genetic material and some of its cytoplasm. Because endospores can resist freezing, heating, and drying, they can survive for many years. Endospores are also light—a breeze can lift and carry them to new places. If an endospore lands in a place where conditions are suitable, it opens up. Then the bacterium can begin to grow and multiply.

☑ *Checkpoint* **How do autotrophic bacteria obtain energy to make food?**

Bacteria and The Living World

When you hear the word *bacteria*, you may think about getting sick. After all, strep throat, many ear infections, and other diseases are caused by bacteria. It is true that some bacteria cause diseases and other harmful effects. However, most bacteria are either harmless or helpful to people. In fact, in many ways, people depend on bacteria. **Bacteria are involved in fuel and food production, environmental recycling and cleanup, and the production of medicines.**

Fuel The next time you use natural gas to boil an egg, grill a hamburger, or heat your house, think of archaebacteria. The archaebacteria that live in oxygen-free environments, such as the thick mud at the bottom of lakes and swamps, produce a gas called methane during respiration. The methane produced by archaebacteria that died millions of years ago is the major component in about 20 percent of Earth's deposits of natural gas.

Bacteria for Breakfast

In this activity, you will observe helpful bacteria in a common food.

1. Put on your apron. Add water to plain yogurt to make a thin mixture.
2. With a plastic dropper, place a drop of the mixture on a glass slide.
3. Use another plastic dropper to add one drop of methylene blue dye to the slide. **CAUTION:** *This dye can stain your skin.*
4. Put a coverslip on the slide.
5. Observe the slide under both the low and high power lenses of a microscope.

Observing Draw a diagram of what you see under high power. Label any cell structures that you see.

Bacteria and the Living World

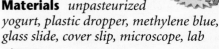 TRY THIS

Skills Focus observing
Materials *unpasteurized yogurt, plastic dropper, methylene blue, glass slide, cover slip, microscope, lab apron*
Time 20 minutes
Tips Students will need to observe with the highest powers of the microscope. As they observe the bacteria in yogurt, have students classify the bacteria according to their shape: spherical, rod, or spiral. Caution them to not drop the glass slides, and to avoid getting methylene blue on their skin or clothing.
Observing The bacteria appear as dark-blue capsule-shaped dots against a cloudy, pale blue background. Bacteria are so small that students will be unable to see them unless they are using high-powered microscopes.
Extend Challenge students to observe yogurt that contains added *Lactobacillus acidophilus* (the contents will be listed on the label) and to draw what they observe under the microscope. **learning modality: visual**

Program Resources

 Science Explorer Series *Earth's Waters*, Chapter 1

Media and Technology

 Exploring Life Science Videodisc
Unit 2, Side 2,
"Positive Bacteria"

Chapter 4

Answers to Self-Assessment

Caption Question
Figure 9 A thin, threadlike bridge that joins the two cells during conjugation allows for the transfer of genetic material.

☑ *Checkpoint*
Some autotrophic bacteria obtain the energy to make food from the sun. Others obtain food-making energy from chemical substances in their environment.

Ongoing Assessment

Oral Presentation Ask students to describe the conditions bacteria need in order to survive and explain one way bacteria can survive when the conditions are not present. (*Food, a way of breaking down food for energy; some bacteria form endospores*)

A ◆ 61

Bacteria and the Living World, continued

SCIENCE & History

Materials *globe or world map*

Time 15 minutes

Tips Have a world map or globe available for students to use to locate the places discussed in the feature. Invite volunteers to read aloud the annotations to the time line. For each food preservation method, encourage students to draw conclusions about the environment in which the bacteria grew and how they affected the food. Ask: **Do you think these methods of food preservation and preparation are still used today? What examples have you seen?** *(Responses will vary. These methods are still used.)*

In Your Journal Suggest students keep the following questions in mind as they do their research.

◆ What techniques were used in the food production method?

◆ What environment existed in the geographical region where the method was developed?

◆ Did the environment have any effect on the development of the method?

Many different cultures have used foods that have been altered by bacteria. You may want to have students do research and write in their journals about such a food from their own culture. Encourage students to share their reports with the class.

Portfolio Students can save their reports in their portfolios.

Food Do you like cheese, yogurt, and apple cider? What about olives and sauerkraut? The activities of helpful bacteria produce all of these foods and more. For example, bacteria that grow in a liquid poured around fresh cucumbers turn the cucumbers into pickles. Bacteria that grow in apple cider change the cider to vinegar. Bacteria that grow in milk produce dairy products such as buttermilk, sour cream, yogurt, and cheeses.

However, some bacteria cause food to spoil when they break down the food's chemicals. Spoiled food usually smells or tastes foul and can make you very sick. Since ancient times, people have

SCIENCE & History

Bacteria and Foods of the World

Ancient cultures lacked refrigeration and other modern methods of preventing food spoilage. People in these cultures developed ways to use bacteria to preserve foods. You may enjoy some of these foods today.

1000 B.C. China

The Chinese salted vegetables and packed them in containers. Naturally-occurring bacteria fed on the vegetables and produced a sour taste. The salt pulled water out of the vegetables and left them crisp. These vegetables were part of the food rations given to workers who built the Great Wall of China.

| 3000 B.C. | 2000 B.C. | 1000 B.C. |

2300 B.C. Egypt

Ancient Egyptians made cheese from milk. Cheesemaking begins when bacteria feed on the sugars in milk. The milk separates into solid curds and liquid whey. The curds are processed into cheeses, which keep longer than milk.

500 B.C. Mediterranean Sea Region

People who lived in the regions around the Mediterranean Sea chopped meat, seasoned it with salt and spices, rolled it, and hung it to dry. Bacteria in the drying meat gave unique flavors to the food. The rolled meat would keep for weeks in cool places.

Background

History of Science Canning as a method of food preservation was developed in 1810 by a Frenchman named Nicolas Appert. The first food-processing plant began operating in England in 1813. The plant sealed meats, vegetables, and soups in tin canisters, then heated the "cans" to a certain temperature for the correct amount of time.

Freezing food to preserve it was not possible until mechanical refrigeration systems were perfected About 1880, fish were frozen and sold in the United States and Europe. At that time, New Zealand began to freeze mutton and ship it to England. Frozen fruits appeared in the United States in 1905 and frozen vegetables in 1923.

Dehydration, or drying food, became commercially important during World War I, when soldiers were given dehydrated foods.

developed ways to slow down food spoilage. They have used such methods as heating, refrigerating, drying, salting, or smoking foods. These methods help to preserve food by preventing the bacteria that cause spoiling from growing in the food.

Environmental Recycling Do you recycle plastic, glass, and other materials? If you do, you have something in common with some heterotrophic eubacteria. These bacteria, which live in the soil, are **decomposers**—organisms that break down large chemicals in dead organisms into small chemicals. Decomposers are

In Your Journal
Find out more about one of these ancient food production methods and the culture that developed it. Write a report about the importance of the food to the culture.

A.D. 1500
The West Indies
People in the West Indies mixed beans from the cocoa plant with bacteria and other microorganisms, then dried and roasted them. The roasted beans were then brewed to produce a beverage with a chocolate flavor. The drink was served cold with honey, spices, and vanilla.

A.D. 1   **A.D. 1000**   **A.D.. 2000**

A.D. 500
China
The Chinese crushed soybeans with wheat, salt, bacteria, and other microorganisms. The microorganisms fed on the proteins in the wheat and soybeans. The salt pulled water out of the mixture. The protein-rich soy paste that remained was used to flavor foods. The soy sauce you may use today is made in a similar manner.

A.D. 1850
United States of America
Gold prospectors in California ate a bread called sourdough bread. The bacteria *Lactobacillus san francisco* gave the bread its sour taste. Each day before baking, cooks would set aside some dough that contained the bacteria to use in the next day's bread.

Chapter 2 **A ◆ 63**

Program Resources

◆ **Integrated Science Laboratory Manual**
A-2, "Eubacteria That Dine on Vegetables"

A ◆ 63

Bacteria and the Living World, continued

Demonstration

To show students how bacteria act as decomposers, put several leaves of lettuce on each of two plates. Place one plate in a refrigerator. Place the other in a warm place. Allow the plates to sit for several days. Show them to students and give them time to observe the lettuce and describe what they observe. *(They should notice that the lettuce that was left out has become rotten and slimy.)* Challenge students to draw conclusions about what made the lettuce get this way. *(bacteria)* Ask: **What effect do you think temperature has on the growth of some bacteria?** *(Lower temperatures may slow the rate of growth.)* Explain that bacteria broke down the components of the lettuce for food. As the cells of the lettuce leaf decompose, the contents are released as a slimy mixture of plant materials. Ask: **How are the bacteria in the lettuce similar to the bacteria that act as decomposers in the environment?** *(Decomposers feed on dead matter and convert it into different forms.)* **learning modality: visual**

Integrating Environmental Science

Explain that many kinds of bacteria are needed to decompose oil. Each one breaks up a specific type of molecule. One mixture used to clean up oil spills contains 117 different species of bacteria. Bacteria are also used to clean waste water. Ask: **What other sources of polluted water could possibly be cleaned up with bacteria?** *(Pollution from industry or farming)* **learning modality: verbal**

Figure 11 Bacteria live in the swellings on the roots of this soybean plant. The bacteria convert nitrogen from the air into substances the plant needs. *Applying Concepts Why might farmers plant soybeans in a field that is low in nitrogen?*

"nature's recyclers"—they return basic chemicals to the environment for other living things to reuse. For example, in the fall, the leaves of many trees die and fall to the ground. Decomposing bacteria spend the next months breaking down the chemicals in the dead leaves. The broken-down chemicals mix with the soil, and can then be absorbed by the roots of nearby plants.

Other recycling eubacteria live in swellings on the roots of some plants, such as peanuts, peas, and soybeans. There, they convert nitrogen gas from the air into nitrogen compounds that the plants need to grow. The plants cannot convert nitrogen from the air into the nitrogen compounds they need. Therefore, the bacteria that live in the roots of plants help the plants to survive.

Environmental Cleanup Some bacteria help to clean up Earth's land and water. Can you imagine having a bowl of oil for dinner instead of soup? Well, there are some bacteria that prefer the oil. They convert the dangerous chemicals in oil into harmless substances. Scientists have put these bacteria to work cleaning up oil spills in oceans and gasoline leaks in the soil under gas stations.

Health and Medicine You may find it hard to believe that many of the bacteria living in your body actually keep you healthy. In your digestive system, for example, your intestines teem with bacteria. This is a natural and healthy situation. Some of the bacteria help you digest your food. Some make vitamins that your body needs. Others compete for space with disease-

Figure 12 Scientists use bacteria such as these *Ochrobactrum anthropi* to help clean up oil spills.

Background

Facts and Figures As well as "eating" oil, bacteria can convert dangerous chemicals in industrial waste products into harmless ones.

Chlorinated compounds such as trichloroethylene (TCE) and perchloroethylene (PCE) are toxic and believed to cause cancer. However, PCE is used to dry-clean clothes, and both compounds are present in antifreeze. Until 1997, scientists could not find a microorganism that would clean up TCE and PCE. In that year, researchers from Cornell University found a microbe, known as Strain 195, in an abandoned sewage plant in Ithaca, New York. Strain 195 is an anaerobic bacterium that extracts energy from the breakdown of chlorinated solvents. It can remove all the chlorine atoms from PCE and convert it to ethene, a natural, biologically important substance.

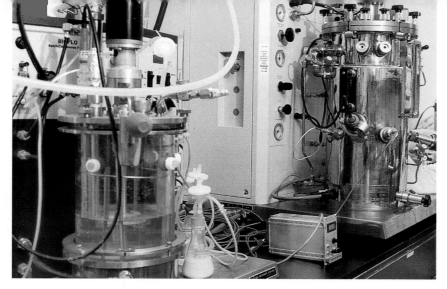

causing organisms. They prevent the harmful bacteria from attaching to your intestines and making you sick.

 INTEGRATING TECHNOLOGY Scientists have put some bacteria to work making medicines and other substances. People can use these substances to live healthy lives. The first medicine-producing bacteria were made in the 1970s. By manipulating the genetic material of bacteria, scientists engineered bacteria to produce human insulin. Although healthy people can make their own insulin, people with diabetes cannot. Many people with diabetes need to take insulin on a daily basis. Thanks to their fast rate of reproduction, large numbers of insulin-making bacteria can be grown in huge vats. The human insulin they produce is then purified and made into medicine.

Figure 13 Today, bacteria can be used to produce medicines. The bacteria can be grown in huge numbers in vats like these.

Section 2 Review

1. How is a bacterial cell different from the cells of other kinds of organisms?
2. List four ways in which bacteria are helpful to people.
3. What happens during binary fission?
4. Describe how a bacterium can survive when conditions are unfavorable for growth.
5. **Thinking Critically Applying Concepts** Why are some foods, such as milk, heated to high temperatures before they are bottled?

Science at Home

With a family member, look around your kitchen for foods that are made using bacteria. Read the labels on the foods to see if the role of bacteria in the food's production is mentioned. Discuss with your family member the helpful roles that bacteria play in the lives of people.

Chapter 2 **A ◆ 65**

 Integrating Technology

Tell students that diabetics used to take insulin that was derived from pigs or sheep. Draw students' attention to the vats in Figure 13. Ask: **Do you think it would take a long time to produce a vat full of insulin-producing bacteria?** *(Students should recall their graphs of bacterial growth and realize it will not take very long.)* **learning modality: visual**

3 Assess

Section 2 Review Answers

1. Bacterial cells are prokaryotic; cells of other organisms are eukaryotic.
2. Bacteria are involved in food and fuel production, environmental recycling and cleanup, and the production of medicines.
3. During binary fission, a cell divides to produce two new cells that are identical to each other.
4. A bacterium survives unfavorable conditions by forming an endospore, a small, round, thick-coated resting cell that contains some of its cytoplasm and all of its genetic material.
5. High temperatures kill any disease-causing bacteria in the milk.

Science at Home

Provide students with a list of keywords to look for on product labels to help them identify bacteria in products. For example, *live* or *active cultures, enzymes.* Encourage students to share their findings from home with classmates.

Program Resources

◆ **Teaching Resources** 2-2 Review and Reinforce, p. 49; 2-2 Enrich, p. 50

Media and Technology

 Interactive Student Tutorial CD-ROM A-2

Answers to Self-Assessment

Caption Question

Figure 11 The bacteria that live on the roots of soybeans can convert the nitrogen compounds into a form that can be used by the plant.

Performance Assessment

Writing Have students write two or three paragraphs describing bacteria that are either helpful or harmful to humans.

A ◆ 65

You, the Consumer

Do Disinfectants Work?

Preparing for Inquiry

Key Concept The growth of bacteria can be controlled through the use of disinfectants.

Skills Objective Students will be able to
- observe bacterial growth on petri dishes;
- infer how well a disinfectant controls bacterial growth;
- draw conclusions regarding the best way to use disinfectants.

Time 30 minutes first day, 15 minutes for each of the next three days

Advance Planning Bring disinfectants, such as pine-scented cleaners or bleach, to class that contain different active ingredients. Dilute disinfectants at least tenfold to reduce the possibility of injury to students. Make sure the room is well ventilated. Review the use of the eyewash apparatus in case disinfectant is accidentally splashed into the eye of a student. Because disinfectants may stain clothes, students may want to bring an old shirt or apron to wear over their clothes during the lab. After opening a package of agar plates, use all the plates right away or dispose of leftover plates, because they will not remain sterile.

Guiding Inquiry

Invitation

Ask students why some cleaning products contain disinfectants. Students should discuss the fact that bacteria are present everywhere around them. Controlling bacteria using disinfectants helps prevent disease transmission and food spoilage. Students should be able to explain how they will test the ability of a disinfectant to control bacteria in this lab.

Introducing the Procedure
- Pour out enough of each disinfectant into small containers so that students can fill their droppers without inserting them into the bottle of disinfectant. Caution students not to mix samples.

You, the Consumer

Do Disinfectants Work?

When your family goes shopping, you may buy cleaning products called disinfectants. Disinfectants kill microorganisms such as bacteria, which may cause infection or decay. In this lab, you will compare the effects of two different disinfectants.

Problem

How well do disinfectants control the growth of bacteria?

Skills Focus

observing, inferring, drawing conclusions

Materials

clock	wax pencil
2 plastic droppers	transparent tape
2 household disinfectants	
3 plastic petri dishes with sterile nutrient agar	

Procedure

1. Copy the data table into your notebook.
2. Work with a partner. Obtain 3 petri dishes containing sterile agar. Without opening them, use a wax pencil to label the bottoms "A," "B," and "C." Write your initials beside each letter.
3. Wash your hands thoroughly with soap, then run a fingertip across the surface of your worktable. Your partner should hold open the cover of petri dish A, while you run that fingertip gently across the agar in a zig-zag motion. Close the dish immediately.
4. Repeat Step 3 for dishes B and C.
5. Use a plastic dropper to transfer 2 drops of one disinfectant to the center of petri dish A. Open the cover just long enough to add the disinfectant to the dish. Close the cover immediately. Record the name of the disinfectant in your data table. **CAUTION:** *Do not inhale vapors from the disinfectant.*
6. Repeat Step 5 for dish B but add 2 drops of the second disinfectant. **CAUTION:** *Do not mix any disinfectants together.*
7. Do not add any disinfectant to dish C.
8. Tape down the covers of all 3 petri dishes so that they will remain tightly closed. Allow the 3 dishes to sit upright on your work surface for at least 5 minutes. **CAUTION:** *Do not open the petri dishes again.* Wash your hands with soap and water.
9. As directed by your teacher, store the petri dishes in a warm, dark place where they can remain for at least 3 days. Remove them only to make a brief examination each day.

DATA TABLE

Petri Dish	Disinfectant	Day 1	Day 2	Day 3
A				
B				
C				

Sample Data Table

Petri Dish	Disinfectant	Day 1	Day 2	Day 3
A				
B				
C				

Program Resources

- **Teaching Resources** Chapter 2 Real-World Lab, pp. 57–59

10. After one day, observe the contents of each dish without removing the covers. Estimate the percentage of the agar surface that shows any changes. Record your observations. Return the dishes to their storage place when you have finished making your observations. Wash your hands with soap.

11. Repeat Step 10 after the second day and again after the third day.

12. After you and your partner have made your last observations, return the petri dishes to your teacher unopened.

Analyze and Conclude

1. How did the appearance of dish C change during the lab?

2. How did the appearance of dishes A and B compare with dish C? Explain any similarities or differences.

3. How did the appearance of dishes A and B compare with each other? How can you account for any differences?

4. Why was it important to set aside one petri dish that did not contain any disinfectant?

5. Apply Based on the results of this lab, what recommendation would you make to your family about the use of disinfectants? Where in the house do you think these products would be needed most?

Design an Experiment

Go to a store and look at soap products that claim to be "antibacterial" soaps. How do their ingredients differ from other soaps? How do their prices compare? Design an experiment to test how well these products control the growth of bacteria.

◆ Explain that students will store petri dishes upside down so that any condensed water will collect on the inside cover of the dish instead of dropping into the agar.

Troubleshooting the Experiment
Stress the safety procedures associated with any lab dealing with bacteria. Emphasize that students must not open the petri dishes after the initial procedures.

Expected Outcome
Several colonies of bacteria should grow on the control dish C. Dishes A and B should have fewer colonies, smaller colonies, or both.

Analyze and Conclude
1. Answers will vary, but students should report numerous bacterial colonies growing on the agar surface.
2. Dishes A and B should have fewer colonies, smaller colonies, or both.
3. Answers will vary depending on the disinfectants used. Any differences between A and B may be due to the relative effectiveness of the two disinfectants. They could also be due to other factors such as the distribution of different kinds of bacteria picked up off the work surface.
4. The dish without disinfectant, dish C, was the control. It shows how bacteria grew when no disinfectant was applied.
5. Students may mention using disinfectants to clean locations and implements associated with food preparation, bathroom facilities, children's rooms, and in cases of family illness.

Extending the Inquiry
Design an Experiment Encourage students to compare the labels of antibacterial soaps with the labels of disinfectants to look for any common ingredients. Students' plans should include clear and safe procedures and should clearly identify the control and the variables to be tested.

SECTION 3 Viruses, Bacteria, and Your Health

Objectives

After completing the lesson, students will be able to

◆ describe how infectious diseases spread from person to person;

◆ describe some ways in which infectious diseases can be treated or prevented.

Key Terms infectious disease, toxin, antibiotic, vaccine

1 Engage/Explore

Activating Prior Knowledge

Invite students to recall the last time they were ill and make inferences as to how they may have gotten the disease. Write their responses on the board. *(Accept all reasonable responses.)*

DISCOVER

Skills Focus predicting

Materials *aprons, plastic cups, eyedroppers, goggles, distilled water, 0.01 M sodium hydroxide solution (enough for one student), phenol red solution (enough for every student)*

Time 20 minutes

Tips Give each student a plastic cup of distilled water. "Infect" one student's cup with sodium hydroxide, but do not inform that student. Caution students not to insert their droppers into another student's solution. Remind them that phenol red will stain their clothing. Phenol red is an acid-base indicator that turns red in contact with the base sodium hydroxide.

Expected Outcome After three rounds, up to eight students will be infected.

Think It Over In a class of 30, all should be infected after five rounds. Some diseases spread the way bacteria grow—one person passes a disease to another, two then spread it, and so on.

SECTION 3 Viruses, Bacteria, and Your Health

DISCOVER

How Do Infectious Diseases Spread?

1. Put on goggles and plastic gloves. Your teacher will give you a plastic dropper and a plastic cup half filled with a liquid. Do not taste, smell, or touch the liquid.

2. In this activity, you will model how some diseases spread. Your teacher will signal the start of a "talking" period. Choose a classmate to talk with briefly. As you talk, exchange a dropperful of the liquid in your cup with your classmate.

3. At your teacher's signal, talk to another classmate. Exchange a dropperful of liquid.

4. Repeat Step 3 two more times.

5. Your teacher will add a few drops of a liquid to each student's cup. If your fluid turns pink, it indicates that you have "contracted a disease" from one of your classmates. Wash your hands when you have finished the activity.

Think It Over

Predicting How many more rounds would it take for everyone in your class to "become infected"? Use your prediction to explain why some diseases can spread quickly through a population.

GUIDE FOR READING

◆ How do infectious diseases spread from person to person?

Reading Tip Before you read, rewrite the section's headings as questions. As you read, write answers to the questions.

It started last night with a tickle in the back of your throat. This morning, when you woke up, your nose felt stuffy. By lunchtime, your muscles started to ache. By the time the big game started after school, your mouth felt dry and your throat was scratchy. Now, in the seventh inning of the game, you feel awful. You're sneezing and talking like you have a clothespin on your nose. You can't seem to get warm, and you're shivering on the bench. You've caught a cold—or maybe more accurately, a cold has caught you!

How Infectious Diseases Spread

Have you ever wondered how you catch a cold, a strep throat, or even the chicken pox? These and many other diseases are called **infectious diseases**—illnesses that pass from one organism to another. **Infectious diseases can spread in one of four ways: through contact with either an infected person, a contaminated object, an infected animal, or an environmental source.** Once contact occurs, some disease-causing agents may enter a person through breaks in the skin, or they may be inhaled or swallowed. Others may enter the body through the moist linings of the eyes, ears, nose, mouth, or other body openings.

READING STRATEGIES

Reading Tip As students generate questions based on the section headings, remind them to rewrite the headings so that they begin with common question words such *who, what, where, when, why, how.* Suggest students predict answers to some or all of the questions. Then direct them to answer the questions in their own words based on their reading.

Study and Comprehension As students read, encourage them to list the similarities and differences between viruses and bacteria and create compare/contrast tables from their lists.

Contact With an Infected Person Direct contact such as touching, hugging, or kissing an infected person can spread some infectious diseases. For example, kissing an infected person can transmit cold sores. Many other infectious diseases can be spread by indirect contact with an infected person. A common form of indirect contact is inhaling the tiny drops of moisture that an infected person sneezes or coughs into the air. This is because the drops of moisture contain disease-causing organisms. For example, the flu can be spread by inhaling drops of moisture that contain the flu virus.

Figure 14 When you sneeze, tiny drops of moisture that contain the disease-causing organisms in your body enter the air.

Contact With a Contaminated Object Some viruses and bacteria can survive for a while outside a person's body. They can be spread via objects, such as eating utensils, or in contaminated food or water. For example, drinking from a cup used by an infected person can spread diseases such as strep throat and mononucleosis. If you touch an object that an infected person has sneezed or coughed on, you may transfer some viruses or bacteria to yourself if you then touch your mouth or eyes. If you drink water or eat food that an infected person has contaminated, you may get sick. Drinking water that contains small amounts of sewage is a common way that disease is spread in many areas of the world.

Contact With an Animal The bites of animals can transmit some serious infectious diseases to humans. For example, the deadly disease rabies can be transferred through the bite of an infected dog, raccoon, or some other animals. The bites of ticks can transmit the bacteria that cause Lyme disease. The bites of mosquitoes can spread the virus that causes encephalitis—a serious disease in which the brain tissues swell.

Figure 15 This mosquito, *Culex nigripalpus*, is feeding on human blood. If this mosquito contains the virus that causes encephalitis, it can transmit the disease through its bite. *Applying Concepts* What other diseases are spread by animal bites?

Answers to Self-Assessment
Caption Question
Figure 15 rabies and Lyme disease

2 Facilitate

How Infectious Diseases Spread

Demonstration
Materials *disposable petri dishes with sterile agar, wax marking pencil, masking tape, cotton swabs*

ACTIVITY

Time 20 minutes for setup; 10 minutes on each of 2 days

Tips Be sure to use all the plates in a package as they are not sterile once the package is opened. Challenge small groups to think of inanimate objects in the classroom on which bacteria might be found. CAUTION: *Do not collect samples from humans or pets.* Compile a list from the group's suggestions and select the top four choices. Have students predict which surface will have the most bacteria. Use the wax pencil to draw a line on the outside of the bottom of a petri dish, dividing it in two. Collect samples by rubbing the swab on the objects and then on the agar on one side of the dish. Cover the prepared dishes and seal them with tape. Label the dishes with the name of the object or surface where the sample was collected. CAUTION: *Once plates are inoculated and sealed, do not reopen them.* Place the dishes upside down in a warm, dark place. Allow students to observe the dishes after 24 and 48 hours. Have groups compare their results and make inferences about the sources of disease-causing bacteria. Review the safety guidelines in Appendix A. Dispose of the petri dishes and all other materials according to the proper procedures. Be sure to check your district's and state's guidelines for the proper disposal of bacterial cultures.
learning modality: visual

Ongoing Assessment
Oral Assessment Have students describe three ways infectious diseases can be spread.

How Infectious Diseases Spread, continued

Real-Life Learning

Invite students to volunteer experiences

ACTIVITY

they have had with cooking chicken or watching chicken being cooked. Have students discuss safety measures that might be used to prevent salmonella poisoning. Inform students that bacteria such as salmonella can survive in poultry that is cooked at low temperatures. The meat may look cooked, but it can still cause intestinal infections. In addition, cooking may kill the bacteria that produce toxins, but it does not necessarily destroy the toxin. Botulism is one example of food poisoning caused by a toxin. Remind students to always wash their hands, as well as cutting boards and utensils, thoroughly after handling chicken. Ask: **What foods are most likely to contain dangerous bacteria?** *(Eggs, dairy products, poultry, meat, fish)* Have students create posters encouraging healthy cooking habits. **learning modality: verbal**

Social Studies
CONNECTION

In the late 1800s, Emil Adolf von Behring, a German bacteriologist, injected animals with dead or weakened toxins from diphtheria bacteria. The animals produced an antitoxin that made them resistant to the disease. This antitoxin was given to humans for the first time in 1891. Ask: **Why are there so few cases of diphtheria in the United States?** *(Most Americans are immunized with the antitoxin.)*

In Your Journal Suggest students find out how weather conditions and terrain on the Iditarod Trail affects dogs and drivers, so they can describe how the dogs and drivers feel when they arrive in Nome. **learning modality: verbal**

Social Studies
CONNECTION

In January 1925, two children died of diphtheria, a bacterial disease, in Nome, Alaska. The disease can be treated with an antitoxin that destroys the toxin that the bacteria produces. But Nome had no antitoxin and was snow-bound. Antitoxin had to be rushed from Anchorage, over 1,500 kilometers away.

The antitoxin went by rail to Nenana, which was still 1,100 kilometers from Nome. Then twenty sled-dog owners organized a relay team. The drivers passed the antitoxin from one sled-dog team to the next, through storms and frigid weather. The sled-dog teams traveled along the Iditarod Trail, which was cut across the wilderness during the 1880s gold rush. After six grueling days, the last team arrived in Nome. The city was saved from the disease.

In Your Journal

It is February 2, 1925, and you are the driver on the last leg of the antitoxin relay. Write a diary entry about your arrival in Nome.

Contact With Environmental Sources Some viruses and bacteria live in food, water, and soil, or on the surfaces of objects. The places where they are naturally found are environmental sources of disease. For example, poultry, eggs, and meat often contain salmonella bacteria. Eating foods that contain these bacteria can lead to one type of food poisoning. Cooking the foods thoroughly kills the bacteria. A soil bacterium called *Clostridium botulinum* can grow in improperly processed canned foods. It produces a poison known as a **toxin**, which soaks into the food. Eating the food causes a serious, often deadly disease known as botulism. *Clostridium tetani*, another soil-dwelling bacteria, can enter a person's body through a wound and cause the deadly disease tetanus.

☑ *Checkpoint* **What is one thing you can do to reduce the risk of food poisoning?**

Common Infectious Diseases

There are thousands of kinds of infectious diseases. Some are common in one part of the world but rare or absent in other places. Many infectious diseases are caused by viruses and bacteria. Others are caused by protists and fungi, which you will learn about in the next chapter. Figure 17 provides important information about some common viral and bacterial diseases in this country.

Figure 16 Today, an event called the Iditarod Trail Dog Sled Race takes place in March each year. Sled-dog teams compete in a 1,930-kilometer race to celebrate the history of the Iditarod Trail.

Background

Facts and Figures In the early 1980s, an American biochemist, Stanley B. Prusiner, found an unusual protein in the brain of an animal that died of scrapie. Prusiner called the protein a *prion* (PREE awn). Researchers later discovered prions in the brains of humans that died of Creutzfeldt-Jakob disease. Prions are abnormal versions of normally harmless proteins that occur in cells such as brain cells. Prions differ from the harmless versions, not in their amino acid sequence, but in the way they are folded. This abnormal folding keeps them from being broken down by enzymes so they build up in the nerve cells in the brain. The prion does not reproduce, but it does multiply by inducing other harmless proteins to refold into the aberrant form. After months or years, the accumulating levels of prions in the brain lead to brain damage.

Common Infectious Diseases

Disease	Disease-Causing Agent	Symptoms	How Spread	Treatment	Prevention
Acquired immuno-deficiency syndrome (AIDS)	Virus	Weight loss; chronic fatigue; fever; diarrhea; frequent infections	Sexual contact; contact with blood; pregnancy, birth, and breast-feeding	Drugs to slow viral multiplication	Avoid contact with infected body fluids
Chicken Pox	Virus	Fever; red itchy rash	Contact with rash; inhale droplets	Antiviral drug (for adults)	Vaccine
Influenza (flu)	Virus	High fever; sore throat; headache; cough	Contact with contaminated objects; inhale droplets	Bed rest; fluids	Vaccine (mainly for high-risk ill, elderly, and young)
Measles	Virus	High fever; sore throat; cough; white spots on cheek lining; rash; puffy eyelids	Inhale droplets	Bed rest, cough medicine	Vaccine
Poliomyelitis (polio)	Virus	Fever; muscle weakness; headache; difficulty swallowing	Inhale droplets	Bed rest	Vaccine
Rabies	Virus	Drooling; skin sensitivity; alternating periods of rage and calm; difficulty swallowing	Animal bite	Vaccine	Avoid wild animals and pets that act abnormally; keep track of pets outside
Food poisoning	Various bacteria	Vomiting; cramps; diarrhea; fever	Eating foods containing the bacteria	Antitoxin medicines; rest	Properly cook and store foods; avoid foods in rusted and swollen cans
Lyme disease	Bacterium	Rash at site of tick bite; chills; fever; body aches; joint swelling	Animal bite	Antibiotic	Tuck pants into socks; wear long-sleeved shirt
Strep throat	Bacterium	Fever; sore throat; swollen glands	Inhale droplets; contact with infected object	Antibiotic	Avoid contact with infected people
Tetanus (lockjaw)	Bacterium	Stiff jaw and neck muscles; spasms; difficulty swallowing	Deep puncture wound	Antibiotic; opening and cleaning wound	Vaccine
Tuberculosis (TB)	Bacterium	Fatigue; mild fever; weight loss; night sweats; cough	Inhale droplets	Antibiotic	Vaccine (for those in high risk occupations only)

Figure 17 Many common infectious diseases are caused by viruses and bacteria. Much is known about how these diseases are spread and how they can be treated or prevented.
Interpreting Charts Which diseases are spread by inhaling droplets in the air?

Program Resources

 Science Explorer Series
Environmental Science, Chapter 5

Answers to Self-Assessment

Caption Question
Figure 17 Chicken pox, influenza, measles, polio, strep throat, and tuberculosis

✓ Checkpoint
Cook foods thoroughly.

Common Infectious Diseases

Using the Visuals: Figure 17
Ask students to imagine that they are doctors examining a patient with a rash and a fever. Ask: **Which diseases could these symptoms be caused by?** *(Sample: Chicken pox, measles, Lyme disease)* **What questions could you ask the patient to determine which disease he or she had?** *(Samples: Were you immunized against the measles? Have you been in the woods lately?)* **learning modality: verbal**

Ongoing Assessment

Oral Presentation Tell students to choose one infectious disease and explain what causes the disease, what its symptoms are, how it is spread, its treatment, and how they could prevent the disease.

A ◆ 71

Treating Infectious Diseases

Demonstration

Materials *disposable petri dish, sterile nutrient agar, sterile cotton swab, sterile tweezers, antibiotic disk of aureomycin, broth culture of Escherichia coli*

ACTIVITY

Time 20 minutes for setup; 10 minutes for observation after 48 hours

This demonstration will show students how an antibiotic affects a common bacteria. Transfer two drops of the *E. coli* culture onto the sterile agar. Using a cotton swab, spread the culture evenly across the agar. Use sterile tweezers to place the aureomycin disk in the middle of the agar. Cover the petri dish, seal it with tape, and place it in a dark, warm spot for 48 hours. CAUTION: *Do not open the petri dish after it has been inoculated. Wash your hands thoroughly. Do not allow students to come into contact with the bacterial culture.* Have students predict what they will observe in the dish. Allow time to observe the culture after 48 hours. Light-colored cloudy areas will indicate the growth of bacteria. A clear area shows where the *E. coli* bacteria were killed or prevented from growing by the aureomycin. Challenge students to infer how effective the antibiotic was against bacterial growth. Dispose of the petri dishes and all other materials according to the proper procedures. Be sure to check your district's and state's guidelines for the proper disposal of bacterial cultures. **limited English proficiency**

Preventing Infectious Diseases

Real-Life Learning

Have students contact a public-health agency or their school administration to learn more about vaccinations. Some topics students might research include making a list of all vaccines that are required for school children, or the schedule for receiving immunizations in childhood. Have students make posters or prepare presentations to share their findings. **learning modality: verbal**

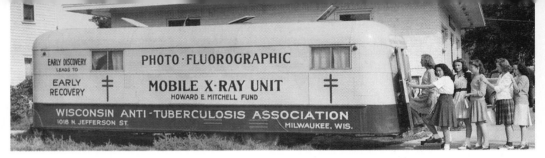

Figure 18 Before antibiotics were available to treat tuberculosis, the deadly disease spread easily. People visited mobile X-ray vans to be screened for tuberculosis. *Relating Cause and Effect How has antibiotic resistance affected the number of tuberculosis cases?*

Treating Infectious Diseases

Once you start to have symptoms of an infectious disease, your attention probably turns quickly to helping yourself feel better. For most infectious diseases, the best treatment is bedrest. Indeed, resting, drinking lots of fluids, and eating well-balanced meals may be all you can do while you recover from some infectious diseases.

Viral Diseases Unfortunately, there are no medications that can cure viral infections. However, while no cures exist, there are many over-the-counter medications that treat the symptoms. These medications are available without a prescription. Over-the-counter medications can make you feel better. But, they can also delay your recovery if you resume your normal routine while you are still sick. They can also hide symptoms that would normally cause you to go to a doctor.

Bacterial Diseases Unlike viral diseases, many bacterial diseases can be cured with medications known as antibiotics. An **antibiotic** is a chemical that can kill bacteria without harming a person's cells. Antibiotics are made naturally by some bacteria and fungi. Today, antibiotics such as penicillin are made in large quantities in factories. Penicillin works by weakening the cell walls of some bacteria and causing the cells to burst.

If you have ever had a strep throat infection, you know that the infection makes swallowing feel like you have a throat full of barbed wire. But soon after you begin taking the antibiotic that your doctor prescribes, your throat feels better. This is because the antibiotic quickly kills the bacteria that cause strep throat.

Unfortunately, antibiotics are less effective today than they once were. This is because many bacteria have become resistant to antibiotics over the years. Resistant bacteria are able to survive in the presence of an antibiotic. The recent increase in tuberculosis cases demonstrates the impact of antibiotic resistance. Between 1950 and 1980, the number of cases of tuberculosis dropped significantly as patients took antibiotics. Unfortunately, there were always a few tuberculosis bacteria that were resistant to the antibiotics. Those bacteria survived and reproduced,

Background

Facts and Figures Most vaccinations involve injections, ingestions, or most recently, inhalations. However, researchers at Washington University in Missouri have found a better way.

The most common cause of salmonella poisoning is through eating uncooked eggs, either directly or in other foods. To prevent salmonella in humans, the researchers decided to vaccinate the chickens that lay the eggs. From 1990–1997, they worked to make a live salmonella strain harmless by deleting two critical genes. These genes regulate the expression of other genes that make the bacteria harmful. The vaccine can be administered in aerosol form or in drinking water, at a cost of less than a penny per bird.

producing more bacteria like themselves. Today, many resistant bacteria exist. Since the mid-1980s, the number of tuberculosis cases has been on the rise despite the use of antibiotics.

Preventing Infectious Diseases

One important tool that helps to prevent the spread of infectious diseases is vaccines. A **vaccine** is a substance that stimulates the body to produce chemicals that destroy viruses or bacteria. A vaccine may be made from dead or altered viruses or bacteria. The viruses or bacteria in the vaccine do not cause disease, but instead activate the body's natural defenses. In effect, the altered viruses or bacteria put the body "on alert." If that virus or bacterium ever invades the body, it is destroyed before it can produce disease. You may have been vaccinated against diseases such as tetanus, pertussis (whooping cough), measles, mumps, and polio. Now there is also a vaccine available for the viral disease chicken pox.

Staying Healthy

The best way to protect against infectious diseases is to keep your body healthy. You need to eat nutritious food, as well as get plenty of rest, fluids, and exercise. You can also protect yourself by washing your hands often and by not sharing eating utensils or drink containers. You should also make sure that you have all recommended vaccinations. Storing food properly, keeping kitchen equipment and surfaces clean, and cooking meats well can prevent food poisoning.

Unfortunately, despite your best efforts, you'll probably get infectious diseases, such as colds, from time to time. When you do get ill, get plenty of rest, follow your doctor's recommendations, and try not to infect others.

Figure 19 By exercising and keeping your body healthy, you can help protect yourself from infectious diseases.

 Section 3 Review

1. List four ways that infectious diseases can be spread.
2. What is an antibiotic? What types of infectious diseases do antibiotics cure?
3. What is a vaccine?
4. **Thinking Critically** *Inferring* Why is washing your hands an effective way to prevent the spread of some infectious diseases?

Check Your Progress

CHAPTER PROJECT 2

By now you should have nearly all of your questionnaires answered. You should be ready to tally your responses. Begin to think about how you will use graphs or other visual ways to organize your results. *(Hint:* You may need to review the research you did earlier to help you make sense of some survey data.)

Chapter 2 **A ◆ 73**

 Media and Technology

 Interactive Student Tutorial CD-ROM A-2

Exploring Life Science Videodisc
Unit 2, Side 2, "Have You Had Your Shots?"
Chapter 3

Answers to Self-Assessment

Caption Question
Figure 18 Since the mid-1980s, the number of tuberculosis cases is on the rise, in spite of the use of antibiotics.

Program Resources

◆ **Teaching Resources** 2-3 Review and Reinforce, p. 53; 2-3 Enrich, p. 54

Staying Healthy

Building Inquiry Skills: Applying Concepts

Have students refer to pages 68–70 and make a list of the ways infectious diseases are spread. Then have them list one specific action they can take to prevent catching an infectious disease for each way disease is spread.

3 Assess

Section 3 Review Answers

1. Infectious diseases are spread through contact with an infected person, contaminated object, infected animal, or environmental source.
2. An antibiotic is a chemical that kills bacteria. Antibiotics can cure only bacterial infections.
3. A vaccine is a substance that stimulates the body to produce chemicals that destroy viruses or bacteria in the host.
4. Washing hands removes many bacteria and viruses from the skin and prevents them from being spread.

Check Your Progress

CHAPTER PROJECT 2

Make sure students have collected most of their survey results, and that they are keeping organized records of their data. Review with the class some of the ways (line graphs, bar charts) in which data can be visually presented.

Performance Assessment

Writing Have students choose one infectious disease that is transmitted by a virus and explain why it cannot and should not be treated with antibiotics.

Antibiotic Resistance —An Alarming Trend

Purpose

To acquaint students with the problems caused by overusing antibiotics and to help them determine ways to reduce the occurrence of antibiotic-resistant bacteria.

Panel Discussion

Materials *encyclopedias and other sources of information on antibiotic use, overuse, and discovery; materials to prepare posters*
Time one class period to prepare; 30 minutes for panel discussion, 30 minutes to create poster

As a class, first discuss the issue of antibiotic resistance. Be sure students understand how antibiotic-resistant populations of bacteria can evolve. Encourage students to think about how antibiotics have altered everyday life. Before the early 1940s, any cut was potentially fatal because of bacterial infection. Very few individuals today die from bacterial infections obtained through cuts. Have students consider the implications of having bacteria that are resistant to all known antibiotics. *(Resistant bacteria are difficult to treat.)*

Divide the class into three groups. Have one group research the question of overprescription of antibiotics and the problems caused when patients do not take all of a prescribed medication. Have the second group research nonmedical uses of antibiotics, and have the third group research the search for new antibiotics. Each group should limit the information they want to share with the class to two or three main points, well supported by facts. Have the groups select two spokespersons to serve on the panel.

On the second day, organize the panel discussion. Allow the spokespersons to present the results of their research (8–10 minutes each) and allow time for the class to ask questions of the panel.

Antibiotic Resistance—An Alarming Trend

Penicillin, the first antibiotic, became available for use in 1943. Soon afterward, antibiotics became known as the "wonder drugs." Over the years, they have reduced the occurrence of many bacterial diseases and saved millions of lives. But each time an antibiotic is used, a few bacteria— those resistant to the drug—survive. They pass on their resistance to the next generation of bacteria. As more and more patients take antibiotics, the number of resistant bacteria increases.

In 1987, penicillin killed more than 99.9 percent of a type of bacteria that causes ear infections. By 1995, 25 percent of those bacteria were resistant to penicillin. Diseases such as tuberculosis are on the increase due in part to growing antibiotic resistance.

The Issues

What Can Doctors and Patients Do?
In a typical year, about 6 billion dollars worth of antibiotics are sold to drugstores and hospitals in the United States. One way to slow down the process that leads to resistance is to decrease the amount of antibiotics people use. About one out of five prescriptions for antibiotics is written for colds and other viral illnesses. Antibiotics, however, do not kill viruses. If doctors could better identify the cause of an infection, they could avoid prescribing unnecessary antibiotics.

Patients can also play an important role. If a doctor prescribes a ten-day course of antibiotics, all of the prescription should be taken. If a patient stops taking the antibiotic, the resistant bacteria will survive and reproduce. Then, a second antibiotic may be necessary. Patients also need to learn that some illnesses are best treated with rest and not with antibiotics.

Limiting Non-medical Uses of Antibiotics About forty percent of the antibiotics used each year are not given to people. Instead, the drugs are fed to food animals, such as cattle and chickens, to prevent illness and increase growth. Reducing this type of use would limit the amount of the drugs in food animals and in the people who eat them. But these actions might increase the risk of disease in animals and lead to higher meat prices.

Finding New Antibiotics Another way to slow the increase of antibiotic resistance might be through more research. Scientists are trying to identify new antibiotics. With more kinds of antibiotics, scientists hope that bacteria will not develop resistances as quickly.

You Decide
1. Identify the Problem
Describe how the use of antibiotics can eventually make these medicines not work as well.

2. Analyze the Options
List all the ways to fight the development of antibiotic resistance in bacteria. For each action, tell who would carry it out and how it would work. Mention any costs or drawbacks.

3. Find a Solution
Make a persuasive poster about one way to deal with antibiotic resistance. Support your viewpoint with sound reasons. Target the group who could make the change.

Background

The problems of antibiotic resistance are often most dramatic in hospitals, where many patients are being treated with antibiotics. Because patients who are already ill are at higher risk because of weakened immune systems, many cases of bacterial infection are acquired in hospitals. One strain of the deadly bacteria *Staphylococcus aureus* was discovered in 1997 to be resistant to the antibiotic vancomycin. Fortunately, this particular strain could be treated with other antibiotics, but many forms of these bacteria have already developed resistance to all drugs except vancomycin.

One way that hospitals can help restrict antibiotic resistance is to treat different patients with different antibiotics. By prescribing different antibiotics for different people, doctors can help slow the spread of resistant bacteria.

SECTION 1 Viruses

Key Ideas

◆ Viruses are considered to be nonliving because viruses are not cells, and they do not use energy to grow and develop, or to respond to their surroundings.

◆ All viruses have two basic parts: an outer coat that protects the virus and an inner core made of genetic material.

◆ Once inside a cell, a virus uses the host cell's functions to make its own proteins and genetic material. The proteins and genetic material assemble into new viruses, which burst out, destroying the host.

Key Terms

virus   parasite
host   bacteriophage

SECTION 2 Bacteria

Key Ideas

◆ Bacteria are prokaryotes. Their cells do not have nuclei that contain the cell's genetic material. Instead, the genetic material floats freely in the cytoplasm.

◆ Bacteria reproduce asexually by binary fission, which results in the production of two cells exactly like the parent cell. Some bacteria have a simple form of sexual reproduction called conjugation. This process results in a cell with a new combination of genetic information.

◆ Bacteria play positive roles in the lives of humans. Bacteria are involved in fuel and food production, in environmental recycling and cleanup, and in the production of medicines.

Key Terms

cytoplasm   sexual reproduction
ribosome   conjugation
flagellum   respiration
binary fission   endospore
asexual reproduction   decomposer

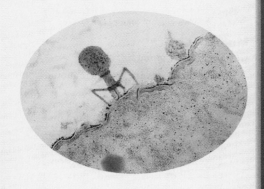

SECTION 3 Viruses, Bacteria, and Your Health

INTEGRATING HEALTH

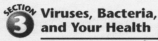

Key Ideas

◆ Infectious disease can spread through contact with an infected person, a contaminated object, an infected animal, or an environmental source.

◆ There is no cure for viral diseases. Bacterial diseases can be cured through the use of antibiotics. Vaccines can prevent some viral and bacterial diseases.

Key Terms

infectious disease   antibiotic
toxin   vaccine

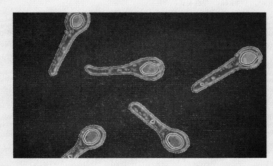

USING THE INTERNET

ACTIVITY

www.science-explorer.phschool.com

Extend Have the groups prepare a community health bulletin on this issue. Encourage them to list the problems and to identify solutions that individuals can implement to prevent antibiotic resistance.

You Decide

Students should respond to the items using information collected during the panel discussion as well as information from the book. Provide students with samples of persuasive or informative posters.

Program Resources

◆ **Teaching Resources** Chapter 2 Project Scoring Rubric, p. 42; Chapter 2 Performance Assessment Teacher Notes, pp. 163–164; Chapter 2 Performance Assessment Student Worksheet, p. 165; Chapter 2 Test, pp. 166–169

Reviewing Content:

Multiple Choice

1. b 2. d 3. c 4. a 5. c

True or False

6. Active viruses 7. virus's 8. true
9. true 10. antibiotic

Checking Concepts

11. Viruses do not have cell structures. Viruses do not carry on the functions of cells, such as food getting and respiration. Viruses cannot reproduce on their own.

12. The proteins in the coat of the virus will only fit with certain proteins on the surface of a cell.

13. A bacteriophage multiplies by injecting its genetic material into a cell. Then it takes over the cell's functions to make new protein coats and genetic material that assemble into new viruses. The cell bursts open and the new viruses are released to invade other cells.

14. Cell wall—protects the cell; cytoplasm—contains ribosomes and genetic material; ribosomes—produce protein; genetic material—contains instructions for the cell's functions; flagellum—helps cell to move

15. Most bacteria reproduce asexually by binary fission, in which one cell divides into two cells. Some bacteria have a simple form of sexual reproduction called conjugation, in which some genetic material from one cell is transferred into another cell, eventually resulting in different cells.

16. The bacteria that live in your intestines help keep you healthy because they help you digest food, make vitamins for you, and keep harmful bacteria and fungi from living in your tissues.

17. Antibiotics kill bacteria without harming body cells. For example, penicillin weakens the cells walls of some bacteria and causes them to burst.

18. Vaccines prevent the spread of infectious diseases by stimulating people who receive them to produce chemicals that fight off invading viruses and bacteria.

19. Students' essays should include the idea that once the virus is suspended in the air it could fall on many different

---

Reviewing Content

 For more review of key concepts, see the Interactive Student Tutorial CD-ROM.

Multiple Choice

Choose the letter of the best answer.

1. Bacteriophages are viruses that attack and destroy
   a. other viruses.   b. bacteria.
   c. plants.   d. humans.

2. Which part of a virus determines which host cells it can infect?
   a. genetic material   b. ribosomes
   c. flagellum   d. outer coat

3. Viruses multiply
   a. slowly inside cells.   b. by binary fission.
   c. by taking over a cell's functions.   d. both asexually and sexually.

4. Most bacteria are surrounded by a rigid protective structure called the
   a. cell wall.   b. cell membrane.
   c. protein coat.   d. flagellum.

5. Which of the following statements about infectious diseases is *not* true?
   a. Some can be spread by contact with an infected person.
   b. Some can be spread by contact with animals.
   c. All can be treated with antibiotics.
   d. Some can be prevented with vaccines.

True or False

If the statement is true, write true. If it is false, change the underlined word or words to make the statement true.

6. Hidden viruses enter a cell and immediately begin to multiply.

7. In gene therapy, scientists take advantage of a bacteria's ability to get inside a host cell.

8. Most archaebacteria live in extreme environments.

9. Bacteria form endospores to survive unfavorable conditions in their surroundings.

10. A vaccine is a chemical that can kill bacteria without harming a person's cells.

Checking Concepts

11. List three ways that viruses are different from cells.

12. Explain why a certain virus will attach to only one or a few types of cells.

13. Describe how a bacteriophage multiplies.

14. What are the parts of a bacterial cell? Explain the role of each part.

15. Describe how bacteria reproduce.

16. How do the bacteria that live in your intestines help you?

17. Explain how antibiotics kill bacteria.

18. How do vaccines prevent the spread of some infectious diseases?

19. **Writing to Learn** Imagine you are a cold virus. The student you infected just sneezed you into the air in the cafeteria. Write a description of what happens to you until you finally attach to a cell in another student.

Thinking Visually

20. Copy the Venn diagram comparing viruses and bacteria onto a separate sheet of paper. Then complete the Venn diagram. (For more on Venn diagrams, see the Skills Handbook.)

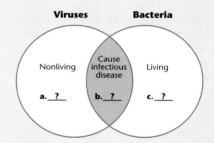

---

kinds of surfaces, many different times, before it finds itself in a person's moist nose and throat. They should demonstrate knowledge of how viruses are spread and should mention the selectivity of viruses for a host.

Thinking Visually

20. a. Can only multiply inside a cell or Not treated with antibiotics b. Microscopic c. Can multiply by itself or Treated with antibiotics

Applying Skills

21. Bacteria are rapidly growing because they have plenty of food available.

22. Sample: The number of bacteria stays constant between points B and C because the amount of food available to the bacteria can only support this number of bacteria.

23. Students might suggest testing their hypotheses from Question 22 by preparing petri dishes with different amounts of food and graphing the growth patterns of the bacteria.

Applying Skills

The graph shows how the number of bacteria that grow on a food source changes over time. Use the graph to answer Questions 21–23.

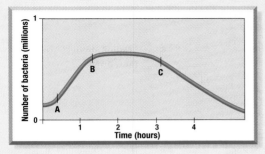

21. **Interpreting Data** Explain what is happening between points A and B.
22. **Developing Hypotheses** Develop a hypothesis that explains why the number of bacteria stays constant between points B and C.

23. **Designing Experiments** How could you test the hypothesis you developed in Question 22? What would your results show?

Thinking Critically

24. **Classifying** You know that viruses vary in shape, size, and the kinds of organisms they infect. Which one of these three characteristics would you use as a basis for a classification system for viruses? Explain your answer.
25. **Comparing and Contrasting** Describe the similarities and differences between active and hidden viruses.
26. **Problem Solving** Bacteria will grow in the laboratory on a gelatin-like substance called agar. Viruses will not grow on agar. If you needed to grow viruses in the laboratory, what kind of substance would you have to use? Explain.

Performance Assessment

CHAPTER PROJECT 2 **Wrap Up**

Present Your Project Your presentation should lead your audience through your project—from your survey to your conclusions. Make sure to explain why you chose the questions and survey group that you did. Use graphs or other visual displays to highlight important similarities or differences you found. Make sure that you support your conclusions with data.

Reflect and Record Do you think that a survey like this one is similar to a science experiment? What makes them alike or different? In your journal, describe what you did to make your survey accurate and complete.

Getting Involved

In Your School With your classmates plan a "Bacteria in Food" display for the other students in your school. Arrange for a place to set up your display. Put out samples of foods that require bacteria for their production. Make posters and models to inform students how bacteria are involved in each food's production. Be prepared to answer questions about the foods and about the bacteria that are used to make the foods.

Thinking Critically

24. Students might choose any of the three methods to classify viruses. Be sure they explain their choice. Scientists usually classify viruses on the basis of the organisms they infect.

25. All viruses invade the host cell and cause it to start producing new viruses. With an active virus, the takeover occurs immediately after entry into the cell. With hidden viruses, the genetic material of the virus is incorporated into the cell's genetic material and it can be years before the virus actively takes over the cell.

26. A substance that includes living cells would have to be used to grow viruses in a laboratory, because viruses need to infect living cells in order to increase their numbers.

Program Resources

◆ **Inquiry Skills Activity Book** Provides teaching and review of all inquiry skills

---

Performance Assessment

Wrap Up
Presenting Your Project Have students present their projects while their classmates take notes. Students' conclusions must be drawn from the results of their own surveys. Encourage students to compare their data with other sources. Prepare classroom space for students to display their posters or visual aids.

Reflect and Record Students should realize that a survey is similar to a science experiment in that they both require careful analysis. Students may express frustration that it is much more difficult to control variables in their surveys.

Getting Involved

In Your School Encourage students to choose a target audience within the school, such as a younger class of students. Guide students to think of the questions their audience might have, and to include foods they are familiar with. If possible, arrange for students to present their displays to their audience. Before the presentation, coach the students through a practice question-and-answer period.

Sections	Time	Student Edition Activities	Other Activities	
CHAPTER PROJECT 3 **A Mushroom Farm** p. 79	Ongoing (1½ weeks)	Check Your Progress, pp. 92, 104 Wrap Up, p. 107	TE	Chapter 3 Project Notes, pp. 78–79
1 **Protists** pp. 80–89 ◆ Describe the characteristics of animal-like, funguslike, and plantlike protists.	5 periods/ 2½ blocks	**Discover** What Lives in a Drop of Pond Water?, p. 80 **Try This** Feeding Paramecia, p. 84 **Sharpen Your Skills** Predicting, p. 87	TE TE TE TE TE TE ISLM	Inquiry Challenge, p. 81 Inquiry Challenge, p. 83 Building Inquiry Skills: Making Models, p. 85 Inquiry Challenge, p. 86 Building Inquiry Skills: Making Models, p. 86 Demonstration, p. 88 A–3, "Comparing Protists"
2 *INTEGRATING ENVIRONMENTAL SCIENCE* **Algal Blooms** pp. 90–94 ◆ Describe how red tides occur and explain why they are dangerous. ◆ Explain how the rapid growth of algae affects a pond or lake.	2½ periods/ 1–2 blocks	**Discover** How Can Algal Growth Affect Pond Life?, p. 90 **Real-World Lab: You and Your Environment** An Explosion of Life, p. 93	TE TE IES	Building Inquiry Skills: Making Models, p. 91 Including All Students, p. 92 "Where River Meets Sea," pp. 28–30
3 **Fungi** pp. 95–104 ◆ Name the characteristics that all fungi share. ◆ Describe how fungi obtain food. ◆ List the roles fungi play in the living world. ◆ Describe the ways that fungi reproduce.	5 periods/ 2½ blocks	**Discover** Do All Models Look Alike?, p. 95 **Try This** Making Spore Prints, p. 97 **Try This** Spreading Spores, p. 98 **Skills Lab: Drawing Conclusions** What's for Lunch?, pp. 100–101	TE TE TE TE TE IES	Building Inquiry Skills: Observing, p. 96 Building Inquiry Skills: Observing, p. 98 Demonstration, p. 99 Building Inquiry Skills: Designing Experiments, p. 102 Integrating Earth Science, p. 104 "A Nation of Immigrants," pp. 12–13
Study Guide/Chapter Review pp. 105–107	1 period/ ½ block		ISAB	Provides teaching and review of all inquiry skills

For Standard or Block Schedule The Resource Pro® CD-ROM gives you maximum flexibility for planning your instruction for any type of schedule. Resource Pro® contains Planning Express®, an advanced scheduling program, as well as the entire contents of the Teaching Resources and the Computer Test Bank.

CHAPTER PLANNING GUIDE

Program Resources	Assessment Strategies	Media and Technology
TR Chapter 3 Project Teacher Notes, pp. 60–61 **TR** Chapter 3 Project Overview and Worksheets, pp. 62–65 **TR** Chapter 3 Project Scoring Rubric, p. 66	**SE** Performance Assessment: Chapter 3 Project Wrap Up, p. 107 **TE** Performance Assessment: Chapter 3 Project Wrap Up, p. 107 **TE** Check Your Progress, pp. 92, 104 **TR** Chapter 3 Project Scoring Rubric, p. 66	Science Explorer Internet Site
TR 3-1 Lesson Plan, p. 67 **TR** 3-1 Section Summary, p. 68 **TR** 3-1 Review and Reinforce, p. 69 **TR** 3-1 Enrich, p. 70 **SES** Book D, *Human Biology and Health*, Chapter 6 **SES** Book G, *Earth's Changing Surface*, Chapter 3	**SE** Section 1 Review, p. 89 **TE** Ongoing Assessment, pp. 81, 83, 85, 87 **TE** Performance Assessment, p. 89 **TR** 3-1 Review and Reinforce, p. 69	Exploring Life Science Videodisc, Unit 2 Side 2, "Fungi and Algae" Audiotapes: English-Spanish Summary 3-1 Transparency 8, "Exploring Protozoans—Ameba" Transparency 9, "Exploring Protozoans—Paramecium" Transparency 10, "The Structure of a Euglena" Interactive Student Tutorial CD-ROM, A-3
TR 3-2 Lesson Plan, p. 71 **TR** 3-2 Section Summary, p. 72 **TR** 3-2 Review and Reinforce, p. 73 **TR** 3-2 Enrich, p. 74 **TR** Chapter 3 Real-World Lab, pp. 79–80 **SES** Book H, *Earth's Waters*, Chapter 5	**SE** Section 2 Review, p. 92 **SE** Analyze and Conclude, p. 93 **TE** Ongoing Assessment, p. 91 **TE** Performance Assessment, p. 92 **TR** 3-2 Review and Reinforce, p. 73	Exploring Life Science Videodisc, Unit 2 Side 2, "Fungi and Algae" Audiotapes: English-Spanish Summary 3-2 Interactive Student Tutorial CD-ROM, A-3
TR 3-3 Lesson Plan, p. 75 **TR** 3-3 Section Summary, p. 76 **TR** 3-3 Review and Reinforce, p. 77 **TR** 3-3 Enrich, p. 78 **TR** Chapter 3 Skills Lab, pp. 81–83 **SES** Book D, *Human Biology and Health*, Chapter 6 **SES** Book F, *Inside Earth*, Chapter 3	**SE** Section 3 Review, p. 104 **SE** Analyze and Conclude, p. 101 **TE** Ongoing Assessment, pp. 97, 99, 103 **TE** Performance Assessment, p. 104 **TR** 3-3 Review and Reinforce, p. 77	Audiotapes: English-Spanish Summary 3-3 Transparency 11, "The Structure of a Mushroom" Interactive Student Tutorial CD-ROM, A-3
TR Chapter 3 Performance Assessment, pp. 170–172 **TR** Chapter 3 Test, pp. 173–176	**SE** Chapter Review, pp. 105–107 **TR** Chapter 3 Performance Assessment, pp. 170–172 **TR** Chapter 3 Test, pp. 173–176 **CTB** Test A-3	Computer Test Bank, Test A-3 Interactive Student Tutorial CD-ROM, A-3

Key: **SE** Student Edition   **TE** Teacher's Edition   **TR** Teaching Resources
      CTB Computer Test Bank   **SES** Science Explorer Series Text   **ISLM** Integrated Science Laboratory Manual
      ISAB Inquiry Skills Activity Book   **PTA** Product Testing Activities by *Consumer Reports*   **IES** Interdisciplinary Explorations Series

Meeting the National Science Education Standards and AAAS Benchmarks

National Science Education Standards	Benchmarks for Science Literacy	Unifying Themes
Science as Inquiry (Content Standard A) ◆ **Ask questions that can be answered by scientific investigations** How does the amount of fertilizer affect algae growth? *(Real-World Lab)* How does the presence of sugar or salt affect the activity of yeast? *(Skills Lab)* ◆ **Use mathematics in all aspects of scientific inquiry** Students use mathematics as variables in scientific investigations. *(Real-World Lab, Skills Lab)* ◆ **Design and conduct a scientific investigation** Students design and conduct an investigation about how light and moisture affect the growth of mushrooms. *(Chapter Project)* **Life Science** (Content Standard C) ◆ **Structure and Function of Living Systems** Students learn the main characteristics of protists and the differences among the protist groups. *(Section 1)* Students learn the characteristics of fungi, how they obtain food, and their role in the living world. *(Section 3; Chapter Project)* ◆ **Populations and Ecosystems** Students learn about the effects of the rapid growth of algae on a pond or a lake. *(Section 2)* ◆ **Diversity and Adaptations of Organisms** Students learn about the diversity among protists and fungi. *(Sections 1 and 3)*	**1B Scientific Inquiry** Students control variables to see the effect of fertilizer on algae growth. Students control variables to see the effect of sugar or salt on yeast. *(Real-World Lab; Skills Lab)* **5A Diversity of Life** Characteristics that describe protists, algae, and fungi are presented in a general format. *(Sections 1, 2, 3)* **5D Interdependence of Life** Interactions between fungi and food, fungi and their relationship to diseases, and fungi and their relationship to the environment are explored. *(Section 3)* **11D Communication Skills** Students organize the results of investigations in data tables and interpret their results. *(Real-World Lab; Skills Lab)*	◆ **Scale and Structure** Protists are unicellular organisms that contain nuclei. Most are microscopic and cannot be seen without the aid of a microscope. Fungi are made of threadlike fibers called *hyphae*. *(Sections 1, 3)* ◆ **Unity and Diversity** There are many types of protists, but they all share basic characteristics. Fungi are alike in the way they reproduce and obtain food. *(Sections 1, 3)* ◆ **Systems and Interactions** Some protists are parasitic in nature and can harm crops and cause disease in humans. Fungi interact with the living world in a variety of ways. *(Section 3)* ◆ **Energy** Animal-like protists are heterotrophic, obtaining food by consuming other organisms; funguslike protists are heterotrophs; and plantlike protists and algae are autotrophs. Fungi are heterotrophs, obtaining energy by absorbing food from living organisms. *(Sections 1, 2, 3)*

Media and Technology

Exploring Life Science Videodisc

◆ **Section 1** "Fungi and Algae" provides examples of fungi and algae as they are found in a variety of habitats.

Interactive Student Tutorial CD-ROM

◆ **Chapter Review** Interactive questions help students to self-assess their mastery of key chapter concepts.

Student Edition Connection Strategies

◆ **Section 1** Integrating Health, p. 84
Integrating Technology, p. 88

◆ **Section 2** Integrating Environmental Science, p. 90
Integrating Technology, p. 91

◆ **Section 3** Integrating Health, p. 102
Language Arts Connection, p. 103
Integrating Earth Science, p. 104

USING THE INTERNET **ACTIVITY**

www.science-explorer.phschool.com

Visit the Science Explorer Internet site to find an up-to-date activity for Chapter 3 of *From Bacteria to Plants*.

ACTIVITY	Time (minutes)	Materials Quantities for one work group	Skills
Section 1			
Discover, p. 80	25	**Consumable** pond dropper **Nonconsumable** plastic dropper, microscope slide, cover slip, microscope	Observing
Try This, p. 84	15	**Consumable** paramecium culture, Chlorella culture, cotton fibers **Nonconsumable** plastic dropper, microscope slide, microscope	Inferring
Sharpen your Skills, p. 87	20	**Consumable** euglena culture, aluminum foil **Nonconsumable** plastic petri dish, compound microscope	Predicting
Section 2			
Discover, p. 90	15	**Consumable** water **Nonconsumable** clear plastic container, green paper punches, spoons	Predicting
Real-World Lab, p. 93	30 min first day, 10 min subsequent days	**Consumable** aged tap water, aquarium water, liquid fertilizer **Nonconsumable** 4 glass jars with lids, graduated cylinder, marking pen	Controlling Variables, Predicting, Drawing Conclusions
Section 3			
Discover, p. 95	15	**Consumable** self-seal bags, tape, old bread, fruit **Nonconsumable** hand lens	Observing
Try This, p. 97	10 min; 15 min for observations two days later	**Consumable** mushroom cap, white paper **Nonconsumable** large plastic container	Predicting
Try This, p. 98	25	**Consumable** tape **Nonconsumable** round balloon, cotton balls, stick or ruler about 30 cm long, modeling clay, pin	Making Models
Skills Lab, pp. 100–101	45	**Consumable** 5 plastic straws, salt, sugar, warm water (40–45°C), dry powdered yeast **Nonconsumable** marking pen, beaker, graduated cylinder, 5 narrow-necked bottles, 5 round balloons	Drawing Conclusions

A list of all materials required for the Student Edition activities can be found on pages T14–T15. You can order Materials Kits by calling 1-800-828-7777 or by accessing the Science Explorer Internet site at **www.science-explorer.phschool.com.**

A Mushroom Farm

Although most students are probably familiar with mushrooms, they may not know very much about their structure or how they grow.

Purpose In this project, students will determine the effect of changing a single variable on the growth of mushrooms.

Skills Focus After completing the Chapter 3 Project, students will be able to
◆ develop a hypothesis concerning how a variable affects mushroom growth;
◆ design and perform an experiment to test their hypothesis;
◆ draw conclusions based on their results;
◆ communicate their results in the form of a poster.

Project Time Line This project will take four to five weeks. It will take one class period to introduce the project, discuss mushrooms, and have students decide what variable to test. Allow students a day or two to come up with an experimental design to test their chosen variables. The experiment will take between two and four weeks, depending on the conditions being tested. Allow one week following the end of the project for data analysis and poster preparation. Before beginning the project, see Chapter 3 Project Teacher Notes on pages 60–61 in Teaching Resources for more details on carrying out the project. Also, distribute the Students' Chapter 3 Project Overview and Worksheets and Scoring Rubric on pages 62–66 in Teaching Resources.

Possible Materials It is difficult to grow mushrooms from spores you collect yourself. Mushroom growing kits are available from most biological supply companies. They provide all the materials necessary to complete this project. You may need additional pots and peat moss. You can use milk cartons, two-liter plastic bottle bottoms, or other such containers with holes cut in the bottom. A spray bottle works well for watering the containers.

CHAPTER
3 Protists and Fungi

WHAT'S AHEAD

SECTION 1 Protists

Discover **What Lives in a Drop of Pond Water?**
Try This **Feeding Paramecia**
Sharpen Your Skills **Predicting**

SECTION 2 *Integrating Environmental Science* **Algal Blooms**

Discover **How Can Algal Growth Affect Pond Life?**
Real-World Lab **An Explosion of Life**

SECTION 3 Fungi

Discover **Do All Molds Look Alike?**
Try This **Making Spore Prints**
Try This **Spreading Spores**
Skills Lab **What's for Lunch?**

For testing variables you will need
◆ a dark location and a light source (to test light);
◆ a thermometer and a warm and a cool location (to test temperature);
◆ substrate lacking nutrients and some fertilizer (to test nutrients).

Launching the Project To introduce the project and to stimulate interest, ask students: **How do you think mushrooms grow? Are they like plants?** Students will probably describe mushrooms growing somewhere damp and

warm, such as in the forest after a rain. Students may know that mushrooms are fungi, but may also think of them as plants because they grow out of the ground in a similar way. Encourage students to discuss similarities and differences between mushrooms and plants.

Allow time for students to read the description of the project in their text and the Chapter 3 Project Overview on pages 62–63 in Teaching Resources. Then discuss experimental design. Make sure students understand the difference between the manipulated and

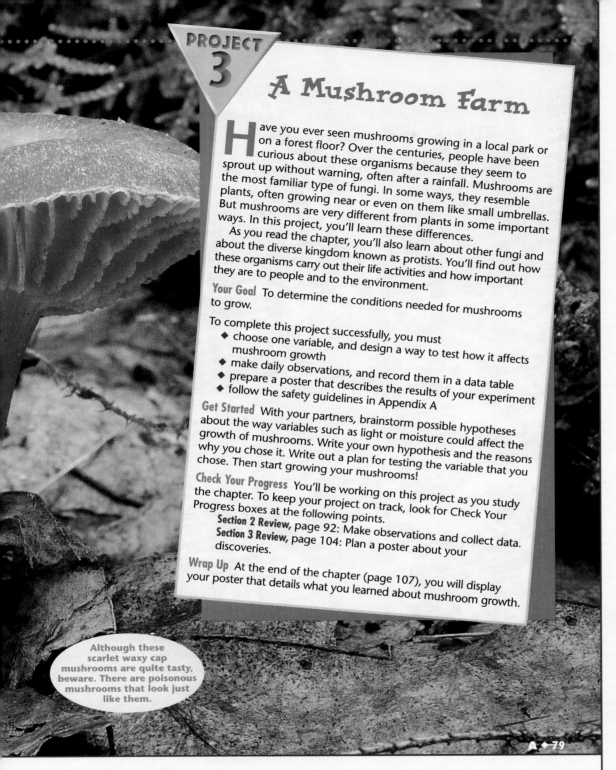

PROJECT 3

A Mushroom Farm

Have you ever seen mushrooms growing in a local park or on a forest floor? Over the centuries, people have been curious about these organisms because they seem to sprout up without warning, often after a rainfall. Mushrooms are the most familiar type of fungi. In some ways, they resemble plants, often growing near or even on them like small umbrellas. But mushrooms are very different from plants in some important ways. In this project, you'll learn these differences.

As you read the chapter, you'll also learn about other fungi and about the diverse kingdom known as protists. You'll find out how these organisms carry out their life activities and how important they are to people and to the environment.

Your Goal To determine the conditions needed for mushrooms to grow.

To complete this project successfully, you must
◆ choose one variable, and design a way to test how it affects mushroom growth
◆ make daily observations, and record them in a data table
◆ prepare a poster that describes the results of your experiment
◆ follow the safety guidelines in Appendix A

Get Started With your partners, brainstorm possible hypotheses about the way variables such as light or moisture could affect the growth of mushrooms. Write your own hypothesis and the reasons why you chose it. Write out a plan for testing the variable that you chose. Then start growing your mushrooms!

Check Your Progress You'll be working on this project as you study the chapter. To keep your project on track, look for Check Your Progress boxes at the following points.
Section 2 Review, page 92: Make observations and collect data.
Section 3 Review, page 104: Plan a poster about your discoveries.

Wrap Up At the end of the chapter (page 107), you will display your poster that details what you learned about mushroom growth.

Although these scarlet waxy cap mushrooms are quite tasty, beware. There are poisonous mushrooms that look just like them.

A ◆ 79

responding variables, and why other variables must be controlled. Pass out copies of the Chapter 3 Project Worksheets on pages 64–65 in Teaching Resources for students to review.

Have students form groups and choose their variables. Check that some groups choose different variables. Students should develop hypotheses about how mushroom growth will be affected by their variable.

Performance Assessment

The Chapter 3 Project Scoring Rubric on page 66 of Teaching Resources will help you evaluate how well students complete the Chapter 3 Project. Students will be assessed on
◆ how well they define and control the variables in their experiment;
◆ how well their experimental design tests their hypothesis, and the thoroughness of their data collection;
◆ their analysis of the results, and the clarity and organization of their poster;
◆ their ability to work cooperatively in a group.
By sharing the Chapter 3 Scoring Rubric with students at the beginning of the project, you will make it clear to them what they are expected to do.

Section 1 Protists

Objective

After completing the lesson, students will be able to

◆ describe the characteristics of animal-like, funguslike, and plantlike protists.

Key Terms protozoan, pseudopod, contractile vacuole, cilia, symbiosis, mutualism, spore, algae, pigment

1 Engage/Explore

Activating Prior Knowledge

Before class, place several drops of vegetable oil in a small dish of water. Add a few drops of green food coloring to the water. To begin, place the dish on an overhead projector. Ask students: **How can you tell whether the blobs you see are alive?** (*Sample: Check for reaction to stimuli, taking in food, breathing, movement*)

·········· **DISCOVER** ··········

Skills Focus observing
Materials *plastic dropper, pond water, microscope slide, cover slip, microscope*
Time 25 minutes
Tips Have students predict what they might observe in the water. Suggest students use their high-power objective lenses if they have them.
Expected Outcome Both algae and protozoans should be visible. Green algae have a greenish tint, but most organisms appear colorless. Organisms with flagella or pseudopods could be either protozoans or algae.
Think It Over Students will probably associate movement with life.

Section 1 Protists

DISCOVER ·································· **ACTIVITY**

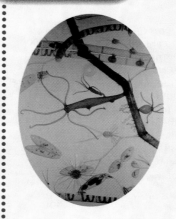

What Lives in a Drop of Pond Water?

1. Use a plastic dropper to place a drop of pond water on a microscope slide.

2. Put the slide under your microscope's low-power lens. Focus on the objects you see.

3. Find at least three different objects that you think might be organisms. Observe them for a few minutes.

4. Draw the three organisms in your notebook. Below each sketch, describe the movements or behaviors of the organism. Wash your hands thoroughly when you have finished.

Think It Over

Observing What characteristics did you observe that made you think that each organism was alive?

GUIDE FOR READING

◆ What are the characteristics of animal-like, funguslike, and plantlike protists?

Reading Tip As you read, use the headings to make an outline of the different kinds of protists.

Look at the objects in Figure 1. What do they look like to you? Jewels? Stained glass windows? Crystal ornaments? You might be surprised to learn that these beautiful, delicate structures are the walls of unicellular organisms called diatoms. Diatoms live in both salt water and fresh water. Believe it or not, these tiny organisms provide food for some of Earth's largest organisms—whales.

What Is a Protist?

Diatoms are only one type of organism classified in the protist kingdom. Protists are so different from each other that you can think of this kingdom as the "junk drawer" kingdom. You may have a drawer in your room where you store ticket stubs, postcards, and other odds and ends. Just as these items don't really fit anywhere else in your room, protists don't really fit into any other biological kingdom. Protists do share some characteristics. They are all eukaryotes, or organisms that have cells with nuclei. In addition, all protists live in moist surroundings.

Despite these common characteristics, the word that best describes the protist kingdom is diversity. For example, most protists are unicellular like the diatoms. On the other hand, some

Figure 1 These delicate-looking diatoms are classified in the protist kingdom.

READING STRATEGIES

Reading Tip Review outlines. Explain that main topics should be written with Roman numerals, subtopics should be written with capital letters, and important details should be written with numerals. Provide an example such as this partial outline for the first main topic in the section:

I. Animal-like Protists
  A. Protozoans with Pseudopods
  B. Protozoans with Cilia

After students read the information under topics A and B, discuss key details that should be included under these headings.

Study and Comprehension Have students make compare/contrast tables to list characteristics of animal-like, funguslike, and plantlike protists. Suggest they list the three types of protists across the top of the table and the characteristics in the left-hand column.

protists are multicellular. In fact, the protists known as giant kelps can be over 100 meters long. Protists also vary in how they obtain food—some are heterotrophs, some are autotrophs, and others are both. Some protists cannot move, while others zoom around their moist surroundings.

Because of the great variety of protists, scientists have proposed different ways of grouping these organisms. One useful way of grouping protists is to divide them into three categories: animal-like protists, funguslike protists, and plantlike protists.

☑ *Checkpoint* **What characteristics do all protists share?**

Animal-like Protists

What image pops into your head when you think of an animal? A tiger chasing its prey? A snake slithering onto a rock? Most people immediately associate animals with movement. In fact, movement is often involved with an important characteristic of animals—obtaining food. All animals are heterotrophs that must obtain food by consuming other organisms.

Like animals, animal-like protists are heterotrophs. And most animal-like protists, or **protozoans** (proh tuh ZOH unz), are able to move from place to place to obtain their food. Unlike animals, however, protozoans are unicellular. Some scientists distinguish between four types of protozoans based on the way these organisms move and live.

Protozoans With Pseudopods The ameba in *Exploring Protozoans* on the next page belongs to the group of protozoans called sarcodines. Sarcodines move and feed by forming **pseudopods** (SOO doh pahdz)—temporary bulges of the cell membrane that fill with cytoplasm. The word *pseudopod* means "false foot." Pseudopods form when the cell membrane pushes outward in one location. The cytoplasm flows into the bulge

Figure 2 The protist kingdom includes animal-like, plantlike, and funguslike organisms. **A.** These shells contained unicellular, animal-like protists called foraminifera. **B.** This red alga is a multicellular, plantlike protist found on ocean floors. **C.** This yellow slime mold is a funguslike protist.
Comparing and Contrasting In what way are animal-like protists similar to animals? How do they differ?

Answers to Self-Assessment

Caption Question

Figure 2 Animal-like protists are like animals in that they are heterotrophs, moving from place to place to obtain food. They are different in that they are unicellular.

☑ *Checkpoint*

All protists are eukaryotes and live in moist surroundings.

---

2 Facilitate

What Is a Protist?

Building Inquiry Skills: Forming Operational Definitions

Display pictures of protists such as slime molds, paramecia, euglenoids, diatoms, and algae in stations around the room. Have small groups list the characteristics they observe. Ask students if it is possible to create an operational definition of a protist. Have students consider this as they read the rest of the section.
learning modality: visual

Animal-like Protists

Inquiry Challenge

ACTIVITY

Materials *plastic dropper, ameba culture, microscope slide, cover slip, microscope*
Time 20 minutes
Tips Challenge students to identify the pseudopod action of an ameba they observe. Have them place a drop of the ameba culture on a slide and carefully add a cover slip, then observe the organisms under low and high power. Ask: **Can you tell when the ameba is using its pseudopods to eat and when it is using them to move?** *(Students may say that when the ameba is eating, it wraps two pseudopods around the food; when it is moving, it puts out a pseudopod and flows into it.)* Students can sketch what they observe and label the parts of the ameba. Observations should include the organism's shape, size, and motion.
learning modality: visual

Ongoing Assessment

Writing Have students explain why protists are thought of as the "junk drawer" kingdom by describing characteristics, categories, and examples of protists.

Animal-like Protists, continued

EXPLORING

Protozoans

Ask students: **What do these protists have in common?** *(They eat the same things, they both have nuclei, cytoplasm, food vacuoles, and contractile vacuoles.)* Ask: **What is different about them?** *(Amebas live in soil and water, paramecia only in water; paramecia move with cilia, amebas move with pseudopods; paramecia ingest food into an oral groove, amebas surround food with pseudopods; amebas have one nucleus, paramecia have two.)* As students list the similarities and differences, include them in a Venn diagram on the board. Then draw students' attention to the number and shapes of the contractile vacuoles in the two protists. Remind students that amebas live in soil or water, and paramecia live only in the water. Then ask: **What characteristics of the ameba do you think make it suited to living in either soil or water?** *(Sample: They can take any shape and flow easily through different substances. The contractile vacuole allows excess water to be expelled.)* **What characteristics of the paramecium do you think make it suited to living only in water?** *(Sample: The cilia act like tiny oars to move the paramecium through the water and sweep food into the oral groove. The cilia may not be as effective in a solid environment such as soil. Their rigid shape may make it difficult to move through compacted soil. The two contractile vacuoles remove excess water from the cell.)* **learning modality: logical/ mathematical**

and the rest of the organism follows. Pseudopods enable sarcodines to move in response to changes in the environment. For example, amebas use psuedopods to move away from bright light. Sarcodines also use pseudopods to trap food. The organism extends a pseudopod on each side of the food particle. The two pseudopods then join together, trapping the particle inside.

Organisms that live in fresh water, such as amebas, have a problem. Small particles, like those of water, pass easily through the cell membrane into the cytoplasm. If the excess water were to build up inside the cell, the ameba would burst. Fortunately, amebas have a **contractile vacuole** (kun TRAK til VAK yoo ohl), a structure that collects the extra water and then expels it from the cell.

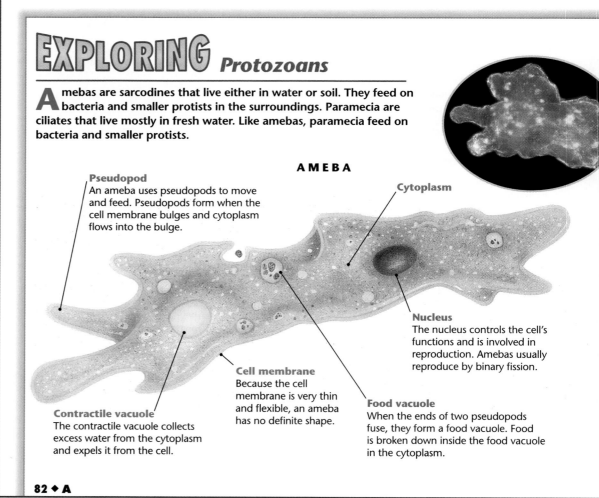

EXPLORING Protozoans

Amebas are sarcodines that live either in water or soil. They feed on bacteria and smaller protists in the surroundings. Paramecia are ciliates that live mostly in fresh water. Like amebas, paramecia feed on bacteria and smaller protists.

AMEBA

Pseudopod
An ameba uses pseudopods to move and feed. Pseudopods form when the cell membrane bulges and cytoplasm flows into the bulge.

Cytoplasm

Nucleus
The nucleus controls the cell's functions and is involved in reproduction. Amebas usually reproduce by binary fission.

Cell membrane
Because the cell membrane is very thin and flexible, an ameba has no definite shape.

Food vacuole
When the ends of two pseudopods fuse, they form a food vacuole. Food is broken down inside the food vacuole in the cytoplasm.

Contractile vacuole
The contractile vacuole collects excess water from the cytoplasm and expels it from the cell.

Background

Facts and Figures Free-living protists encounter changes in temperature, water acidity, food supply, moisture, and light. Many survive during these changes by entering a dormant stage—forming cysts with tough walls that act as protective coverings. During encystment, protozoans that have flagella and cilia lose them, and the contractile vacuole and food vacuoles disappear. Many protozoans can form cysts, and biologists believe this ability formed early in their evolutionary history.

Some parasitic protozoans, such as the one that causes amebic dysentery, also form cysts. The cysts are excreted and survive in the soil or water, and humans who come into contact with the cysts can be infected.

Protozoans With Cilia The second type of animal-like protist is the ciliate. Ciliates have structures called **cilia** (SIL ee uh) which are hairlike projections from cells that move with a wavelike pattern. They use cilia to move, obtain food, and sense the environment. Cilia act something like tiny oars to move a ciliate. Their movement sweeps food into the organism.

Ciliates have complex cells. In *Exploring Protozoans*, you see a ciliate called a paramecium. Notice that the paramecium has two nuclei. The large nucleus controls the everyday tasks of the cell. The small nucleus functions in reproduction. Paramecia usually reproduce asexually by binary fission. Sometimes, they reproduce by conjugation. This occurs when two paramecia join together and exchange genetic material.

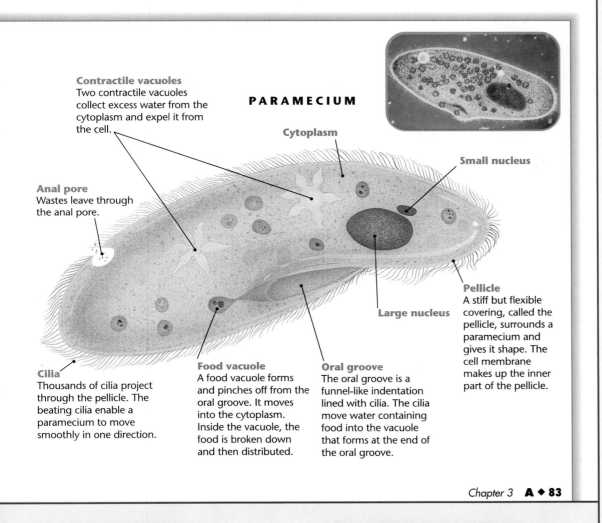

PARAMECIUM

Contractile vacuoles
Two contractile vacuoles collect excess water from the cytoplasm and expel it from the cell.

Cytoplasm

Small nucleus

Anal pore
Wastes leave through the anal pore.

Pellicle
A stiff but flexible covering, called the pellicle, surrounds a paramecium and gives it shape. The cell membrane makes up the inner part of the pellicle.

Large nucleus

Cilia
Thousands of cilia project through the pellicle. The beating cilia enable a paramecium to move smoothly in one direction.

Food vacuole
A food vacuole forms and pinches off from the oral groove. It moves into the cytoplasm. Inside the vacuole, the food is broken down and then distributed.

Oral groove
The oral groove is a funnel-like indentation lined with cilia. The cilia move water containing food into the vacuole that forms at the end of the oral groove.

Chapter 3 **A ◆ 83**

Program Resources

 Science Explorer Series *Human Biology and Health,* Chapter 6
 Science Explorer Series *Earth's Changing Surface,* Chapter 3

Media and Technology

 Transparencies "Exploring Protozoans—Ameba," Transparency 8

Transparencies "Exploring Protozoans—Paramecium," Transparency 9

Inquiry Challenge

Materials *microscope, slide and cover slip, water, plastic dropper, paramecium culture, ice*
Time 30 minutes

Challenge students to form hypotheses about how water temperature affects the activity level of a paramecium, then design experiments using the materials above to test their hypotheses. *(Sample design: materials— two or more paramecium cultures, plastic dropper, microscope, slides, cover slips; procedure— put the paramecia in water of varying temperatures, then examine them under the microscope; results— paramecia are active at room temperature and slow down at about 2°C.)* After you review their designs, have students carry out their experiments and report their findings to the class. **learning modality: logical/mathematical**

Ongoing Assessment

Oral Presentation Have students compare and contrast the characteristics of an ameba and a paramecium.

A ◆ 83

Animal-like Protists, continued

Skills Focus inferring
Materials *plastic dropper, paramecium culture,* Chlorella *culture, microscope slide, cotton fibers, microscope*
Time 15 minutes
Tips As well as using cotton fibers, students can slow down the paramecia by placing a cover slip over the drop of culture and absorbing some of the water by holding the edge of a piece of lens paper against the edge of the cover slip. Another option is to add one drop of a 2–3% solution of clear gelatin to the drop of culture on the slide. Make sure students wash their hands immediately after the activity.
Inferring Students should see green food vacuoles form inside the paramecia. Students should conclude that paramecia are heterotrophs because they ingest the *Chlorella. Chlorella* behave like autotrophs because they do not seem to be ingesting food and are green like plants.
Extend Have students predict how long it will take the paramecia to ingest all the *Chlorella,* then check their slides at regular intervals to test their predictions. Have students turn off the lights on the microscopes when they are not making observations to avoid overheating the paramecia. **learning modality: visual**

 Integrating Health

Ask students to describe ways that hikers can avoid ingesting *Giardia. (Samples: Carry enough water, use water purifying treatments, boil water before using)* Inform students that the safest way to purify water of organisms is to boil it for at least three minutes. This will kill the organisms, but it will not necessarily make the water safe if the water also contains chemical pollutants. **learning modality: verbal**

Feeding Paramecia

In this activity you will feed *Chlorella,* a plantlike protist, to paramecia.

1. Use a plastic dropper to place one drop of paramecium culture on a micrscope slide. Add some cotton fibers to slow down the paramecia.
2. Use the microscope's low-power objective to find some paramecia.
3. Add one drop of *Chlorella* to the paramecium culture on your slide.
4. Switch to high power and locate a paramecium. Observe what happens. Then wash your hands.

Inferring What evidence do you have that paramecia are heterotrophs? That *Chlorella* are autotrophs?

Figure 3 When people drink from freshwater streams and lakes, they can get hiker's disease. Below you see the organism responsible for the disease, a protozoan called *Giardia lamblia.*

Protozoans With Flagella The third type of protozoans are called zooflagellates (zoh uh FLAJ uh lits)—animal-like protists that use flagella to move. Most zooflagellates have one to eight long, whiplike flagella that help them move.

Many zooflagellates live inside the bodies of other organisms. For example, one type of zooflagellate lives in the intestines of termites. The zooflagellates produce chemicals that help the termites digest the wood that they eat. In turn, the termites protect the zooflagellates. The interaction between these two species is an example of **symbiosis** (sim bee OH sis)—a close relationship where at least one of the species benefits. When both partners benefit from living together, the relationship is a type of symbiosis called **mutualism.**

 INTEGRATING HEALTH Sometimes a zooflagellate harms the animal in which it lives. In Figure 3 you see a zooflagellate called *Giardia.* This zooflagellate is a parasite in humans. Wild animals, such as beavers, deposit *Giardia* organisms in freshwater streams, rivers, and lakes. When a person drinks water containing *Giardia,* the zooflagellates attach to the person's intestine, where they feed and reproduce. The person develops a serious intestinal condition commonly called hiker's disease.

Other Protozoans The fourth type of protozoans, the sporozoans, are characterized more by the way they live than by the way they move. Sporozoans are parasites that feed on the cells and body fluids of their hosts. They move in a variety of ways. Some have flagella and some depend on hosts for transport. One even slides from place to place on a layer of slime that it produces.

Many sporozoans have more than one host. For example, *Plasmodium* is a sporozoan that causes malaria, a serious disease

---

Background

History of Science Malarial infection, mentioned in medical records as early as the fifth century B.C., has plagued human populations since ancient times. Early doctors knew that malaria was associated with swampy and marshy areas, but they did not know about *Plasmodium* and the *Anopheles* mosquito.

A French army surgeon, Alphonse Laveran, was working in Algeria in 1880 when he became the first person to discover that the sporozoan *Plasmodium* was the parasite that causes human malaria. A British army doctor, Sir Ronald Ross, was in India in 1892. He was able to demonstrate that malaria was transmitted from infected birds to healthy ones by the bite of the mosquito, suggesting that the same transmission was possible in humans.

of the blood. Two hosts are involved in *Plasmodium's* life cycle—humans and a species of mosquitoes found in tropical areas. The disease spreads when a healthy mosquito bites a person with malaria, becomes infected, and then bites a healthy person. Symptoms of malaria include high fevers that alternate with severe chills. These symptoms can last for weeks, then disappear, only to reappear a few months later.

☑ *Checkpoint* **What structures do protozoans use to move?**

Funguslike Protists

The second group of protists are the funguslike protists. Recall from Chapter 1 that fungi include organisms such as mushrooms and yeast. Until you learn more about fungi in Section 3, you can think of fungi as the "sort of like" organisms. Fungi are "sort of like" animals because they are heterotrophs. They are "sort of like" plants because their cells have cell walls. In addition, most fungi use spores to reproduce. A **spore** is a tiny cell that is able to grow into a new organism.

Like fungi, funguslike protists are heterotrophs, have cell walls, and use spores to reproduce. Unlike fungi, however, all funguslike protists are able to move at some point in their lives. The three types of funguslike protists are water molds, downy mildews, and slime molds.

Water Molds and Downy Mildews Most water molds and downy mildews live in water or in moist places. These organisms grow as tiny threads that look like a fuzzy covering. Figure 5 shows a fish attacked by a water mold.

Water molds and downy mildews also attack food crops, such as potatoes, cabbages, corn, and grapes. A water mold destroyed the Irish potato crops in 1845 and 1846. The loss of these crops led to a famine that resulted in the deaths of over one million Irish people. Many others left Ireland and moved to other countries, such as Canada and the United States.

Figure 4 *Anopheles* mosquitoes can carry a sporozoan, *Plasmodium*, which causes malaria in people. *Relating Cause and Effect Why do you think it is difficult to control the spread of malaria?*

Figure 5 This threadlike water mold is a parasite that grows on fish. The water mold eventually kills the fish.

Answers to Self-Assessment

Caption Question

Figure 4 It is difficult to control the populations of mosquitoes that carry the parasite.

☑ *Checkpoint*

Protozoans use pseudopods, cilia, or flagella to move.

Building Inquiry Skills:
Making Models

Materials *clay, paint, string, pipe cleaners, cardboard, and other materials of students' choice*
Time 30 minutes
Tips Challenge small groups to design models of one of the four kinds of animal-like protists. Have students consult photos in the text or in reference materials. Models should include the details of each organism that make it unique, with labels. Have students compare and contrast the models, explaining similarities and differences. They should note the structures, shapes, and methods of movement of the various animal-like protozoans. Challenge groups to use their models to demonstrate how these organisms move, eat, or reproduce. **cooperative learning**

Funguslike Protists

Building Inquiry Skills:
Organizing Information

On the board, write the headings *Plants and Animals*. Then call on students to tell you the characteristics of each type of organism and list them under the appropriate heading. Then ask a volunteer to put a star next to each item that is a characteristic of a funguslike protist. (*Heterotrophs, cells have cell walls, reproduce by spores*) **learning modality: verbal**

Ongoing Assessment

Writing Ask students to describe the characteristics of zooflagellates, sporozoans, or funguslike protists.

Funguslike Protists, continued

Inquiry Challenge

Materials *compound microscope, slime mold culture, plastic petri dish with cover, oatmeal*

Time 15 minutes for setup, 10 minutes for observation after 24 hours

Tips Pair students. Give each pair a covered petri dish containing slime mold culture to observe under the microscope. Partners can take turns observing and sketching what they see. Ask students to predict how slime molds will react when oatmeal is placed in the dish. They can test their predictions by uncovering the dish, putting a few flakes about one mm from a branch of the slime mold and putting the cover back on. Allow students to place the dish in a cool, dark place. After 24 hours, the slime mold should increase in size, spread across, then engulf the oatmeal flakes. Ask: **What did you observe that suggests the slime mold is alive?** *(It moved toward the oatmeal and engulfed it.)* **How is a slime mold similar to an ameba?** *(It engulfs its food with pseudopods.)* Caution students to wash their hands thoroughly after the activity. Review the safety guidelines in Appendix A. Dispose of the petri dishes and all other materials according to the proper procedures. Be sure to check your district's and state's guidelines for the proper disposal of fungal cultures.

learning modality: visual

Plantlike Protists

Building Inquiry Skills: Making Models

Divide the class into three groups: unicellular algae, multicellular algae, and a colony of algae. Have each student act out the role of an individual algae cell. Give each group a deck of cards to use as a food source, and encourage the "cells" to act out how each organism accomplishes food intake and waste elimination. *(Sample: unicellular: individual students pick up and put down cards without interacting; multicellular: cooperative model; one student picks up a card and passes it on; another puts it down; colony: individual and cooperative)*

learning modality: kinesthetic

Figure 6 Slime molds, like the chocolate tube slime mold (left), feed on microorganisms on the surfaces of decaying materials. When food runs low, they grow stalks that produce spores (right).

Slime Molds Slime molds live in moist soil and on decaying plants and trees. Slime molds are often beautifully colored. Many are bright yellow, like the one in Figure 6. Their glistening bodies creep over fallen logs and dead leaves on shady, moist forest floors. They move in an amebalike way by forming pseudopods and oozing along the surfaces of decaying materials. Slime molds feed on bacteria and other microorganisms.

Some slime molds are large enough to be seen with the naked eye. Many, however, are so small that you need a microscope to see them. When the food supply decreases or other conditions change, some tiny slime molds creep together and form a multicellular mass. Spore-producing structures grow out of the mass and release spores, which can develop into a new generation of slime molds.

✓ *Checkpoint* *In what environments are slime molds found?*

Plantlike Protists

If you've ever seen seaweed at a beach, then you are familiar with a type of plantlike protist. Plantlike protists, which are commonly called **algae** (AL jee), are even more varied than the animal-like and funguslike protists. **The one characteristic that all algae share is that, like plants, they are autotrophs.**

Some algae live in the soil, others live on the barks of trees, and still others live in fresh water and salt water. Algae that live on the surface of ponds, lakes, and oceans are an important food source for other organisms in the water. In addition, most of the oxygen in Earth's atmosphere is made by these algae.

Algae range greatly in size. Some algae, such as diatoms, are unicellular. Others are groups of unicellular organisms that live together in colonies. Still others, such as seaweeds, are multicellular. Recall from Chapter 1 that a unicellular organism carries

Background

Facts and Figures The cryophyte alga *Chlamydomonas nivalis* is one of several responsible for a phenomenon known as red (or pink) snow. During the late spring or the summer, snowbanks in mountain regions all over the world may be colored beautiful shades of red by "blooms" or patches of various snow algae. Scientists estimate that one teaspoon of melted snow may contain more than a million cells of algae.

Although *Chlamydomonas nivalis* is classified as a green alga, its color comes from a bright red carotenoid pigment that probably helps to protect the algae from intense solar radiation at high altitudes. The nutrients for the algae are minerals leached from boulders and soil, as well as organic material that blows onto the snow from nearby plants.

out all the functions necessary for life. But the cells of a multi-cellular organism are specialized to do certain tasks. When single-celled algae come together to form colonies, some of the cells may become specialized to perform certain functions, such as reproduction. However, most cells in a colony continue to carry out all functions. Colonies can contain from four up to thousands of cells.

Algae exist in a wide variety of colors because they contain many types of **pigments**—chemicals that produce color. Depending on their pigments, algae can be green, yellow, red, brown, orange, or even black. Read on to learn about the types of algae that live on Earth.

Euglenoids Euglenoids are green, unicellular algae that are found mostly in fresh water. Unlike other algae, euglenoids have one animal-like characteristic—they can be heterotrophs under certain conditions. When sunlight is available, euglenoids are autotrophs that produce their own food. However, when sunlight is not available, euglenoids will act like heterotrophs by finding and taking in food from their environment.

In Figure 7 you see a euglena, which is a common euglenoid. Notice the long whiplike flagellum that helps the organism move. Locate the eyespot near the flagellum. Although the eyespot is not really an eye, it contains pigments. These pigments are sensitive to light and help a euglena recognize the direction of a light source. You can imagine how important this response is to an organism that needs light to make food.

Sharpen your Skills

Predicting ACTIVITY

Predict what will happen when you pour a culture of euglena into a petri dish, then cover half the dish with aluminum foil. Give a reason for your prediction.

Then carry out the experiment with a culture of euglena in a plastic petri dish. Cover half the dish with aluminum foil as shown. After 10 minutes, uncover the dish. What do you observe? Was your prediction correct? Explain why euglena behave this way.

Figure 7 Euglenas are unicellular algae that live in fresh water. In sunlight, euglenas make their own food. Without sunlight, they obtain food from their environment.
Interpreting Diagrams What structures help a euglena find and move toward light?

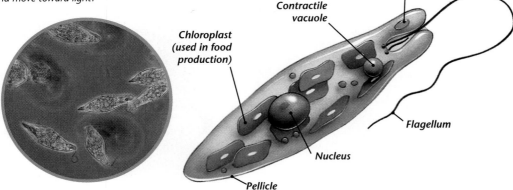

Eyespot
Contractile vacuole
Chloroplast (used in food production)
Flagellum
Nucleus
Pellicle

Ask students: **How many cells does a Euglena have?** *(one)* Point out that the structures such as flagella, the eyespot, and the chloroplast are all part of the same cell. Some students may be confused that a unicellular organism has so many parts. Explain that cells are the smallest structures capable of performing all the functions required for life. Ask: **Is the cell shown in the figure specialized to do certain tasks?** *(No, it performs all the functions necessary to maintain the Euglena's life.)* **learning modality: visual**

Sharpen your Skills

Predicting

Materials *euglena culture, plastic petri dish, aluminum foil, compound microscope* ACTIVITY
Time 20 minutes
Tips Tell students to record their predictions and the reasons for them.
Expected Outcome Students will probably predict that the euglena will move toward the light because it needs light to make food. The result of the experiment will confirm this prediction. The covered area will no longer be green, because the euglena have moved to the uncovered area and the light.
Extend Ask students to identify the source of the green tint of the euglena culture. *(chloroplasts)* **learning modality: visual**

Answers to Self-Assessment

Caption Question

Figure 7 The eyespot helps the euglena find light, and the flagellum helps the euglena move toward light.

☑ *Checkpoint*

Slime molds are found in moist soil and on decaying plants and trees.

Ongoing Assessment

Oral Presentation Ask students to give the other names for funguslike protists and plantlike protists. *(Funguslike—water molds, downy mildews, slime molds; plantlike—algae)*

Plantlike Protists,
continued

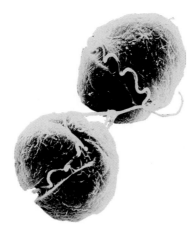

Figure 8 Dinoflagellates, such as these *Gonyaulax,* have rigid plates for protection. They use flagella to move through the water.

Figure 9 Green algae range in size from unicellular organisms to multicellular seaweeds. **A.** The multicellular sea lettuce, *Ulva,* lives in oceans. **B.** This unicellular algae, *Closterium,* lives in fresh water.

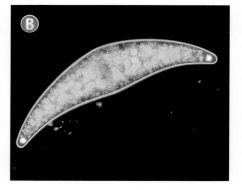

88 ◆ A

Dinoflagellates Dinoflagellates are unicellular algae covered by stiff plates that look like a suit of armor. Because they have different amounts of green, red, and other pigments, dinoflagellates exist in a variety of colors.

All dinoflagellates have two flagella held in grooves between their plates. When the flagella beat, the dinoflagellates twirl like toy tops through the water. Many glow in the dark and look like miniature fireflies dancing on the ocean's surface at night.

Diatoms Diatoms are unicellular protists with beautiful glasslike cell walls. Some float on the surface of freshwater and saltwater environments. Others attach to objects such as rocks in shallow water. Diatoms move by shooting chemicals out of slits in their cell walls. This gives them a kind of jet propulsion. Diatoms are a food source for heterotrophs in the water.

INTEGRATING TECHNOLOGY When diatoms die, their cell walls collect on the bottoms of oceans and lakes. Over time, they form layers of a coarse material called diatomaceous (dy uh tuh MAY shus) earth. This makes a good polishing agent. Manufacturers add diatomaceous earth to most toothpastes. Diatomaceous earth is also used in many household scouring products as well as in swimming pool filters. It is even used as an insecticide. The sharp edges puncture the bodies of insects.

Green Algae As their name suggests, all green algae contain green pigments. Otherwise, green algae are quite diverse, as you can see in Figure 9. Although most green algae are unicellular, some form colonies, and a few are multicellular. You might have seen multicellular green algae, or green seaweed, washed up on a beach. Most green algae live in either freshwater or saltwater surroundings. The few that live on land are found along the bases of trees or in moist soils.

Red Algae Almost all red algae are multicellular seaweeds. Divers have found red algae growing at depths greater than 260 meters below the ocean's surface. Their red pigments are especially good at absorbing the small amount of light that enters deep ocean waters.

Red algae are used by humans in a variety of ways. Carrageenan (kar uh JEE nun), a substance extracted from red algae, is used in products such as ice creams and hair conditioners. For people in many Asians cultures, red algae is a nutrient-rich delicacy that is eaten fresh, dried, or toasted.

Brown Algae Many of the organisms that are commonly called seaweeds are brown algae. In addition to their brown pigment, brown algae also contain green, yellow, and orange pigments. As you can see in Figure 10, a typical brown alga has many plantlike structures. Holdfasts anchor the alga to rocks. Stalks support the blades, which are the leaflike structures of the alga. Brown algae also have gas-filled sacs called bladders that allow the algae to float upright in the water.

Brown algae flourish in cool, rocky waters. Brown algae called rockweed live along the Atlantic coast of North America. Giant kelps, which can grow to 100 meters in length, live in some Pacific coastal waters. The giant kelps form large underwater "forests" where many organisms, including sea otters and abalone, live. Some people eat brown algae for their nutrients. Substances called algins are extracted from brown algae and used as thickeners in foods such as puddings and salad dressings.

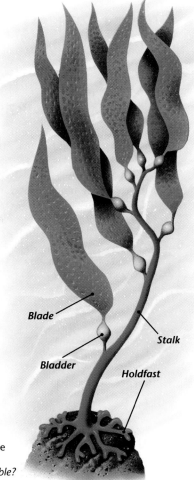

Blade

Stalk

Bladder

Holdfast

Figure 10 Giant kelps have many plantlike structures. *Applying Concepts What plant structures do the holdfasts and blades resemble?*

Section 1 Review

1. What characteristic do all protozoans share?
2. What are three characteristics of the funguslike protists?
3. What characteristic do algae share with plants?
4. **Thinking Critically Making Judgments** Would you classify euglena as an animal-like protist or as a plantlike protist? Explain your answer.

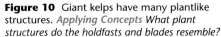
Science at Home

Look through your kitchen with a family member to find products that contain substances made from algae. Look at both food and non-food items. Before you begin, tell your family member that words such as diatomaceous earth, algin, and carrageenan are substances that come from algae. Make a list of the products and the algae-based ingredient they contain. Share your list with the class.

Program Resources

◆ **Teaching Resources** 3-1 Review and Reinforce, p. 69; 3-1 Enrich, p. 70
◆ **Integrated Science Laboratory Manual** A-3, "Comparing Protists"

Answers to Self-Assessment

Caption Question

Figure 10 The holdfasts resemble roots and the blades resemble leaves.

Media and Technology

Interactive Student Tutorial CD-ROM A-3

3 Assess

Section 1 Review Answers

1. All protozoans are unicellular heterotrophs.
2. Funguslike protists have cell walls, use spores to reproduce, are heterotrophs, and are able to move at some point in their lives.
3. Both plants and algae are autotrophs that use sunlight to make their food.
4. Students may argue that euglena are either plantlike or animal-like protists. They are animal-like because they can feed like heterotrophs when there is no light. They are plantlike because they can make their own food and are usually green.

Science at Home

Encourage students to explain to family members that algae can be found in many products such as ice cream, hair conditioners, toothpaste, and scouring products. They may wish to see who can find the most products containing algae.

Performance Assessment

Writing Ask students to imagine they are the size of a protozoan. Have them write a short story of their encounters with other microscopic life forms such as amebas, euglenoids, slime molds, and other protists. Encourage students to describe how these organisms behave and how they identify them. Students can save their stories in their portfolios.

SECTION 2 Algal Blooms

Objectives

After completing the lesson, students will be able to

◆ describe how red tides occur and explain why they are dangerous;

◆ explain how the rapid growth of algae affects a pond or lake.

Key Terms algal bloom, red tide, eutrophication

1 Engage/Explore

Activating Prior Knowledge

Remind students that in Section 1, they learned that algae live on the surface of ponds, lakes, and oceans. Ask: **What do you think would happen if there were so many algae on the water's surface that they blocked sunlight from getting into the water?** *(Sample: The organisms in the water that need sunlight to make food will die.)*

⸱⸱⸱⸱⸱⸱⸱ DISCOVER ⸱⸱⸱⸱⸱⸱⸱

Skills Focus predicting
Materials *clear plastic container, water, green paper punches, spoons*
Time 15 minutes
Tips Use a hole punch to make green paper punches. After students complete their models, ask: **What does your model show about how algae can grow on a pond?** *(How rapidly the number of algae can increase)*
Expected Outcome The green paper punches will eventually cover the surface of the water.
Think It Over If algae cover the pond's surface, less light and air will reach the bottom, and organisms deep in the pond will die.

SECTION 2 Algal Blooms

DISCOVER ⸱⸱⸱⸱⸱⸱⸱⸱⸱⸱⸱⸱⸱⸱⸱⸱⸱⸱⸱⸱⸱⸱⸱⸱⸱⸱⸱⸱⸱⸱ ACTIVITY

How Can Algal Growth Affect Pond Life?

1. Pour water into a plastic petri dish until the dish is half full. The petri dish will represent a pond.

2. Sprinkle a spoonful of green paper punches into the water in the petri dish to represent green algae growing in the pond water.

3. Sprinkle two more spoonfuls of paper punches into the water to represent one cycle of algae reproduction.

4. Sprinkle four more spoonfuls of paper punches into the water to represent the next reproduction cycle of the algae.

Think It Over
Predicting How might algae growing on the surface affect organisms living deep in a pond?

GUIDE FOR READING

◆ What makes red tides dangerous?

◆ How does the rapid growth of algae affect a pond or lake?

Reading Tip As you read, look for evidence of the dangers of algal blooms.

Over a five week period one year, the bodies of 14 humpback whales washed up along beaches on Cape Cod, Massachusetts. The whales showed no outward signs of sickness. Their stomachs were full of food. Their bodies contained plenty of blubber to insulate them from changes in water temperature. What caused such healthy-looking animals to die?

When biologists examined the dead whales' tissues, they identified the cause of the puzzling deaths. The whales' cells contained a deadly toxin produced by a dinoflagellate called *Alexandrium tamarense*. For reasons that scientists don't fully understand, the population of these algae grew rapidly in the ocean waters through which the whales were migrating. When the whales fed on the toxin-producing algae or on fishes that had eaten the algae, the toxins reached a deadly level and killed the whales.

Algae are common in both saltwater and freshwater environments on Earth. They float on the surface of the waters and use sunlight to make food. The rapid growth of a population of algae is called an **algal bloom.** The deaths of the humpbacks is one example of the damage that an algal bloom can cause.

◀ A humpback whale

READING STRATEGIES

Reading Tip Before students read, have them preview the pictures and read the captions. Then have them predict the dangers of algal blooms. As students read, instruct them to list the dangers of algal blooms on a sheet of notebook paper. Suggest to students that they divide their paper into two columns with the headings Saltwater Blooms and Freshwater Blooms.

Study and Comprehension After students read the section, have them imagine that they are newspaper or television reporters. Direct them to write news stories about an algal bloom. Ask students to include the most important points about the rapid growth of algae populations. Suggest that students use their notes from the Reading Tip to help them decide what information to include about the dangers of algal blooms.

Saltwater Blooms

In Figure 11, you see an algal bloom in ocean water. Saltwater algal blooms are commonly called **red tides.** This is because the algae that grow rapidly often contain red pigments and turn the color of the water red. But red tides do not always look red. Some red tides are brown, green, or colorless depending on the species of algae that blooms. Dinoflagellates and diatoms are two algae that frequently bloom in red tides.

Scientists are not sure why some saltwater algal populations increase rapidly at times. But red tides occur most often when there is an increase in nutrients in the water. Increases in ocean temperature due to climate changes also affect the occurrence of red tides. Some red tides occur regularly in certain seasons. The cold bottom layers of the ocean contain a lot of nutrients. When the cold water mixes with the surface waters, more nutrients become available to surface organisms. With excess nutrients present in the surface waters, blooms of algae occur.

Red tides are dangerous when the toxins that the algae produce become concentrated in the bodies of organisms that consume the algae. Shellfish feed on large numbers of the algae and store the toxins in their cells. Fishes may also feed on the algae and store the toxins. When people or other large organisms eat these shellfish and fishes, it may lead to serious illness or even death. Public health officials close beaches in areas of red tides and prohibit people from gathering shellfish or fishing.

 INTEGRATING TECHNOLOGY Red tides occur more frequently worldwide today than they did a decade ago. Scientists cannot yet predict when red tides will occur. They use images taken by satellites in space to track how red tides move with ocean currents. Satellite images can also detect increases in ocean temperatures, which may put an area at risk for red tide.

✓ *Checkpoint* Why are red tides often red in color?

Figure 11 Rapid algae growth has caused a red tide in this small bay off the coast of California. *Relating Cause and Effect What organisms are most often responsible for causing red tides?*

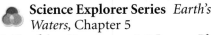
Answers to Self-Assessment

Caption Question

Figure 11 Dinoflagellates and diatoms are the algae most often responsible for causing red tides.

✓ *Checkpoint*

The algae that form the red tides often contain red pigments that change the color of the water to red.

---

2 Facilitate

Saltwater Blooms

Building Inquiry Skills: Making Models

Materials *index cards, red and black markers*

 ACTIVITY

In this activity, students role-play how toxic algae in a red tide eventually affect humans. Divide the class into several groups, choosing one "fish," one "shellfish," and one "person" from each group. The rest of the students in each group will be algae. Give each "alga" three cards, and have the "algae" write *Nutrient* on two cards in black and *Toxin* on the third card in red. Then direct the "fish" and "shellfish" to "eat" all the "algae" in their group by taking their cards. Ask: **What do the fish and shellfish gain from eating algae?** (*Lots of nutrients and a little bit of toxins*) Instruct the fish and shellfish to discard two out of every three *Nutrient* cards. Ask: **What happens to the nutrients?** (*They get used up.*) **What happens to the toxins?** (*They stay in the bodies of the fish and shellfish.*) Now instruct the "person" in each group to eat the fish and shellfish by taking all their cards. Ask: **What does the human gain from eating the toxic fish?** (*A little nutrients and a lot of toxins*) **cooperative learning**

Integrating Technology

Ask students why satellite images are used to study activity, such as oil spills, in the oceans. (*Sample: Satellite images show large parts of the ocean, which are difficult for scientists on Earth to observe.*)

Ongoing Assessment

Writing Have students explain how red tides can affect the health of people in a shore community.

Freshwater Blooms

Including All Students

This activity will benefit students who need extra help. Challenge groups of students to create wall-size flowcharts that show the process of eutrophication, including both the natural events and the human activities that affect the rate of eutrophication. **learning modality: logical/mathematical**

3 Assess

Section 2 Review Answers

1. Toxins that the algae produce become concentrated in the bodies of the organisms that consume the algae.

2. An increase of nutrients in the water causes an increase in algae growth, beginning a series of events that affect all organisms in the lake or pond.

3. When bottom plants die, organisms break them down, using up the oxygen in the water in the process. Without oxygen, fishes die.

4. Sample: Plan a good sewage system so that excess nutrients do not get into the lake and increase the rate of eutrophication. Design landscaping to prevent runoff into the lake, and encourage residents to limit use of fertilizers.

Check Your Progress

CHAPTER PROJECT 3

Encourage students to develop a standard procedure to make sure they measure from the same place every day.

Figure 12 Increased nutrient levels in lakes and ponds can lead to algal blooms. The thick layer of algae on the surface can threaten other organisms in the water. *Problem Solving Outline a series of steps that could help slow down the rapid growth of algae in a lake.*

Freshwater Blooms

Algal blooms also occur in bodies of fresh water. Have you ever seen a pond or lake that looked as if it was coated with a layer of green paint? The green layer of surface scum usually consists of huge numbers of unicellular green algae.

Lakes and ponds undergo natural processes of change over time. In a process called **eutrophication** (yoo troh fih KAY shun), nutrients, such as nitrogen and phosphorus, build up in a lake or pond over time, causing an increase in the growth of algae.

Certain natural events and human activities can increase the rate of eutrophication. For example, when farmers spread fertilizers on fields, some of these chemicals can run off into nearby lakes and ponds. In addition, poorly designed or aging septic systems can leak their contents into the soil. The nutrients make their way from the soil into water that leads into lakes and ponds. These events cause a rapid increase in algae growth.

The rapid growth of algae in a pond or lake triggers a series of events with serious consequences. First, the layer of algae prevents sunlight from reaching plants and other algae beneath the surface. Those organisms die and sink to the bottom. Then organisms, such as bacteria, which break down the bodies of the dead plants and algae, increase in number. Soon the bacteria use up the oxygen in the water. Fishes and other organisms in the water die without the oxygen they need to survive. About the only life that survives is the algae on the surface.

Algal blooms in fresh water can be easier to control than those in salt water because lakes and ponds have definite boundaries. To slow eutrophication, scientists first need to find the sources of the excess nutrients and then eliminate them. If the source can be eliminated and the nutrients used up, eutrophication slows to its natural rate.

Section 2 Review

1. Why are red tides dangerous?
2. What causes a freshwater bloom?
3. How does the death of bottom plants in a shallow pond affect the rest of the pond?
4. **Thinking Critically Problem Solving** A new housing development is to be built along a recreational lake. What factors should the developers consider to protect the lake from rapid eutrophication?

Check Your Progress

CHAPTER PROJECT 3

By now, you should have your teacher's approval for your plan, and you should have started growing your mushrooms. Make careful observations of growth every day. Include sketches and measurements as appropriate. Use a data table to organize the data you collect. (*Hint:* As you make your observations, be careful not to disturb the experiment or introduce any new variables.)

Performance Assessment

Writing Have students describe each step in the processes involved in red tides or freshwater blooms.

 Students can save their descriptions in their portfolios.

Media and Technology

 Audiotapes English-Spanish Summary 3-2

Exploring Life Science Videodisc Unit 2, Side 2, "Fungi and Algae"

Chapter 5

Answers to Self-Assessment

Caption Question

Figure 12 The sources of excess nutrients must be located and eliminated. This may include reducing fertilization on nearby farms and improving aging septic systems.

Program Resources

◆ **Teaching Resources** 3-2 Review and Reinforce, p. 73; 3-2 Enrich, p. 74

AN EXPLOSION OF LIFE

Living things are interconnected with their surroundings in many ways. In this lab, you will investigate how one change in a freshwater environment can affect everything that lives in that environment.

Problem

How does the amount of fertilizer affect algae growth?

Skills Focus

controlling variables, predicting, drawing conclusions

Materials

4 glass jars with lids   marking pen
aged tap water   aquarium water
graduated cylinder   liquid fertilizer

Procedure

1. Read through the steps in the procedure. Then write a prediction describing what you think will happen in each of the four jars.
2. Copy the data table into your notebook. Be sure to allow enough lines to make entries for a two-week period.
3. Label four jars A, B, C, and D. Fill each jar half full with aged tap water.
4. Add aquarium water to each jar until the jar is three-fourths full.
5. Add 3 mL of liquid fertilizer to jar B; 6 mL to jar C; and 12 mL to jar D. Do not add any fertilizer to jar A. Loosely screw the lid on each jar. Place all the jars in a sunny location where they will receive the same amount of direct sunlight.

DATA TABLE				
	Observations			
Date	Jar A no fertilizer	Jar B 3 mL fertilizer	Jar C 6 mL fertilizer	Jar D 12 mL fertilizer
Day 1				
Day 2				

6. Observe the jars every day for two weeks. Compare the color of the water in the four jars. Record your observations in your data table.

Analyze and Conclude

1. How did the color in the four jars compare at the end of the two-week period? How can you account for any differences that you observed?
2. What was the purpose of jar A?
3. Describe the process that led to the overall color change in the water. What organisms were responsible for causing that color change?
4. Predict what would have happened if you placed the four jars in a dark location instead of in sunlight. Explain your prediction.
5. **Apply** What do you think might happen to fish and other living organisms when fertilizer gets into a body of fresh water? What are some ways that fertilizer might get into a body of water?

Design an Experiment

Some detergents contain phosphates, which are an ingredient in many kinds of fertilizer. Design an experiment to compare how regular detergent and low-phosphate detergent affect the growth of algae.

Safety

Remind students to wear safety goggles, handle the glass jars with care, and wash their hands immediately after setting up the activity and making observations. Review the safety guidelines in Appendix A. Dispose of the algae and all other materials according to the proper procedures. Be sure to check your district's and state's guidelines for the proper disposal of algal cultures.

Program Resources

◆ **Teaching Resources** Chapter 3 Real-World Lab, pp. 79–80

An Explosion of Life

Preparing for Inquiry

Key Concept Algae grow better in the presence of fertilizer.
Skills Objective Students will be able to
◆ control variables;
◆ predict relative algae growth;
◆ draw conclusions about nutrient use.
Time 30 minutes first day, 10 minutes subsequent days
Advance Planning The tap water should stand for 3 days before the lab.
Alternative Materials You can use pond water or algae cultures from a biological supply house.

Guiding Inquiry

Invitation

Ask students what agricultural runoff after a rainstorm might contain. (*Soil, fertilizers*) Students will test the effect of fertilizer on algal growth.

Analyze and Conclude

1. Jar D was the darkest green, with jars C and B increasingly lighter, and jar A the lightest. The difference: fertilizer.
2. Jar A served as the control.
3. Algae in the water used the nutrients to grow. The intensity of the green color also increased with the numbers of algae.
4. Without light to make food, the jars would stay the same as the first day.
5. Reproduction of algae would use up oxygen in the water. Organisms would die without sufficient oxygen. Fertilizer could get into the water in runoff from farm fields or golf courses.

Extending the Inquiry

Design an Experiment Use regular detergent in one set of jars and low-phosphate detergent in another.

Eutrophication— The Threat to Clear, Clean Water

Purpose

Discuss the problems associated with eutrophication in Weiss Lake. Identify the pros and cons of different plans and consider their implementation.

Panel Discussion

Time 45 minutes to prepare, 30 minutes for panel discussion.

Review eutrophication and ask students to explain why adding nutrients to rivers and lakes is harmful. Divide the class into five groups; farmers, residents, environmentalists, local officials, and industry representatives. Encourage groups to identify the problem and discuss the nutrient sources that are polluting Weiss Lake. Have each group choose a spokesperson and prepare their viewpoints. In the panel discussion, each spokesperson should assess the problem by presenting his or her concerns and possible solutions, along with the economic impact of the final proposal. Students may choose to consider restricting fertilizer use, reducing factory emissions of phosphorus, additional processing of wastewater, or landscaping to prevent soil erosion.

Extend Encourage students to research pollution issues for a local body of water. If possible, have students watch local proceedings in which community members address this problem.

You Decide

Students should complete the first part with their interest groups as they prepare for the discussion. The second part could be completed after the panel discussion. Then have students create a prevention plan based on what they learn in the discussion. Students should indicate an understanding of how each solution will affect different groups of people.

Eutrophication — The Threat to Clear, Clean Water

Weiss Lake, on the Georgia-Alabama border, is a popular vacation area. People come to this lake to fish, boat, and swim. But every year about 2 million pounds of phosphorus pour into Weiss Lake from rivers. These excess nutrients are threatening the lake's good fishing and clean, clear water.

Weiss Lake is just one of thousands of lakes and ponds in the United States threatened by eutrophication. The threat is not just to recreation. Drinking water for nearly 70 percent of Americans comes from lakes, reservoirs, and other surface water.

The Issues

Where Does the Pollution Come From?
The two main sources of excess nutrients are wastes and fertilizers from farms and wastewater from sewage treatment plants. When farmers fertilize crops, the plants absorb only some of these nutrients. The excess nutrients can be washed with soil into lakes and ponds. When wastewater from homes and factories is treated, large amounts of nutrients still remain in the water. For example, about 380 million liters of treated wastewater flow toward Weiss Lake daily. This treated wastewater still contains large amounts of phosphorus produced by many factories.

What Are the Costs of Eutrophication?
People who live near Weiss Lake depend on the lake for jobs and money. But as the fish die in the oxygen-poor waters, swimming and boating in the murky water become less appealing and possibly unsafe. Over 4,000 jobs and millions of dollars each year would be lost if Weiss Lake were to close down. But upgrading or building new water-treatment plants would cost millions of dollars in higher taxes to citizens.

What Can Be Done? Even as cities, farms, and factories grow, the amount of nutrients reaching lakes and ponds can be reduced. Factories can install water-treatment facilities that remove more nitrogen and phosphorus from their wastewater. Farmers can often reduce the use of fertilizers. People can plant trees along the banks of lakes to reduce the amount of soil entering the lake. These solutions can cost millions of dollars, but they can reverse the problem.

You Decide

1. Identify the Problem
In your own words, describe the eutrophication issues that affect Weiss Lake.

2. Analyze the Options
Make a chart of different ways to slow the eutrophication process. How would each work? What groups of people would be affected?

3. Find a Solution
Create a "prevention plan" advising town leaders how to reduce eutrophication in lakes and ponds.

Background

Although most commonly seen in lakes, the problems of eutrophication are also present in oceans. In general, coastal areas that do not have strong winds or tides to mix the sea water, such as bays and gulfs, are most at risk. In these areas, freshwater runoff tends to float on top of the denser sea water. Without being mixed, the water on the surface begins to develop a rich overabundance of life forms. The bottom layers fill with dead plant matter, which decomposes and rapidly consumes oxygen. Entire bays can suffer from the suffocation below the surface. In the Gulf of Mexico, an 18,000-sq km area goes through this deadly process every summer. This lifeless region in open waters is known as the "dead zone."

SECTION 3 Fungi

SECTION 3 Fungi

DISCOVER ●●●●●●●●●●●●●●●●●●●●●●●●●●●●●●●●●●●●●● ACTIVITY

Do All Molds Look Alike?

1. Your teacher will give you two sealed, clear plastic bags—one containing moldy bread and another containing moldy fruit. **CAUTION:** *Do not open the sealed bags at any time.*
2. Examine each mold. In your notebook, describe what you see.
3. Then, use a hand lens to examine each mold. Sketch each mold in your notebook and list its characteristics.
4. Return the sealed bags to your teacher. Wash your hands.

Think It Over
Observing How are the molds similar? How do they differ?

U nnoticed, a speck of dust lands on a cricket's back. But this is no ordinary dust—it is alive! Tiny glistening threads emerge from the dust and begin to grow into the cricket's moist body. As they grow, the threads release chemicals that slowly dissolve the cricket's living tissues. The threads continue to grow deeper into the cricket's body. Within a few days, the cricket's body is little more than a hollow shell filled with a tangle of the deadly threads. Then the threads begin to grow up and out of the dead cricket. They produce long stalks with knobs at their tips. When one of the knobs breaks open, it will release thousands of dustlike specks, which the wind can carry to new victims.

GUIDE FOR READING

◆ What characteristics do fungi share?
◆ How do fungi obtain food?
◆ What roles do fungi play in the living world?

Reading Tip Before you read, preview the headings. Record them in outline form, leaving space for writing notes.

What Are Fungi?

The strange cricket-killing organism is a member of the fungi kingdom. Although you may not have heard of a cricket-killing fungus before, you are probably familiar with other kinds of fungi. For example, the molds that grow on stale bread or on decaying fruit are all fungi. Mushrooms that sprout in forests or yards are also fungi.

▼ A bush cricket attacked by a killer fungus

Chapter 3 **A ◆ 95**

READING STRATEGIES

Reading Tip Before students preview the headings, remind them that main topics in an outline appear with Roman numerals. Ask them how many main topics their outlines will have. *(six)* Have a volunteer name the six main topics. Then have them name the subtopics for each heading. *(Sample answer for the topic Reproduction in Fungi: Asexual Reproduction, Sexual Reproduction)*

Program Resources

◆ **Teaching Resources** 3-3 Lesson Plan, p. 75; 3-3 Section Summary, p. 76

Media and Technology

 Audiotapes English-Spanish Summary 3-3

SECTION 3 Fungi

Objectives

After completing the lesson, students will be able to
◆ name the characteristics that all fungi share;
◆ describe how fungi obtain food;
◆ list the roles fungi play in the living world;
◆ describe the ways that fungi reproduce.

Key Terms hypha, fruiting body, budding, lichen

1 Engage/Explore

Activating Prior Knowledge

Ask students to describe what they know about how mushrooms grow. Some students may have seen mushrooms growing in the woods, while others may have seen cultivated mushrooms. Encourage students to think about how mushrooms are similar to plants.

●●●●●●●● DISCOVER ●●●●●●●●

Skills Focus observing
Materials *self-seal bags, tape, hand lens, old bread, fruit*
Time 15 minutes
Tips At least one week before the activity, place pieces of moist bread and fruit in separate self-seal bags. Seal the bags, then make an extra seal with tape. Keep them in a dark place at room temperature. Make sure students do not open the bags. Dispose of the sealed bags and all other materials according to the proper procedures. Be sure to check your district's and state's guidelines for the proper disposal of fungal cultures.
Expected Outcome Observations will depend on the kinds of fungi that grow on the foods. Students should see more detail with the hand lens.
Think It Over The molds will probably have similar threadlike appearances and fruiting bodies but will probably be of different colors.

A ◆ 95

What Are Fungi?

Using the Visuals: Figures 13 and 14

As students study the two figures, ask: **How are the hyphae of the mushroom similar to those of the mold growing on the orange?** *(Both make up the bodies of the organism, and both grow down into the nutrient source.)* In each example, the hyphae within the body of the organism are more tightly packed than the hyphae under the surface. **learning modality: visual**

Cell Structure

Building Inquiry Skills: Observing

Materials *various types of mushrooms from the grocery store, hand lens*

Time 15 minutes

Tips Give groups of students a selection of mushrooms to observe. Caution students not to eat any part of the mushrooms. Challenge them to identify mushroom structures including gills, cap, and stalk, then sketch the mushrooms and label each part. Encourage each group to compare and contrast the different fruiting bodies. Finally, have students gently twist off the cap of one mushroom and break open the stalk from end to end. Ask: **Can you pull any threadlike structures from the stalk?** *(Answers may vary depending on the mushroom.)* **Using your knowledge of mushrooms, what do you think these threadlike structures are? What are they made of?** *(Hyphae; the cells of the fungus)* Make sure students wash their hands immediately after the activity. **learning modality: visual**

Fungi vary in size from the unicellular yeasts to the multicellular fungi, such as mushrooms and the bracket fungi that look like shelves growing on tree trunks. **Most fungi share three important characteristics: They are eukaryotes, use spores to reproduce, and are heterotrophs that feed in a similar way.** In addition, fungi need moist, warm places in which to grow. They thrive on moist foods, damp tree barks, lawns coated with dew, damp forest floors, and even wet bathroom tiles.

Cell Structure

Except for yeast cells, which are unicellular, the cells of fungi are arranged in structures called hyphae. **Hyphae** (HY fee) (singular *hypha*) are the branching, threadlike tubes that make up the bodies of multicellular fungi. The hyphae of some fungi are continuous threads of cytoplasm that contain many nuclei. Substances move quickly and freely through the hyphae.

The appearance of a fungus depends on how its hyphae are arranged. In some fungi, the threadlike hyphae are loosely tangled. Fuzzy-looking molds that grow on old foods have loosely tangled hyphae. In other fungi, hyphae are packed tightly together. For example, the stalk and cap of the mushrooms in Figure 13 are made of hyphae packed so tightly that they appear solid. Underground, however, a mushroom's hyphae form a loose, threadlike maze in the soil.

☑ *Checkpoint* What structures make up the bodies of multicellular fungi?

Cap

Gills

Stalk

Hyphae

Underground hyphae

Figure 13 The hyphae in the stalk and cap of a mushroom are packed tightly to form very firm structures. Underground hyphae, on the other hand, are arranged loosely. *Inferring What function do you think the underground hyphae perform?*

Background

Facts and Figures There are over 3,000 kinds of mushrooms in North America. Their colors and shapes vary widely.

Two common poisonous mushrooms in North America are the Fly Agaric (*Amanita muscaria*) and the Death Cap (*Amanita phalloides*). The 3 to 30-cm cap on Fly Agaric mushrooms is a straw-yellow to reddish-orange color, and its surface is spotted with white or pale-yellow warts. Fly Agaric

mushrooms contain muscarine and other toxic alkaloids, but eating one does not usually cause death.

The Death Cap is 5 to 15 cm wide, and a pale, grayish brown color near the center, but white on the margin. The poisons in the Death Cap cause damage to cells throughout the body. This damage can lead to a coma, and over half of the victims who go into a coma die.

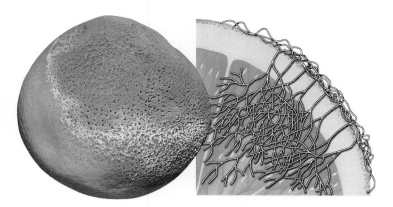

Figure 14 The mold *Penicillium* often grows on old fruits such as this orange. Notice that some hyphae grow deep inside the orange. These hyphae digest the food and absorb the smaller chemicals.

How Do Fungi Obtain Food?

Although fungi are heterotrophs, they do not take food into their bodies as you do. Instead fungi absorb food through hyphae that grow into the food source.

Look at Figure 14 to see how a fungus feeds. **First, the fungus grows hyphae into a food source. Then digestive chemicals ooze from the tips of the hyphae into the food. The digestive chemicals break down the food into small substances that can be absorbed by the hyphae.** Imagine yourself sinking your fingers down into a chocolate cake and dripping digestive chemicals out of your fingertips. Then imagine your fingers absorbing the digested particles of the cake. That's how a fungus feeds.

Some fungi feed on the remains of dead organisms. Other fungi are parasites that break down the chemicals in living organisms. For example, athlete's foot is a disease caused by a fungus that feeds on chemicals in a person's skin. Dutch elm disease is caused by a fungus that feeds on elm trees and eventually kills the trees.

Reproduction in Fungi

Like it or not, fungi are everywhere. The way they reproduce guarantees their survival and spread. Fungi usually reproduce by producing lightweight spores that are surrounded by a protective covering. Spores can be carried easily through air or water to new sites. Fungi produce many more spores than will ever grow into new fungi. Only a few of the thousands of spores that a fungus releases will fall where conditions are right for them to grow into new organisms.

Making Spore Prints

In this activity, you will examine the reproductive structures of a mushroom.

1. Place a fresh mushroom cap, gill side down, on a sheet of white paper. **CAUTION:** *Do not eat the mushroom.*
2. Cover the mushroom cap with a plastic container. Wash your hands with soap.
3. After two days, carefully remove the container and then the cap. You should find a spore print on the paper.
4. Examine the print with a hand lens. Then wash your hands with soap.

Predicting Use your spore print to estimate how many spores a mushroom could produce. Where would spores be most likely to grow into new mushrooms?

Skills Focus predicting
Materials *mushroom cap, white paper, large plastic container*
Time 10 minutes; 15 minutes for observations two days later
Tips Use only mushrooms from a grocery store. Carefully twist the caps off the stalks. The color of spores is a characteristic used to identify mushrooms. Using white paper will help ensure accurate observations.
Expected Results Students should obtain a spore print consisting of lines radiating outward like spokes. Students can estimate the number of spores in a radiating line and multiply the estimate by the number of lines. Spores would grow in a moist warm place with adequate food.
Extend Provide students with different varieties of edible mushrooms and allow them to compare spore prints.

Portfolio Students can save their spore prints in their portfolios.

Program Resources

- **Science Explorer Series** *Human Biology and Health*, Chapter 6
- ◆ **Interdisciplinary Exploration Series** "A Nation of Immigrants," pp. 12–13

Media and Technology

 Transparencies "The Structure of a Mushroom," Transparency 11

Answers to Self-Assessment

Caption Question

Figure 13 Students may suspect that the underground hyphae hold the mushroom in place and help it get water, or they may suggest that the hyphae help absorb food.

☑ *Checkpoint*

hyphae

Ongoing Assessment

Writing Have students briefly describe the structure and function of hyphae.

Reproduction in Fungi, continued

Building Inquiry Skills: Observing

Materials *mushroom spores, eyedropper, water, microscope, slide, and cover slip*
Tips Students can observe the spores they collected in the Try This activity on the previous page. Have them use the eyedropper to place a drop of water on the spore print. Then, they can draw up the water with the dropper, place a drop on a microscope slide, and cover it with a cover slip. Allow them to observe the spores under a microscope. Encourage students to sketch their observations and include the color and shape of the spores. Ask: **What is the function of these spores?** *(Spores are the reproductive cells that will produce new mushrooms.)*
learning modality: visual

TRY THIS

Skills Focus making models
Materials *round balloon, cotton balls, tape, stick or ruler about 30 cm long, modeling clay, pin*
Time 25 minutes
Tips If possible, blow up the balloons with a pump or compressed air so that the cotton balls do not get wet. Suggest students make the cotton balls as small as possible so the balls will not just fall to the ground when expelled from the balloon.
Expected Outcome The "spores" should fly out from the balloons and land in many directions and fairly far from the balloons. Students should explain that, just like air in the balloon scattered the cotton balls from the balloon, air currents catch and carry spores from the tall fruiting bodies.
Extend Allow students to repeat the activity in front of a fan to model the effects of wind on the dispersal of spores. **learning modality: visual**

Spreading Spores

In this activity you will make a model of a fruiting body.

1. Break a cotton ball into five equal-sized pieces. Roll each piece into a tiny ball.
2. Insert the cotton balls into a balloon through the opening in its neck.
3. Repeat Steps 1 and 2 until the balloon is almost full.
4. Inflate the balloon. Tie a knot in its neck. Tape the knotted end of the balloon to a stick.
5. Stand the stick upright in a mound of modeling clay.
6. ✂ Pop the balloon with a pin. Observe what happens.

Making Models Draw a diagram of the model you made. Label the stalk, the spore case, and the spores. Use your model to explain why fungi are found just about everywhere.

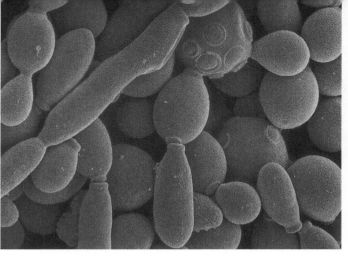

Figure 15 Budding is a form of asexual reproduction that occurs in yeast. The small yeast cell that grows from the body of a parent cell is identical to the parent.

Fungi produce spores in structures called **fruiting bodies,** which are reproductive hyphae that grow out of a fungus. The appearances of fruiting bodies vary from one type of fungus to another. For some fungi, such as mushrooms and puffballs, the part of the fungus that you see is the fruiting body. In other fungi, such as bread molds, the stalklike fruiting bodies grow upward from the hyphae on the surface of the bread. The knoblike structure, or spore case, at the tip of a stalk contains the spores.

Asexual Reproduction Most fungi reproduce both asexually and sexually. When there is adequate moisture and food, most fungi reproduce asexually by growing fruiting bodies that release thousands of spores.

Unicellular yeast cells undergo a form of asexual reproduction called **budding.** In budding, no spores are produced. Instead, a small yeast cell grows from the body of a large, well-fed parent cell in a way that might remind you of a bud forming on the branch of a tree. The new cell then breaks away and lives on its own.

Sexual Reproduction When growing conditions become unfavorable, fungi may reproduce sexually. In sexual reproduction, the hyphae of two fungi grow together. A new spore-producing structure grows from the joined hyphae. The new structure produces spores, which can develop into fungi that differ from either parent.

☑ *Checkpoint* *What is a fruiting body?*

Background

Integrating Science Yeasts are often grown for use in the fermentation process or for use by scientists in research. There are about 600 known species of yeasts. The most familiar, *Saccharomyces cereviseae,* is used in the fermentation process to produce the alcohol in wine and beer. During the fermentation process, enzymes in the yeast enable its cells to extract oxygen from starch or sugar molecules, producing alcohol or carbon dioxide.

Yeasts are also used to produce the carbon dioxide gas that causes bread dough to rise. In bread making, the temperature of the water is very important. The yeast will be killed if the water is even slightly overheated. If the water is too cold, it will slow the growth of the yeast.

Classification of Fungi

Fungi are classified into groups based on the shape of the spore-producing structures and on their ability to reproduce sexually. The four groups of fungi—the threadlike fungi, the sac fungi, the club fungi, and the imperfect fungi—are shown in Figure 16.

▲ **Threadlike Fungi**

This group contains about 600 different species of molds, including many common bread molds, such as this *Rhizopus nigrens*. These fungi produce spores in their threadlike hyphae.

▲ **Sac Fungi**

This group contains over 30,000 diverse species of fungi, including yeast, morels, truffles, and some fungi that cause plant diseases, such as Dutch elm disease. They are called sac fungi because they produce spores in structures that look like sacks. The sac fungi in the photo are called bird's nest fungi.

◀ **Club Fungi**

This group includes about 25,000 species of mushrooms, bracket fungi, plant parasites, and puffballs. Club fungi produce spores in structures that look like clubs. One of the puffballs in the photo is shooting out its spores.

▲ **Imperfect Fungi**

The 25,000 species in this group include this *Penicillium*, the source of an important antibiotic. The fungi in this group are not known to reproduce sexually.

Figure 16 The four groups of fungi differ in the appearance of their spore-producing structures and in how they reproduce. *Classifying* To which group do mushrooms belong?

Program Resources

 Science Explorer Series *Inside Earth*, Chapter 3

Answers to Self-Assessment

Caption Question

Figure 16 Mushrooms are a kind of club fungi.

☑ *Checkpoint*

A fruiting body is a reproductive hypha that grows out of a fungus.

Demonstration

Materials *warm water (40°C–45°C), large beaker, package of dry yeast, sugar, tablespoon, iodine, high-power microscope*
Time 20 minutes for setup; 10 minutes for observations about 30 minutes later
Tips To encourage students who may be having difficulty understanding the text, demonstrate how yeast reproduce by budding. Dissolve several tablespoons of sugar in a jar that is about one-quarter full of warm water. Pour the yeast into the water. Ask students to predict what will happen. Set the jar aside for about 30 minutes. At that time, collect a small sample of yeast from the water. Place the sample on a slide, stain it with a drop of iodine, and cover with a cover slip. Set up the microscope at a central location and allow students to make observations. *(Students should be able to see buds on some yeasts.)* **limited English proficiency**

Classification of Fungi

Using the Visuals: Figure 16

Students may be confused when they look at the puffball, because it does not resemble a club. Inform them that the club-shaped spore cases are located inside the puffball. Point out that the *Penicillium* is classified as an imperfect fungus because sexual reproduction has never been observed in *Penicillium*. Then ask: **What questions would a scientist have to ask to classify a fungus he or she found?** *(Sample: Does it have a spore case, and if so, what shape is it?)* **learning modality: verbal**

Ongoing Assessment

Writing Have students explain why and how fungi reproduce asexually and sexually.

Drawing Conclusions

What's for Lunch?

Preparing for Inquiry

Key Concept The activity of yeast varies, depending on the amount of available food.

Skills Objective Students will be able to
◆ draw conclusions about whether sugar and salt act as food sources for yeast.

Time 45 minutes

Advance Planning Before the lab, check a sample of yeast in warm water with sugar for 20 minutes to make sure the yeasts are alive.

Guiding Inquiry

Invitation

Tell students that yeasts produce carbon dioxide when they break down food. Carbon dioxide production can be measured to determine whether yeasts are feeding. Have students explain how carbon dioxide production will be measured in this lab.

Introducing the Procedure

Help students understand that when carbon dioxide gas forms in water, much of it will escape from the water's surface.

Troubleshooting the Experiment

◆ Have groups walk through Steps 5–11 before they actually carry them out so that they will be sure what to add to each bottle. Have students use the data table as a guide.
◆ Do not let students overfill the bottles.
◆ Caution students to use a fresh straw for each mixing. This is particularly important when mixing bottle E, because students must not introduce yeast by accident.
◆ Balloons may pop off the bottles during the lab.

Expected Outcome

Balloon D should inflate the most. Balloon C should also inflate but noticeably less than balloon D. Balloons A, B, and E should not inflate.

Skills Lab

What's for Lunch?

In this lab, you will draw conclusions about the effects of two substances on the activity of yeast.

Problem

How does the presence of sugar or salt affect the activity of yeast?

Materials

marking pen	5 round balloons
5 plastic straws	sugar
salt	warm water (40–45°C)
beaker	dry powdered yeast
graduated cylinder	
5 small narrow-necked bottles	

Procedure

1. Copy the data table into your notebook. Then read over the entire procedure to see how you will test the activity of the yeast cells in bottles A through E. Write a prediction about what will happen in each bottle.

2. Gently stretch each of the 5 balloons so that they will inflate easily.

3. Using the marking pen, label the bottles A, B, C, D, and E.

4. Use a beaker to fill each bottle with the same amount of warm water. **CAUTION:** *Glass is fragile. Handle the bottles and beaker gently to avoid breakage. Do not touch broken glass.*

5. Put 5 mL of salt into bottle B.

6. Put 5 mL of sugar into bottles C and E.

7. Put 30 mL of sugar into bottle D.

8. Put 2 mL of powdered yeast into bottle A, and stir the mixture with a clean straw. Remove the straw and discard it.

9. Immediately place a balloon over the opening of bottle A. Make sure that the balloon opening fits very tightly around the neck of the bottle.

10. Repeat Steps 8 and 9 for bottle B, bottle C, and bottle D.

DATA TABLE

Bottle	Contents	Prediction	Observations
A	Yeast alone		
B	Yeast and 5 mL of salt		
C	Yeast and 5 mL of sugar		
D	Yeast and 30 mL of sugar		
E	No yeast and 5 mL of sugar		

Sample Data Table

Bottle	Contents	Prediction	Observations
A	Yeast alone	Balloon will inflate	Did not inflate
B	Yeast and 5 mL of salt	Balloon will not inflate	Did not inflate
C	Yeast and 5 mL of sugar	Balloon will inflate	Inflated to small size
D	Yeast and 30 mL of sugar	Balloon will inflate	Inflated to large size
E	No yeast and 5 mL of sugar	Balloon will not inflate	Did not inflate

1. Balloons C and D changed during the lab. Balloon C filled up a little, and balloon D filled up a lot.
2. Some balloons were inflated by carbon dioxide gas. Other balloons remained unchanged because no carbon dioxide gas was produced by the yeast.
3. Yes. Balloons C and D inflated, indicating that the yeast was using the sugar as a source of energy.
4. No. Bottle B produced no gas, indicating that the yeast was not active.
5. The balloon on bottle C did not inflate as much as the balloon on bottle D. When less sugar was available to the yeast (5 mL in bottle C versus 30 mL in D), the yeast gave off less carbon dioxide.
6. No, because there would be no way of knowing whether the gas was being produced by the sugar alone as it dissolved in the water.

Extending the Inquiry

Design an Experiment Students could prepare another bottle D and place it in the dark. They would find that yeasts (unlike algae) do not require light to carry out their basic life processes.

---

11. Place a balloon over bottle E without adding yeast to the bottle.
12. Place the 5 bottles in a warm spot away from drafts. Observe and record what happens.

Analyze and Conclude

1. Which balloons changed in size during this lab? How did they change?
2. Explain why the balloon changed size in some bottles and not in others. What caused that change in size?
3. Do yeast cells use sugar as a food source? How do you know?
4. Do yeast cells use salt as a food source? How do you know?
5. What did the results from bottle C show, compared with the results from bottle D?
6. **Think About It** If you removed bottle E from your experiment, would you be able to conclude whether or not sugar is a food source for the yeast cells? Why or why not?

Design an Experiment

Develop a hypothesis about whether yeast cells need light to carry out their life activities. Then design an experiment to test your hypothesis. Obtain your teacher's permission before you carry out the experiment.

Program Resources

◆ **Teaching Resources** Chapter 3 Skills Lab, pp. 81–83
◆ **Inquiry Skills Activity Book** Provides teaching and review of all inquiry skills

Safety

Students should wear safety goggles in case a balloon pops off a bottle or a bottle is accidentally dropped. Review the safety guidelines in Appendix A.

Fungi and the Living World

Real-Life Learning

Ask students: **Does your family or anyone you know have a compost pile?** Explain that compost piles are made by alternating layers of soil, animal manure, and vegetable materials such as weeds, grass clippings, leaves, and food waste. After several months, the material in a compost pile becomes a rich mixture that can be used to supply nutrients necessary for the plants in a garden to grow. Ask: **How do fungi help to produce compost?** (*Fungi are decomposers. They live in the soil in the compost pile and break down the chemicals in the dead plant matter.*) Students interested in gardening may want to find out more about composting. **learning modality: verbal**

Building Inquiry Skills: Designing Experiments

Challenge small groups of students to work together **ACTIVITY** to design experiments that show how yeast reacts with other ingredients to make bread. Suggest that students find simple bread recipes and vary the ingredients for their experiments. Students can make predictions about how different quantities of ingredients will affect the outcome of the baked bread. Bring a bread machine into class so students can try out their recipes. **cooperative learning**

Integrating Health

Encourage students to share what they know about athlete's foot. Ask: **How do you get athlete's foot?** (*Spores fall off infected feet and are picked up by your feet.*) **Where does this usually occur?** (*Public showers, gyms, etc.*) **What can you do to avoid getting athlete's foot?** (*Dry between your toes; wear shoes in public areas.*) **How would you treat this fungus if you got it?** (*With a fungicide*) **learning modality: verbal**

Fungi and the Living World

Fungi affect humans and other organisms in many ways. **Fungi play an important role as decomposers on Earth. In addition, many fungi provide foods for people. Some cause disease and some fight disease. Still other fungi live in symbiosis with other organisms.**

Environmental Recycling Like bacteria, fungi are decomposers—organisms that break down the chemicals in dead organisms. For example, many fungi live in the soil and break down the chemicals in dead plant matter. This process returns important nutrients to the soil. Without fungi and bacteria, Earth would be buried under dead plants and animals.

Food and Fungi When you eat a slice of bread, you benefit from the work of yeast. Bakers add yeast to bread dough to make it rise. Yeast cells use the sugar in the dough for food and produce carbon dioxide gas as they feed. The gas forms bubbles, which cause the dough to rise. You see these bubbles as holes in a slice of bread. Without yeast, bread would be flat and solid. Yeast is also used to make wine from grapes. Yeast cells feed on the sugar in the grapes and produce carbon dioxide and alcohol.

Other fungi are also important sources of foods. Molds are used in the production of foods such as some cheeses. The blue streaks in blue cheese, for example, are actually growths of

Figure 17 Many food crops are lost each year due to fungal diseases. The ear of corn in the photo has been attacked by a fungus called corn smut. *Making Generalizations Why is the spread of fungal diseases difficult to control?*

Penicillium roqueforti. People enjoy eating mushrooms in salads and soups and on pizza. Because some mushrooms are poisonous, however, you should never pick or eat wild mushrooms.

☑ *Checkpoint* *What are three foods that fungi help to produce?*

Disease-Causing Fungi Many fungi cause serious diseases in plants that result in huge crop losses every year. Corn smut and wheat rust are two club fungi that cause diseases in important food crops. Fungal plant diseases also affect other crops, including rice, cotton, and soybeans.

INTEGRATING HEALTH Some fungi cause diseases in humans as well. Athlete's foot causes an itchy irritation in the damp places between toes. Ringworm, another fungal disease, causes an itchy, circular rash on the skin. Because the fungi that cause these

---

Background

Facts and Figures Many species of soil fungi have their hyphae attached to the roots of forest trees. These associations, called *mycorrhizae,* can benefit both the fungi and the tree.

Because hyphae grow very rapidly under favorable conditions, mycorrhizae can be enormous. In northern Michigan, a single *Armillaria bulbosa* fungus has been discovered that continues under more than 30 acres of forest. Although this may be one of the world's largest organisms, scientists think it came from a single spore released thousands of years ago. In Washington State, another *Armillaria* fungus—consisting of an underground network of hyphae and aboveground mushrooms—covers more than 1,000 acres.

diseases produce spores at the site of infection, the diseases can spread easily from person to person. Both diseases can be treated with antifungal medications.

Disease-Fighting Fungi In 1928 a Scottish biologist, Alexander Fleming, was examining petri dishes in which he was growing bacteria. To his surprise, Fleming noticed a spot of a bluish-green mold growing in one dish. Curiously, no bacteria were growing near the mold. Fleming hypothesized that the mold, a fungus named *Penicillium*, produced a substance that killed the bacteria growing near it. Fleming's work led to the development of the first antibiotic, penicillin. It has saved the lives of millions of people with bacterial infections. Since the discovery of penicillin, many additional antibiotics have been isolated from both fungi and eubacteria.

Fungus-Plant Root Associations Some fungi help plants grow larger and healthier when their hyphae grow among the plant's roots. The hyphae spread out underground and absorb water and nutrients from the soil for the plant. With more water and nutrients, the plant grows larger than it would have grown without its fungal partner. The plant is not the only partner that benefits. The fungi get to feed on the extra food that the plant makes and stores.

Many plants are so dependent on their fungal partners that they cannot survive well without them. For example, orchids cannot grow without their fungal partners.

Figure 18 The fruiting bodies of these mushrooms have emerged in an almost perfect circular pattern. This pattern is called a fairy ring. The mushrooms share the same network of underground hyphae.

Language Arts CONNECTION

Folk tales are ancient stories that were passed down by word of mouth over many generations. Folk tales often involve magical elements, such as fairies—supernatural beings with powers to become invisible, change form, and affect the lives of people.

The circle of mushrooms in Figure 18 was often mentioned in folk tales. These circles were said to be the footprints of fairies who danced there at midnight. These mushroom circles were given the name "fairy rings"—a name that is still used today. People believed that the area inside a fairy ring was a magical location. Cutting down the tree inside a fairy ring was believed to bring bad luck.

In Your Journal

A type of mushroom called a toadstool is mentioned in some folk tales. Write a paragraph that could be part of a folk tale that reveals how toadstools got their name.

Language Arts CONNECTION

Ask students if they know of other mushrooms with interesting names. Some are named for their appearance, like the bird's nest, cauliflower, earthstar, old-man-of-the-woods, parasol, squirrel's bread, and thimble mushrooms. Chicken-of-the-woods and milk cap are named for their taste, and destroying angel, fly agaric, and inky cap are named for distinguishing traits or uses. Others, like fairy cups, elves' saddle, and morel have names rooted in folklore.

In Your Journal Students' paragraphs may include the idea that a toad used a "toadstool" to sit upon. Students should try to include a magical element in their paragraphs. Inform students that although the word *toadstool* commonly refers to poisonous mushrooms, there is no scientific distinction between mushrooms and toadstools. Many families of fungi include both edible and poisonous mushrooms. **learning modality: verbal**

Answers to Self-Assessment

Caption Question

Figure 17 Disease-causing fungi produce spores at the site of infection. The spores are easily dispersed, so disease spreads rapidly.

☑ *Checkpoint*

Fungi help produce bread, cheese, and wine.

Ongoing Assessment

Skills Check Have students list ways that fungi affect humans and identify each as beneficial or harmful.

Provide students with hand lenses and samples of lichens on rocks or tree bark. As students observe the lichens, challenge them to infer why lichens are sensitive to environmental pollution. *(Lichens rapidly absorb substances directly from rainwater, so they are very susceptible to airborne pollutants.)* **learning modality: visual**

3 Assess

Section 3 Review Answers

1. Fungi are eukaryotes, reproduce by spores, and are heterotrophs that feed in a similar way. They also live in warm, moist places.

2. Hyphae secrete digestive chemicals into a food source. The chemicals break down the food into smaller chemicals which the hyphae absorb. Fungi feed on dead organisms or are parasites in living organisms.

3. Fungi recycle chemical substances on Earth. They may cause human diseases, help cure diseases, provide a source of food, or live in symbiotic relationships with plants.

4. Mushrooms cannot make their own food so they are not classified as plants.

Check Your Progress
CHAPTER PROJECT 3

Students will need help drawing conclusions about their results. As you review students' sketches, point out questions that are not addressed by the poster. If necessary, list some ideas for information students should include on their posters before they make their sketches.

Figure 19 Lichens consist of a fungus living together with either algae or autotrophic bacteria. **A.** This lichen—a British soldier—probably gets its name from its scarlet red tops, which stand upright. **B.** The lichens covering these rocks are slowly breaking down the rocks to create soil.

Lichens A **lichen** (LY kun) consists of a fungus and either algae or autotrophic bacteria that also live together in a mutualistic relationship. You have probably seen some familiar lichens—irregular, flat, crusty patches that grow on tree barks or rocks. The fungus benefits from the food produced by the algae or bacteria. The algae or bacteria, in turn, obtain water and minerals from the fungus.

INTEGRATING EARTH SCIENCE Lichens are often called "pioneer" organisms because they are the first organisms to appear on the bare rocks in an area after a volcano, fire, or rock slide has occurred. Over time, the lichens break down the rock into soil in which other organisms can grow. Lichens are also useful as indicators of air pollution. Many species of lichens are very sensitive to pollutants and die when pollution levels rise. By monitoring the growth of lichens, scientists can assess the air quality in an area.

Section 3 Review

1. List three characteristics that fungi share.
2. Explain how a fungus feeds. What do fungi feed on?
3. Describe three roles that fungi play in the world.
4. Thinking Critically Classifying Explain why mushrooms are classified as fungi rather than as plants.

Check Your Progress
CHAPTER PROJECT 3

Continue to observe your mushrooms and collect data. Begin to review your data to see which conditions favored mushroom growth. How do your results compare with your hypothesis? Begin to plan your poster now. Think about how you can use graphs and diagrams to display your results. *(Hint:* Draw a rough sketch of your poster, and show it to your teacher. Include a labeled drawing of a mushroom.)

Performance Assessment

Oral Presentation Have small groups make presentations on the structure of fungi, how they obtain food, their reproduction, types of fungi, or how fungi interact with the living world. Presentations should include labeled sketches.

Background

History of Science Beatrix Potter (the creator of Peter Rabbit) thought that lichens were composed of algae and fungi living in a mutualistic relationship. Potter was an avid naturalist and scientific illustrator. She wrote a paper that included drawings of her observations of lichens through the microscope. The paper was read at a scholarly society in the 1890s, but because she was a woman, Potter was not allowed to appear.

Program Resources

◆ **Teaching Resources** 3-3 Review and Reinforce, p. 77; 3-3 Enrich, p. 78

SECTION 1 Protists

Key Ideas

◆ Animal-like protists, or protozoans, include sarcodines, ciliates, zooflagellates, and sporozoans. Like animals, these protists are heterotrophs. Most protozoans move by using pseudopods, cilia, or flagella.

◆ Funguslike protists include water molds, downy mildews, and slime molds. Like fungi, these protists are heterotrophs, have cell walls, and use spores to reproduce.

◆ Plantlike protists, or algae, include euglenoids, dinoflagellates, diatoms, green algae, red algae, and brown algae. Like plants, these organisms are autotrophs.

Key Terms

protozoan   mutualism
pseudopod   spore
contractile vacuole   algae
cilia   pigment
symbiosis

SECTION 2 Algal Blooms
INTEGRATING ENVIRONMENTAL SCIENCE

Key Ideas

◆ Red tides occur when a population of algae increases quickly in ocean waters. Some algae can secrete toxins that poison animals.

◆ Nutrients in a lake or pond build up over time, causing an increase in the numbers of algae. An accelerated rate of eutrophication can lead to the deaths of many organisms in the lake or pond.

Key Terms

algal bloom   eutrophication
red tide

SECTION 3 Fungi

Key Ideas

◆ Most fungi are eukaryotes, use spores to reproduce, and are heterotrophs.

◆ Most fungi feed by absorbing food through their hyphae. The hyphae secrete digestive chemicals into a food source, which is broken down into small substances that are absorbed by the hyphae.

◆ Fungi produce spores in structures called fruiting bodies. The majority of fungi reproduce both asexually and sexually.

◆ Fungi are decomposers that recycle Earth's chemicals. In addition, some fungi cause disease while some fight disease. Many produce important foods for people. Some fungi live in symbiotic relationships with other organisms.

Key Terms

hypha
fruiting body
budding
lichen

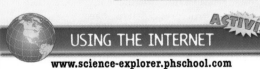

USING THE INTERNET ACTIVITY

www.science-explorer.phschool.com

Program Resources

◆ **Teaching Resources** Chapter 3 Project Scoring Rubric, p. 66; Chapter 3 Performance Assessment Teacher Notes, pp. 170–171; Chapter 3 Performance Assessment Student Worksheet, p. 172; Chapter 3 Test, pp. 173–176

Media and Technology

Interactive Student Tutorial CD-ROM A-3

Reviewing Content:
Multiple Choice
1. c 2. c 3. d 4. c 5. b

True or False
6. pseudopods 7. true 8. true 9. club
10. true

Checking Concepts

11. An ameba extends pseudopods on each side of a food particle to engulf it.
12. Algae range greatly in size. Some are unicellular, others are multicellular, and some form large colonies.
13. Animal-like and funguslike protists are heterotrophs. Plantlike protists are autotrophs, but some can also be heterotrophs.
14. In sexual reproduction, two hyphae grow together and produce a fruiting body.
15. The fungus benefits from food produced by the algae or bacteria, which obtains water and minerals from the fungus.
16. Students should explain that the puffball is the fruiting body and that the spores are spread by wind, water, or other organisms. They should also know that spores will only germinate in a suitable environment.

Thinking Visually

17. Sample title: The Effect of Excess Nutrients in a Lake; **a.** Algal bloom occurs. **b.** Excess algae block the sun and plants on the bottom die. **c.** As decomposers feed on the dead bodies, they use up the oxygen in the water.

Applying Skills

18. The amount of carbon dioxide produced is highest between 20°C and 30°C. As the temperature gets cooler or warmer than this range, the carbon dioxide production decreases sharply. Below 0°C and above 50°C, no carbon dioxide is produced.
19. Yeast must be active and produce carbon dioxide so the dough will rise, and it is more active in warm water.
20. No. For the most part the dough would not continue to rise because yeast are usually inactive at that temperature.

Reviewing Content

 For more review of key concepts, see the Interactive Student Tutorial CD-ROM.

Multiple Choice
Choose the letter of the best answer.

1. Which of the following characteristics describes *all* protists?
   a. They are unicellular.
   b. They can be seen with the unaided eye.
   c. Their cells have nuclei.
   d. They are unable to move on their own.
2. Which protist uses cilia to move?
   a. euglena
   b. ameba
   c. paramecium
   d. diatom
3. Which statement is true of slime molds?
   a. They are always unicellular.
   b. They are autotrophs.
   c. They are animal-like protists.
   d. They use spores to reproduce.
4. An overpopulation of saltwater algae is called a(n)
   a. pigment.
   b. lichen.
   c. red tide.
   d. eutrophication.
5. A lichen is a symbiotic association between which of the following?
   a. fungi and plant roots
   b. algae and fungi
   c. algae and bacteria
   d. protozoans and algae

True or False
If the statement is true, write true. If it is false, change the underlined word or words to make the statement true.

6. Sarcodines use <u>flagella</u> to move.
7. <u>Eutrophication</u> is the process by which nutrients in a lake build up over time, causing an increase in the growth of algae.
8. Most fungi are made up of threadlike structures called <u>hyphae</u>.
9. All mushrooms are classified as <u>sac</u> fungi.
10. Most fungi that live among the roots of plants are <u>beneficial</u> to the plants.

Checking Concepts

11. Describe how an ameba obtains its food.
12. How do algae differ in terms of size?
13. Compare how animal-like, funguslike, and plantlike protists obtain food.
14. How does sexual reproduction occur in fungi?
15. Explain how both organisms in a lichen benefit from their symbiotic relationship.
16. **Writing to Learn** Imagine you are a spore in a ripe puffball. An animal passing by punctures the outer covering of your spore case. Describe what happens to you next.

Thinking Visually

17. **Flowchart** Copy this flowchart about changes in a lake onto a separate sheet of paper. Then complete the flowchart and add a title. (For more on flowcharts, see the Skills Handbook.)

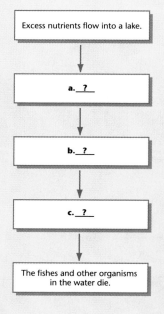

Thinking Critically

21. Amebas and paramecia are both unicellular heterotrophs that move. Amebas move with pseudopods, but paramecia move with cilia.
22. There could be excess nutrients in the water, or it may be old and need to be changed. The scum could be from eutrophication, a natural process that occurs over time.
23. Most other life forms would probably disappear also. Algae provide food and oxygen for water animals and help maintain the oxygen in the atmosphere.

24. Keep it aired out, dry, and cool. Mildew is a funguslike protist that thrives in moist, warm environments.

Applying Skills

When yeast is added to bread dough, the yeast cells produce carbon dioxide, which causes the dough to rise. The graph below shows how temperature affects the amount of carbon dioxide that is produced. Use the graph to answer Questions 18–20.

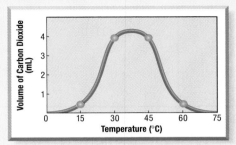

18. **Interpreting Data** Explain how temperature affects the amount of carbon dioxide that the yeast cells produce.
19. **Inferring** Use the graph to explain why yeast is dissolved in warm water rather than cold water when it is used to make bread.

20. **Predicting** Based on the graph, would you expect bread dough to continue to rise if it were placed in a refrigerator (about 2°–5°C)? Explain.

Thinking Critically

21. **Comparing and Contrasting** How are amebas and paramecia similar to one another? How are they different?
22. **Relating Cause and Effect** You see a layer of green scum growing on the walls of your aquarium at home. List some possible reasons why this growth has occurred.
23. **Predicting** If algae disappeared from Earth's waters, what would happen to living things on Earth? Explain your answer.
24. **Problem Solving** What actions could homeowners take to discourage the growth of mildew in their basement? Explain why these actions might help solve the problem.

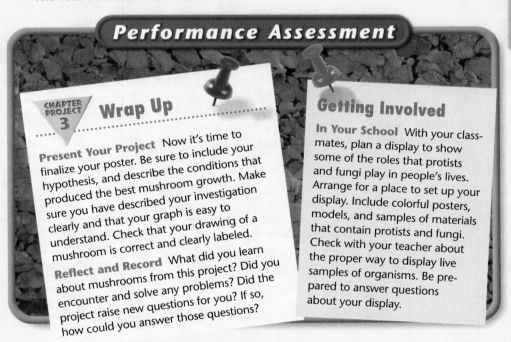

Performance Assessment

CHAPTER PROJECT 3 **Wrap Up**

Present Your Project Now it's time to finalize your poster. Be sure to include your hypothesis, and describe the conditions that produced the best mushroom growth. Make sure you have described your investigation clearly and that your graph is easy to understand. Check that your drawing of a mushroom is correct and clearly labeled.

Reflect and Record What did you learn about mushrooms from this project? Did you encounter and solve any problems? Did the project raise new questions for you? If so, how could you answer those questions?

Getting Involved

In Your School With your classmates, plan a display to show some of the roles that protists and fungi play in people's lives. Arrange for a place to set up your display. Include colorful posters, models, and samples of materials that contain protists and fungi. Check with your teacher about the proper way to display live samples of organisms. Be prepared to answer questions about your display.

Program Resources

◆ **Inquiry Skills Handbook** Provides teaching and review of all inquiry skills.

Performance Assessment

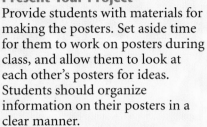

Wrap Up
Present Your Project
Provide students with materials for making the posters. Set aside time for them to work on posters during class, and allow them to look at each other's posters for ideas. Students should organize information on their posters in a clear manner.

Reflect and Record
Some students may have found it difficult to organize their results because they changed the variables too often or were not confident of their results. Students may propose another experiment or talking to an expert as a way of answering their questions.

Getting Involved

In Your School The students could display beneficial and harmful protists and fungi and have a few examples of both (do not use living samples of harmful protists). Or the display could illustrate the diversity of protists and fungi. Small protists could be displayed under a microscope or dissection scope. Larger protists and fungi should be in petri dishes, sealed plastic bags, or jars.

A ◆ 107

4 Introduction to Plants

Sections	Time	Student Edition Activities	Other Activities	
CHAPTER PROJECT 4 **Become a Moss Expert** p. 109	Ongoing (2 weeks)	Check Your Progress, pp. 117, 128, 134 Wrap Up, p. 137	TE	Chapter 4 Project Notes, pp. 108–109
1 The Plant Kingdom pp. 110–119 ◆ Identify the characteristics that all plants share. ◆ Name all the things that plants need to live successfully and describe the plant life cycle.	5 periods/ 2–3 blocks	**Discover** What Do Leaves Reveal About Plants?, p. 110 **Sharpen Your Skills** Interpreting Data, p. 113 **Skills Lab: Designing Experiments** Eye on Photosynthesis, pp. 118–119	TE TE TE	Building Inquiry Skills: Observing, pp. 111, 114, 115, 116; Comparing and Contrasting, p. 112; Inferring, p. 113 Addressing Naive Conceptions, p. 112 Demonstration, p. 116
2 *INTEGRATING PHYSICS* **Photosynthesis and Light** pp. 120–124 ◆ Explain what happens when light strikes a green leaf. ◆ Describe the overall process of photosynthesis.	$2\frac{1}{2}$ periods/ 1–2 blocks	**Discover** What Colors Make Up Sunlight?, p. 120	TE TE IES ISLM	Building Inquiry Skills: Observing, p. 121 Integrating Chemistry, p. 123 "Where River Meets Sea," pp. 15–16 A-4, "Investigating Stomata"
3 Mosses, Liverworts, and Hornworts pp. 125–129 ◆ Name some nonvascular plants and list the characteristics that they all share. ◆ Describe the structure of a moss plant.	$2\frac{1}{2}$ periods/ 1–2 blocks	**Discover** Will Mosses Absorb Water?, p. 125 **Skills Lab: Observing** Masses of Mosses, p. 129	TE TE IES	Demonstration, p. 126 Building Inquiry Skills: Observing, p. 127 "Fate of the Rain Forest," pp. 12–13
4 Ferns and Their Relatives pp. 130–134 ◆ Name some seedless vascular plants and list the characteristics that they share. ◆ Describe the structure of a fern plant.	$2\frac{1}{2}$ periods/ 1–2 blocks	**Discover** How Quickly Can Water Move Upward?, p. 130 **Try This** Examining a Fern, p. 132	TE TE IES	Visual Arts Connection, p. 132 Building Inquiry Skills: Classifying, p. 133 "Fate of the Rain Forest," pp. 6–9; 17–19
Study Guide/Chapter Review pp. 135–137	1 period/ $\frac{1}{2}$ block		ISAB	Provides teaching and review of all inquiry skills

For Standard or Block Schedule The Resource Pro® CD-ROM gives you maximum flexibility for planning your instruction for any type of schedule. Resource Pro® contains Planning Express®, an advanced scheduling program, as well as the entire contents of the Teaching Resources and the Computer Test Bank.

CHAPTER PLANNING GUIDE

Program Resources	Assessment Strategies	Media and Technology
TR Chapter 4 Project Teacher Notes, pp. 84–87 **TR** Chapter 4 Project Overview and Worksheets, pp. 88–89 **TR** Chapter 4 Project Scoring Rubric, p. 90	**SE** Performance Assessment: Chapter 4 Project Wrap Up, p. 137 **TE** Check Your Progress, pp. 117, 128, 134 **TE** Performance Assessment: Chapter 4 Project Wrap Up, p. 137 **TR** Chapter 4 Project Scoring Rubric, p. 90	Science Explorer Internet Site
TR 4-1 Lesson Plan, p. 91 **TR** 4-1 Section Summary, p. 92 **TR** 4-1 Review and Reinforce, p. 93 **TR** 4-1 Enrich, p. 94 **TR** Chapter 4 Skills Lab, pp. 107–109	**SE** Section 1 Review, p. 117 **SE** Analyze and Conclude, p. 119 **TE** Ongoing Assessment, pp. 111, 113, 115 **TE** Performance Assessment, p. 117 **TR** 4-1 Review and Reinforce, p. 93	Audiotapes: English-Spanish Summary 4-1 Transparency 12, "The Plant Cell" Transparency 13, "The Life Cycle of Plants" Interactive Student Tutorial CD-ROM, A-4
TR 4-2 Lesson Plan, p. 95 **TR** 4-2 Section Summary, p. 96 **TR** 4-2 Review and Reinforce, p. 97 **TR** 4-2 Enrich, p. 98 **SES** Book L, *Chemical Interactions,* Chapter 1 **SES** Book O, *Sound and Light,* Chapter 4	**SE** Section 2 Review, p. 124 **TE** Ongoing Assessment, pp. 121, 123 **TE** Performance Assessment, p. 124 **TR** 4-2 Review and Reinforce, p. 97	Exploring Life Science Videodisc, Unit 1 Side 2, "Space Shuttle Air Systems" Audiotapes: English-Spanish Summary 4-2 Transparency 14, "Photosynthesis" Interactive Student Tutorial CD-ROM, A-4
TR 4-3 Lesson Plan, p. 99 **TR** 4-3 Section Summary, p. 100 **TR** 4-3 Review and Reinforce, p. 101 **TR** 4-3 Enrich, p. 102 **TR** Chapter 4 Skills Lab, pp. 110–111 **SES** Book E, *Environmental Science,* Chapter 3	**SE** Section 3 Review, p. 128 **SE** Analyze and Conclude, p. 129 **TE** Ongoing Assessment, p. 127 **TE** Performance Assessment, p. 128 **TR** 4-3 Review and Reinforce, p. 101	Audiotapes: English-Spanish Summary 4-3 Interactive Student Tutorial CD-ROM, A-4
TR 4-4 Lesson Plan, p. 103 **TR** 4-4 Section Summary, p. 104 **TR** 4-4 Review and Reinforce, p. 105 **TR** 4-4 Enrich, p. 106 **SES** Book G, *Earth's Changing Surface,* Chapter 2	**SE** Section 4 Review, p. 134 **TE** Ongoing Assessment, pp. 131, 133 **TE** Performance Assessment, p. 134 **TR** 4-4 Review and Reinforce, p. 105	Audiotapes: English-Spanish Summary 4-4 Interactive Student Tutorial CD-ROM, A-4
TR Chapter 4 Performance Assessment, pp. 177–179 **TR** Chapter 4 Test, pp. 180–183	**SE** Chapter Review, pp. 135–137 **TR** Chapter 4 Performance Assessment, pp. 177–179 **TR** Chapter 4 Test, pp. 180–183 **CTB** Test A-4	Computer Test Bank, Test A-4 Interactive Student Tutorial CD-ROM, A-4

Key: **SE** Student Edition   **TE** Teacher's Edition   **TR** Teaching Resources
      CTB Computer Test Bank   **SES** Science Explorer Series Text   **ISLM** Integrated Science Laboratory Manual
      ISAB Inquiry Skills Activity Book   **PTA** Product Testing Activities by *Consumer Reports*   **IES** Interdisciplinary Explorations Series

Meeting the National Science Education Standards and AAAS Benchmarks

National Science Education Standards	Benchmarks for Science Literacy	Unifying Themes
Science as Inquiry (Content Standard A) ◆ **Design and conduct a scientific investigation** Students design experiments to identify the raw materials and conditions that are involved in photosynthesis. *(Skills Lab: Designing Experiments)* ◆ **Communicate scientific procedures and explanations** Students create a brochure describing how to grow moss. *(Chapter Project)* **Physical Science** (Content Standard B) ◆ **Transfer of energy** Light can pass through objects, be absorbed by objects, or be reflected by objects. The energy from the sun is stored in plants during photosynthesis. *(Section 2; Skills Lab: Designing Experiments)* **Life Science** (Content Standard C) ◆ **Structure and function in living systems** Plants are multicellular and have a variety of structures that carry out life functions. *(Sections 1, 2, 3, 4; Chapter Project; Skills Lab: Designing Experiments; Skills Lab: Observing)* ◆ **Reproduction and heredity** Mosses and ferns have life cycles that include gametophyte and sporophyte stages. *(Sections 3, 4)* ◆ **Diversity and adaptations of organisms** There are many kinds of plant species. Mosses and ferns evolved adaptations that allowed them to survive on land. *(Sections 1, 3, 4; Skills Lab: Observing)*	**1A The Scientific World View** Knowledge about photosynthesis has been repeatedly modified as scientists learned more about the process. *(Section 2)* **1B Scientific Inquiry** Controlling variables and conducting experiments are emphasized as students investigate photosynthesis. *(Skills Lab: Designing Experiments)* **5A Diversity of Life** Plants have a wide array of adaptations. All plants share certain characteristics. *(Sections 1, 3, 4; Chapter Project; Skills Lab: Observing)* **5C Cells** Plant cells contain cell walls and chlorophyll. *(Section 1)* **5E Flow of Matter and Energy** Plants store energy from the sun as carbohydrates. *(Section 2; Skills Lab: Designing Experiments)*	◆ **Energy** Plants use energy from sunlight to make food during photosynthesis. Peat and coal resources formed from the ancient remains of mosses and ferns. *(Sections 2, 3, 4; Skills Lab: Designing Experiments)* ◆ **Evolution** Land plants evolved from green algae. Land plants evolved in ways that made them better suited to life on land. Vascular plants are better suited to drier conditions than are nonvascular plants. *(Section 1)* ◆ **Scale and Structure** Plants are made up of cells that have cell walls and chlorophyll. All plants have adaptations for obtaining and transporting water and other materials, support, and reproduction. *(Sections 1, 3, 4; Chapter Project; Skills Lab: Observing)* ◆ **Unity and Diversity** Although each kind of plant has unique adaptations, all plants share basic characteristics. *(Sections 1, 3, 4; Chapter Project; Skills Lab: Observing; Skills Lab: Designing Experiments)*

Media and Technology

Exploring Life Science Videodisc

◆ **Section 2** "Space Shuttle Air Systems" compares the recycling of oxygen and carbon dioxide on the space shuttle to photosynthesis. Pollution, overpopulation, and deforestation are discussed.

Interactive Student Tutorial CD-ROM

◆ **Chapter Review** Interactive questions help students to self-assess their mastery of key chapter concepts.

Student Edition Connection Strategies

◆ **Section 2** Integrating Physics, p. 120
               Science & History, pp. 122–123
               Integrating Chemistry, p. 123

◆ **Section 3** Social Studies Connection, p. 127
               Integrating Earth Science, p. 127

◆ **Section 4** Integrating Earth Science, p. 131

USING THE INTERNET

www.science-explorer.phschool.com

Visit the Science Explorer Internet site to find an up-to-date activity for Chapter 4 of *From Bacteria to Plants*.

ACTIVITY	Time (minutes)	Materials *Quantities for one work group*	Skills
Section 1			
Discover, p. 110	10	**Consumable** leaf from a jade plant or a plant with thick, fleshy leaves; leaf of a temperate-climate plant, such as a maple, oak, or common garden plant **Nonconsumable** hand lens	Inferring
Sharpen your Skills, p. 113	15	**Consumable** No special materials are required.	Interpreting Data
Skills Lab, pp. 118–119	45	**Consumable** *Elodea* plants, water (boiled, then cooled), sodium bicarbonate solution **Nonconsumable** wide-mouthed container, 2 test tubes, 2 wax pencils, lamp (optional)	Designing Experiments
Section 2			
Discover, p. 120	10	**Consumable** shoe box, glue, white paper **Nonconsumable** hand mirror, prism	Observing
Section 3			
Discover, p. 125	15	**Consumable** 20 mL sand, 20 mL peat moss, water **Nonconsumable** 3 plastic graduated cylinders, dropper, stopwatch	Predicting
Skills Lab, p. 129	45	**Consumable** clump of moss, toothpicks, water **Nonconsumable** metric ruler, plastic dropper, hand lens	Observing
Section 4			
Discover, p. 130	10	**Consumable** water, food coloring **Nonconsumable** goggles, plastic petri dish, narrow glass tube, dropper	Inferring
Try This, p. 132	20	**Consumable** fern plant, water **Nonconsumable** hand lens, plastic dropper	Inferring

A list of all materials required for the Student Edition activities can be found on pages T14–T15. You can order Materials Kits by calling 1-800-828-7777 or by accessing the Science Explorer Internet site at **www.science-explorer.phschool.com.**

Become a Moss Expert

Mosses are so low growing, soft, and velvety that students may not realize they are plants at all. By growing mosses in a terrarium, students will be able to make detailed observations of mosses and learn more about plant structure.

Purpose In this project, students construct a terrarium, observe and record the growth of a moss, and determine the requirements for mosses to grow.

Skills Focus After completing the Chapter 4 Project, students will be able to
- plan and construct a terrarium and provide the necessary conditions for growth;
- observe the response of the moss and determine the growth requirements for mosses;
- communicate their results in a brochure describing how to grow mosses;

Project Time Line The entire project will take three to four weeks. Spend one or two days introducing and planning the project. Students may need a day or two to find and collect mosses for their terrariums. It will take one class period to build and set up the terrariums. Mosses should be observed in the terrariums for two to three weeks. Afterward, a few days will be needed for students to write their brochures and prepare their presentations. Before beginning the project, see Chapter 4 Project Teacher Notes on pages 84–85 in Teaching Resources for more details on carrying out the project. Also distribute to students the Chapter 4 Project Overview and Worksheets and Scoring Rubric on pages 86–90 in Teaching Resources.

Possible Materials
- Provide materials for construction of the terrarium. Each group could use a 2-liter soda bottle, a nail (to punch open a cutting hole), scissors, gravel, sand, soil, and charcoal.
- Have students collect mosses or provide the mosses for them. If students collect the mosses themselves, caution them to make sure to remove

CHAPTER 4 Introduction to Plants

WHAT'S AHEAD

SECTION 1 The Plant Kingdom

Discover **What Do Leaves Reveal About Plants?**
Sharpen Your Skills **Interpreting Data**

Integrating Physics
SECTION 2 Photosynthesis and Light

Skills Lab **Eye on Photosynthesis**
Discover **What Colors Make Up Sunlight?**

SECTION 3 Mosses, Liverworts, and Hornworts

Discover **Will Mosses Absorb Water?**
Skills Lab **Masses of Mosses**

108 ◆ A

the plant carefully, including rhizoids, and to take only a small sample.
- Supply materials for the presentations including poster board, graphing paper, and unlined paper.
- Provide research material for students who wish to include additional information on mosses in their brochures.

Launching the Project Have students discuss where they have seen mosses and brainstorm a list of conditions that are present in all these locations. Once they have identified the

conditions they think are suitable, they can use that information to plan their terrariums.

Allow time for students to read the description of the project in their text and the Chapter Project Overview on pages 86–87 in Teaching Resources. Explain to students that, unlike most plants, mosses do not have vascular tissue. Vascular tissue functions in support and in transport of water. Without it, mosses cannot grow tall and must transport water from cell to cell. Caution students to be careful when using scissors to cut the top off the 2-liter plastic

PROJECT 4

Become a Moss Expert

In a shady valley, mosses cover the banks of a stream. Overhead, trees stretch their branches toward the light. Each type of plant has its own requirements for growth. In this project, you'll care for one type of plant, a moss similar to the ones growing on these rocks. By the time you're finished, you'll be able to tell others what conditions are needed for mosses to grow.

Your Goal To create a brochure titled "How to Raise Mosses" to share with an audience of your choice.

To successfully complete this project you must
◆ grow moss in a terrarium you construct from a 2-liter bottle
◆ observe the moss daily, and keep a log of the amount of light, water, and other conditions you provide for it
◆ publish information about caring for mosses
◆ follow the safety guidelines in Appendix A

Get Started In a small group, create a list of places where you've seen mosses growing. Compare the list your group makes with those from other groups. What are some locations that many groups identified? What do you notice about the environments where mosses are found? List possible ways to create a similar environment in a terrarium. Start to write out a plan for making the terrarium.

Check Your Progress You'll be working on this project as you study this chapter. To keep your project on track, look for Check Your Progress boxes at the following points.
Section 1 Review, page 117: Plan your terrarium.
Section 3 Review, page 128: Provide the proper conditions as you care for your moss.
Section 4 Review, page 134: Plan and produce your brochure.

Wrap Up At the end of the chapter (page 137), you'll share your brochure about mosses with your audience.

Mosses carpet the rocks along this stream in Pennsylvania's Pocono Mountains.

SECTION 4 Ferns and Their Relatives
Discover How Quickly Can Water Move Upward?
Try This Examining a Fern

Program Resources

◆ **Teaching Resources** Chapter 4 Project Teacher Notes, pp. 84–85; Chapter 4 Project Overview and Worksheets, pp. 86–89; Chapter 4 Project Scoring Rubric, p. 90

bottle. Address any initial questions students may have. Pass out copies of the Chapter 4 Project Worksheets on pages 88–89 in Teaching Resources for students to review.

You can have students work in small groups as a cooperative learning task. To ensure that every student will have ample opportunity to participate in terrarium construction, data recording, and brochure preparation, each group should consist of no more than four students.

Performance Assessment

The Chapter 4 Project Scoring Rubric on page 90 of Teaching Resources will help you evaluate how well students complete the Chapter 4 Project. Students will be assessed on
◆ how well they construct their terrarium, and the clarity of their procedure;
◆ the completeness of their daily observations and how well they follow their procedure;
◆ the quality of their brochure and presentation;
◆ their group participation (optional).
By sharing the Chapter 4 Scoring Rubric with students at the beginning of the project, you will make it clear to them what they are expected to do.

Objectives

After completing the lesson, students will be able to
- ◆ identify the characteristics that all plants share;
- ◆ name all the things that plants need to live successfully and describe the plant life cycle.

Key Terms photosynthesis, cell wall, cellulose, chloroplast, vacuole, tissue, chlorophyll, cuticle, vascular tissue, fertilization, zygote, sporophyte, gametophyte, gamete

1 Engage/Explore

Activating Prior Knowledge

Show students a potted plant and ask them to name two ways that it is different from an animal. *(Sample: It cannot make noise and does not walk around.)*

‥‥‥‥ DISCOVER ‥‥‥‥

Skills Focus inferring
Materials *hand lens, leaf from a jade plant or a plant with thick, fleshy leaves; leaf of a temperate-climate plant, such as a maple, oak, or common garden plant*
Time 10 minutes
Tips Select leaves that display adaptations easily associated with protection from bright sun and dry weather. Both leaves should be green in color.
Expected Outcome Students should observe a difference in leaf thickness, texture, and size.
Think It Over Students should infer that the plant with the small, thick, fleshy leaf lives in the desert, and that the plant with the larger, thinner, more delicate leaf lives in an area of average rainfall. Students will probably say that the thick leaf looks like it has water in it.

SECTION
① The Plant Kingdom

DISCOVER ‥‥‥‥‥‥‥‥‥‥‥‥‥‥‥‥‥‥ ACTIVITY

What Do Leaves Reveal About Plants?

1. Your teacher will give you two leaves from plants that grow in two very different environments: a desert and an area with average rainfall.

2. Carefully observe the color, size, shape, and texture of the leaves. Touch the surfaces of each leaf. Examine each leaf with a hand lens. Record your observations in your notebook.

3. When you have finished, wash your hands thoroughly with soap and water.

Think It Over
Inferring Use your observations to determine which plant lives in the desert and which does not. Give at least one reason to support your inference.

GUIDE FOR READING

- ◆ What characteristics do all plants share?
- ◆ What do plants need to live successfully on land?

Reading Tip Before you read, list the boldfaced vocabulary words in your notebook. Leave space to add notes as you read.

Imagine a forest where a thick growth of fungi, mosses, and ferns carpets the floor. Because there is no bare soil, seedlings start their lives on fallen logs. Ferns hang like curtains from the limbs of giant hemlock trees. Douglas fir trees grow taller than 20-story buildings. Other plants with strange names—scouler willow, vanilla leaf, self-heal, and licorice fern—also grow in the forest.

Such a forest exists on the western slopes of the Olympic Mountains in Washington State. Native Americans named the forest *Hoh*, which means "fast white water," after a river there. In some areas of the forest, over 300 centimeters of rain fall each year, which makes the area a rain forest. But unlike rain forests in the tropics, the most common trees in the Hoh rain forest are maples, spruces, red cedars, and firs.

▼ The Hoh rain forest

110 ◆ A

READING STRATEGIES

Reading Tip Before students read the section, direct them to discuss what they already know about each boldfaced vocabulary word.

Study and Comprehension Instruct students to use the main headings and subheadings in the section to create an outline that shows main points and key details. Write a beginning outline, such as the one shown below, as a guide for students.

I. Plants Share Two Main Characteristics.
  A. They are autotrophs that use photosynthesis to make food.
  B. They are eukaryotes that contain many cells.
    1. The cells are enclosed by a cell wall.
    2. The cell wall is made of cellulose.

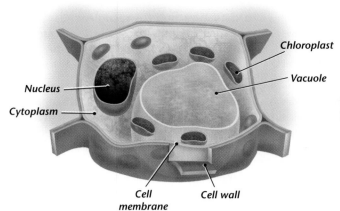

Nucleus

Cytoplasm

Chloroplast

Vacuole

Cell membrane

Cell wall

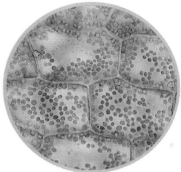

Figure 1 Plants have eukaryotic cells that are enclosed by a cell wall. *Interpreting Photographs Which plant cell structures can you find in the photograph on the right? What roles do these structures play?*

What Is a Plant?

You would probably recognize many of the plants that grow in the Hoh rain forest. You encounter other familiar plants when you pick flowers, run across freshly cut grass, or eat vegetables such as carrots. Members of the plant kingdom share some important characteristics. **Plants are autotrophs that produce their own food. In addition, all plants are eukaryotes that contain many cells.**

Plants Are Autotrophs You can think of a plant as a sun-powered, food-making factory. The process by which plants make food is called **photosynthesis** (foh toh SIN thuh sis). The word *photosynthesis* comes from two Greek words. *Photo* means "light," and *synthesis* means "to make." During photosynthesis, a plant uses carbon dioxide gas and water to make food and oxygen. The process occurs in a series of complex chemical reactions. Sunlight provides the energy that powers the entire process. You will learn more about the process of photosynthesis in the next section.

Plant Cells If you were to look at a plant's cells under a microscope, you would see that plants are eukaryotes. But unlike the cells of some other eukaryotes, a plant's cells are enclosed by a cell wall. The **cell wall** is a boundary that surrounds the cell membrane and separates the cell from the environment. Plant cell walls are made mostly of **cellulose** (SEL yuh lohs), a chemical that makes the walls rigid. Because of the rigid cell walls, plant cells look something like boxes, as Figure 1 shows.

Plant cells also contain many structures called chloroplasts. **Chloroplasts** (KLAWR uh plasts), which look similar to green jelly beans, are the structures in which food is made. The Greek word *chloro* means "green."

Program Resources

◆ **Teaching Resources** 4-1 Lesson Plan, p. 91; 4-1 Section Summary, p. 92

Media and Technology

 Audiotapes English-Spanish Summary 4-1

Answers to Self-Assessment

Caption Question

Figure 1 The cell wall, chloroplasts, and vacuoles. The cell wall separates the cell from its environment. Chloroplasts make food. Vacuoles store food, water, and wastes.

2 Facilitate

What Is a Plant?

Including All Students

Give students who need extra help time to review terms such as *autotroph, eukaryote, photosynthesis, cellulose,* and *chloroplast.* Suggest students create a glossary of words that includes the phonetic English pronunciation and the definition in English. Encourage students to use clues to unlock the meaning of the terms. For example, the term *autotroph* can be broken down into *auto,* which means "from the self," and *troph,* which means "nutrition." **limited English proficiency**

Building Inquiry Skills: Observing

Materials *onion, tweezers, slide, slide cover, light microscope, water, iodine, toothpick*
Time 20 minutes

 Allow students to prepare a wet mount of a very thin piece of onion skin. Using tweezers will allow students to pull off a thin piece of onion. Students should add a drop of iodine to the onion using the tip of a toothpick, then place the cover slip on top. Students should begin at low power, and then switch to high power. Have students sketch and label what they see. Challenge them to point out the cell wall and vacuole. Ask: **Did you see any chloroplasts? How do you know?** (*No, chloroplasts would be green, and there were no green structures.*) **learning modality: visual**

Ongoing Assessment

Drawing Have students make diagrams of a plant cell and label the cell wall, chloroplasts, and vacuoles. Students can save their diagrams in their portfolios.

What Is a Plant?, continued

Addressing Naive Conceptions

Materials *leaves, stems, roots, flowers, other plant parts*

Time 10 minutes

Students may have the notion that a leaf, a root, or some other plant part is a separate plant tissue. Distribute the materials and allow students to examine them with a hand lens or low-power microscope. Ask them to predict how many separate tissues are in a leaf. *(At least four or five)* CAUTION: *Some students may be allergic to certain plants. Allow these students to observe from a safe distance.* **learning modality: kinesthetic**

Origin of Plants

Building Inquiry Skills: Comparing and Contrasting

Materials *microscope, samples of green algae, plant leaves, prepared slides of leaf cross sections, glass slides, tweezers, water, cover slips, dropper*

Time 30 minutes

Allow students to work in groups to compare samples of green algae to a green houseplant. Have students describe similarities and differences between them. Place a drop of water containing algae on a glass slide, and cover with a cover slip. Students should look at the algae slides and plant cross sections under the microscope and compare the cells. Ask students: **What evidence did you see to support the idea that plants are descended from green algae?** *(Answers will vary. Students may say that both types of cells contain chlorophyll.)* Encourage students to speculate on how scientists determined that the chlorophyll is the same. *(Sample: They performed tests to find the chemical structure.)* **learning modality: visual**

Plant cells also contain vacuoles. A **vacuole** is a large, sack-like storage area. The vacuole stores many substances, including water, wastes, and food. A vacuole expands like a balloon when water enters it and shrinks when water leaves it. If too much water leaves a plant's vacuoles, the plant wilts.

Plants Are Multicellular You don't need a microscope to see plants because they are multicellular. Plants do vary greatly in size, however. For example, mosses are among the smallest plants—many are only a few millimeters tall. But some redwood trees can grow over 80 meters tall.

No matter how large or small a plant is, its cells are organized into **tissues**—groups of similar cells that perform a specific function in an organism. For example, most plants that live on land have tissues that transport materials throughout their bodies. You will learn about some important plant tissues later in this chapter.

☑ *Checkpoint* **What is the function of the vacuole in a plant cell?**

Origin of Plants

Which organisms were the ancestors of today's plants? To answer this question, biologists study fossils, the traces of ancient life forms preserved in rock and other substances. The oldest plant fossils are about 400 million years old. These fossils show that early plants resembled small algae.

Other clues to the origin of plants come from analyzing the chemical makeup of plants. In particular, biologists study a green pigment called **chlorophyll** (KLAWR uh fil), which is found in the chloroplasts of plants as well as in algae and some bacteria. Like ice cream, chlorophyll comes in different "flavors," or forms, that have slightly different chemical structures. Scientists have found that plants and green algae contain the same form of chlorophyll. For this reason, biologists infer that ancient green algae were the ancestors of today's plants.

Figure 2 These fossils are from two plants that lived about 300 million years ago. The larger fossil is of a fern's leaf. The small star-shaped fossil is of a plant called a horsetail. *Inferring What organisms do scientists think gave rise to today's plants?*

Background

History of Science The scientist Robert Hooke (1635–1703) first observed cells by looking at plant parts. In 1665, Hooke published a book called *Microphagia,* which reported the research he performed using a compound microscope that he perfected. He described a thin section of cork as "perforated and porous." What Hooke then called "cells" were actually the cell walls left behind in dead cork tissue. Hooke later turned his microscope on samples of petrified wood.

Comparisons of fossilized wood with living wood samples helped lead Hooke to the conclusion that fossils were the remnants of extinct plants and animals. In addition to his contributions in biology, Hooke studied physics, geology, and chemistry. As an important individual in the seventeenth-century scientific community, Hooke collaborated with many great thinkers of his time, including Anton van Leeuwenhoek, Robert Boyle, and Isaac Newton.

Figure 3 Plants have adaptations that help them retain water. The shiny, waterproof cuticle on this leaf slows down evaporation.

Living on Land

Unlike algae, most plants live on land. How is living on land different from living in water? Imagine multicellular green algae floating in the ocean. Their bodies are held up toward the sunlight by the water around them. The algae obtain water and other materials directly from their watery surroundings. When algae reproduce, sperm cells swim to egg cells through the water.

Now imagine the same green algae living on land. Would the algae be able to stand upright? Could they absorb water and other materials from their surroundings? Could their sperm cells swim to egg cells? The answer to all of these questions is no. **For plants to survive on land, they must have ways to obtain water and other materials from their surroundings, retain water, transport materials throughout the plant, support their bodies, and reproduce successfully.** In *Exploring Plant Adaptations* on the next page, you can see some of the ways in which plants are adapted to live on land.

Obtaining Water and Other Materials Recall that all organisms need water to survive. Obtaining water is easy for algae because water surrounds them. To live on land, though, plants need adaptations for obtaining water from the soil. Plants must also have ways of obtaining other nutrients from the soil.

Retaining Water Have you ever noticed that a puddle of rainwater gradually shrinks and then disappears after the rain stops? This happens because there is more water in the puddle than in the air. As a result, the water evaporates into the air. The same principle explains why a plant on land can dry out. Because there is more water in plant cells than in air, water evaporates into the air. Plants need adaptations to reduce water loss to the air. One common adaptation is a waxy, waterproof layer called the **cuticle** that covers the leaves of most plants.

Sharpen your Skills

Interpreting Data

ACTIVITY

The table shows how much water a certain plant loses during the hours listed.

Time	Water Loss (grams)
7 to 8 AM	190
9 to 10 AM	209
11 to Noon	221
1 to 2 PM	233
3 to 4 PM	227
5 to 6 PM	213
7 to 8 PM	190
9 to 10 PM	100
11 to Midnight	90

When does the plant lose the most water? The least water? How could you account for the pattern you see?

Living on Land

Building Inquiry Skills: Inferring

Materials *2 cut flowers, 2 vases, water*

ACTIVITY

Time 15 minutes

Place one cut flower in a vase of water and a second cut flower in an empty vase. Ask students to predict what will happen overnight. The next day, ask: **How do the flowers differ?** *(The flower in the empty vase has withered. The flower in the water is still alive.)* Then ask students to infer how flowers obtain water and compare it to the way algae obtain water. *(The water moves through the stem to the flower. Algae are completely surrounded by water, so they obtain water directly.)* **learning modality: visual**

Sharpen your Skills

Interpreting Data

Time 15 minutes

ACTIVITY

Have students compare the water lost in each time interval. Make sure students understand that the numbers in the right column do not represent the mass of the plant. Ask: **What measurements are used to find these numbers?** *(The mass of the plant is measured every hour, then the mass is subtracted from the measurement made an hour before.)* The plant loses the most water from 1 to 2 P.M. and the least water from 11 P.M. to midnight. The plant loses the most water during the hottest part of the day.

Extend Suggest students graph the data in the table and predict how the line graph would change if the data were collected during a hot summer day or during a cold, rainy day. **learning modality: logical/mathematical**

Answers to Self-Assessment

Caption Question

Figure 2 Scientists think ancient green algae gave rise to today's plants.

✓ *Checkpoint*

A vacuole stores substances in a cell.

Ongoing Assessment

Organizing Information Have students create Venn diagrams that show the similarities and differences between green algae and modern plants.

EXPLORING
Plant Adaptations

After students examine the visual essay, ask them to infer the answers to the following questions:

◆ **Considering that the Venus fly trap catches and digests insects, why do you think scientists classify it as a plant?** *(Sample: Although it gets nitrogen from insects, its leaves perform photosynthesis to make food.)*

◆ **How could water lilies be used to judge whether excess salt water was migrating into a freshwater coastal marsh?** *(Sample: Water lilies only live in fresh water; if the water becomes too salty, they will die.)*

◆ **What is the long-term effect of mangrove roots trapping soil and sand?** *(Sample: The island or beach gradually increases in size.)* **learning modality: visual**

Building Inquiry Skills: Observing

Materials *notebook, pencil*
Time 25 minutes

ACTIVITY

Invite students to explore the diversity of plants in your area. Take students on a walk around the school and have them record descriptions of ten different plants that they see. Each description should include the place where they found the plant, the plant's estimated size, any distinguishing characteristics, and a sketch or photograph of the plant. Make sure students describe at least one adaptation the helps the plant to live in its environment. **learning modality: visual**

EXPLORING *Plant Adaptations*

Today, plants are found in almost every environment on Earth—deserts, lakes, jungles, and even the polar regions. As you read about each plant, notice how it is adapted to living in its specific environment.

◄ **Pasque Flower**
Pasque flowers, such as this *Anemone patens,* often grow on cold, rocky mountain slopes. The flower's petals trap sunlight, keeping the flower up to 10° C warmer than the surrounding air. This feature enables the plant to survive in cold environments.

Staghorn Fern ►
Staghorn ferns do not grow in soil. Instead, they cling to the bark of trees in tropical areas. The leaves that hug the bark store water and nutrients. The leaves that hang down are involved in reproduction.

▲ **Bristlecone Pine**
Because the needles of bristlecone pines live more than 15 years, the trees survive long periods of drought. Bristlecone pine trees can live more than 4,000 years. This is because they grow slowly in high altitude areas where there are few harmful insects or other disease-causing organisims.

◄ **Water Lily**
Water lilies live only in fresh water. Large, flat leaves and sweet-smelling flowers float on the water's surface. The plants have long stems under the water. Roots anchor the plant in the mud at the bottom of the pond.

Background

Facts and Figures Humans use a wide variety of plants to treat pain and disease. These plants are often helpful if used in small amounts or special preparations, but can be deadly or dangerous if used otherwise. The opium poppy is used to make morphine and codeine, which physicians use to treat pain. However, the illegal drug heroin can also be derived from the plant. Similarly, the leaves of the coca plant contain small amounts of cocaine. They have been used as a painkiller for thousands of years. However, in larger doses, cocaine is dangerously addictive. The foxglove plant produces digitalis. In small doses, digitalis is a useful treatment for heart conditions, but in large doses it can be fatal. A plant called belladonna, or deadly nightshade, is lethal when swallowed, but is also the source of atropine, used to dilate the eyes in eye examinations.

Rafflesia ▶
The rafflesia plant produces the largest flowers on Earth. This flower that grew in Borneo measures over 83 centimeters in diameter. Rafflesia flowers have a foul odor—something like rotting meat. The odor attracts insects that help the plant reproduce.

▲ Mangrove
Mangrove trees, such as these on Guadalcanal Island in the Pacific Ocean, grow in salt water in tropical areas. The tree's huge root system makes the tree appear as if it is on stilts. The roots trap soil and sand around them, providing a material in which to anchor as they grow.

◀ Date Palm
Date palms, such as these growing on a date farm in southern California, grow in warm climates. These flowering trees can grow up to 23 meters tall. The leaves are long and narrow, reducing the amount of surface area for evaporation. The female trees produce dates that hang from the stems in large clusters.

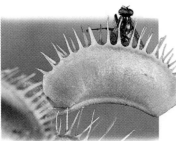

◀ Venus Fly Trap
The Venus fly trap can grow in soil that is low in nitrogen. This is because the plant obtains its nitrogen by digesting insects that it traps. When an insect touches sensitive hairs on the inner surface of a leaf, the two parts of the leaf quickly snap shut. It takes about ten days for the plant to digest an insect.

Chapter 4 **A ◆ 115**

Cultural Diversity

Every culture relies on plants as a resource for food, construction materials, medicines, clothing, and decoration. Date palms are very important in North Africa and the Middle East, where the dates are used for food and the leaves and stalks are woven into baskets, furniture, rugs, and rope. Mangrove trees are used for their wood and sweet fruit, as well as for an astringent tanning solution produced by the bark. Assign students a country or region to investigate. Students should prepare a display showing the kinds of plants that grow in that region and how the plants are used by native populations. Some areas to assign include the Philippine Islands, the Amazon River basin, Kenya, Puerto Rico, and Thailand. **learning modality: verbal**

Building Inquiry Skills: Observing

Suggest students make detailed observations of a common indoor houseplant, such as a rubber plant (*Ficus elastica*). They should describe what adaptations make it a desirable indoor plant. (*Tolerant of low light levels*) Then have them find out the plant's natural environment. (*Tropical forests*) Ask: **How would the feature that makes this plant a desirable houseplant help it in its natural environment?** (*In the plant's natural environment, tolerance of low light levels allowed it to thrive in the limited light beneath the forest canopy.*)
learning modality: visual

Ongoing Assessment

Oral Presentation Ask students to describe a plant they know or one from Exploring Plant Adaptations and tell about one adaptation that helps the plant survive in its environment. (*Sample: Petals of the Pasque flower help the flower stay warm in a cold environment. Date palms have long, narrow leaves that reduce water loss in a hot environment.*)

Living on Land, continued

Demonstration

Materials *clear vase, blue food coloring, white carnation*

Time 10 minutes for setup and observation, 24 hours waiting time

Help students see how a plant's vascular system works. Fill the vase with water and 10 drops of the food coloring. Cut the stem of the carnation. Place the carnation in the vase. Then ask students to predict what will happen if the carnation sits overnight. The next day, have students describe the carnation. (*It has blue streaks on the leaves.*) Allow them to examine the flower closely. They should notice thin veins of color in the petals. Ask: **How did the color move up the flower?** (*Through the tubes of the vascular system*) **learning modality: visual**

Building Inquiry Skills: Observing

Materials *hand lens, celery leaf stalk, dissecting knife*

Time 20 minutes

Explain to students that they will analyze the transport and support systems in a celery leaf stalk. Give each student a celery leaf stalk to examine. Students should cut the base of the stalk cleanly with a knife. CAUTION: *Knives are sharp and should be handled with care.* Students can then look at different parts of the stalk using a hand lens. Allow them to pull off strands of the stalk or cut the stalk lengthwise to make observations. Ask: **What is the function of the long fibers in a celery stalk?** (*The stalk is made up of long, narrow tubes or fibers that are bundled together. These carry materials and provide support.*)
learning modality: visual

Figure 4 The vascular tissue in these tree ferns transports water and nutrients inside the plants. Vascular tissue also strengthens and supports the plants' stems and leaves.

Transporting Materials A plant needs to transport food, water, minerals, and other materials from one part of its body to another. In general, water and minerals are taken up by the bottom part of the plant. Food is made in the top part. But all the plant's cells need water, minerals, and food. To supply all cells with the materials they need, water and minerals must be transported up to the top of the plant. Then food must be transported throughout the plant.

Some plants have transporting tissue called **vascular tissue.** Vascular tissue is an internal system of tubelike structures through which water and food move inside the plant. Plants that have vascular tissue are called vascular plants. Vascular plants can grow quite tall because they have an effective way of transporting substances to distant cells.

Support While algae are supported by the surrounding water, a plant on land must support its own body. Because plants need sunlight for photosynthesis, the food-making parts of the plant must be exposed to as much sunlight as possible. In vascular plants, vascular tissue strengthens and supports the large bodies of the plants.

Reproduction All plants undergo sexual reproduction that involves fertilization. **Fertilization** occurs when a sperm cell unites with an egg cell. The fertilized egg is called a **zygote.** For algae and some plants, fertilization can only occur if there is water in the environment. This is because sperm cells swim through the water to egg cells. Other plants, however, have an adaptation that make it possible for fertilization to occur in dry environments. You will learn more about this adaptation in the next chapter.

✓ *Checkpoint* *Why do plants need adaptations to prevent water loss?*

Background

Facts and Figures Certain plant species have remarkable growth rates or growth patterns. The average plant grows about 1 centimeter per day. Some plants, however, grow much faster. For example, the titan arum has a flowering structure that may grow as much as 10 centimeters per day. In the spring, some bamboo shoots can grow as fast as 0.3 meters per day.

While many plants live for a year or two, others continue living and growing for much longer. A bristlecone pine tree in California is estimated to be over 4,600 years old—and it is still alive!

California also has the tallest and biggest trees in the world. Some coast redwoods are up to 112 meters tall, but the biggest living plant on Earth is a giant sequoia that is 83 meters tall with a trunk that is 31 meters in circumference at its base.

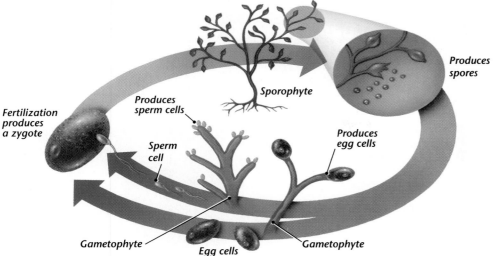

Produces
spores

Sporophyte

Produces
sperm cells

Fertilization
produces
a zygote

Produces
egg cells

Sperm
cell

Gametophyte

Egg cells

Gametophyte

Complex Life Cycles

Unlike most animals, plants have complex life cycles that are made up of two different stages, or generations. In one stage, called the **sporophyte** (SPAWR uh fyt), the plant produces spores, the tiny cells that can grow into new organisms. A spore develops into the plant's other stage, called the gametophyte. In the **gametophyte** (guh MEE tuh fyt) stage, the plant produces two kinds of sex cells, or **gametes**—sperm cells and egg cells.

Figure 5 shows a typical plant life cycle. A sperm cell and egg cell join to form a zygote. The zygote then develops into a sporophyte. The sporophyte produces spores, which develop into the gameophyte. Then the gameophyte produces sperm cells and egg cells and the cycle starts again. The sporophyte of a plant usually looks quite different than the gametophyte.

Figure 5 Plants have complex life cycles that consist of two stages—the sporophyte stage and the gametophyte stage. *Interpreting Diagrams During which stage are sperm and egg cells produced?*

Section 1 Review

1. List three characteristics that all plants share.
2. What are five adaptations that plants need to survive on land?
3. What evidence led scientists to think that green algae were the ancestors of plants?
4. **Thinking Critically** **Classifying** Suppose you found a tall plant living in the desert. Do you think it would be a vascular plant? Explain.

> **Check Your Progress**   CHAPTER PROJECT 4
> At this point, your plan for creating a terrarium should be complete. On a sheet of paper, list the conditions that will affect moss growth. Explain how you'll provide those conditions in your terrarium. (*Hint:* Use a sketch to show what your bottle terrarium will look like.)

Chapter 4 **A ◆ 117**

Program Resources

◆ **Teaching Resources** 4-1 Review and Reinforce, p. 93; 4-1 Enrich, p. 94

Media and Technology

 Transparencies "The Life Cycle of Plants," Transparency 13

Answers to Self-Assessment

Caption Question
Figure 5 Sperm and egg cells are produced during the gametophyte stage.

☑ *Checkpoint*
Plants need adaptations to prevent water loss because every cell of a plant needs water to live.

Complex Life Cycles

Using the Visuals: Figure 5
Point out that plants have both a sexual and an asexual phase in their life cycles. Ask students: **Which stage involves asexual reproduction? How can you tell?** (*The sporophyte stage; the plant produces spores that develop into new organisms.*) Ask: **Which stage involves sexual reproduction?** (*Gametophyte, when sperm cells and egg cells are produced*) **learning modality: logical/mathematical**

3 Assess

Section 1 Review Answers
1. All plants are multicellular, autotrophic eukaryotes.
2. To survive on land, plants must be able to obtain water and other materials from their environment, retain moisture, support their bodies, transport materials throughout their bodies, and reproduce.
3. Scientists think that green algae were the ancestors of plants because both algae and plants contain the same form of chlorophyll.
4. Yes. Due to the scarcity of water in the desert, a tall plant living in the desert must have vascular tissue to supply its cells with water.

> **Check Your Progress**   CHAPTER PROJECT 4
> As you check students' plans, make sure the sketches of the terrariums show details of their construction. Students' plans should indicate how much water will be given and the location of the terrarium to meet their temperature and light requirements. Students should realize that they do not need to add food to the terrarium because mosses make their own food.

Performance Assessment

Writing Have students write paragraphs identifying several ways that an oak tree is adapted to live on land.

Designing Experiments

Eye on Photosynthesis

Preparing for Inquiry

Key Concept Plants require several factors to be present before they can perform photosynthesis.

Skills Objective Students will be able to
◆ design experiments to investigate what substances and conditions are necessary for photosynthesis;
◆ perform tests on several variables;
◆ analyze the results of their tests and draw conclusions.

Time 45 minutes

Advance Planning Obtain *Elodea* plants. Prepare the sodium bicarbonate solution by using 0.5 g of sodium bicarbonate for each 100 mL of water. Boil water for Part 2 and let it cool.

Alternative Materials If *Elodea* plants are not available, you may be able to find appropriate small water plants at a tropical fish supply fish store.

Guiding Inquiry

Invitation Ask students to describe what might happen to a plant to make it turn brown instead of green. *(Sample: Too much sun, not enough water, disease, change of seasons, poor soil)* Then have them describe the things plants need in order to be green and healthy.

Introducing the Procedure
◆ Have students use water to perfect their techniques of immersing a filled test tube before they use the sodium bicarbonate solution or boiled water.
◆ As students read through Steps 3 and 4, make sure they refer to the photograph on page 118.

Troubleshooting the Experiment
◆ Make sure students do not grip the test tubes too tightly. Remind students to inform you of any breakage immediately.
◆ Tell students not to expect dramatic results. Have them look for small bubbles of oxygen.
◆ Remind students to move on to the next procedure while they are waiting for results.

Designing Experiments

Eye on Photosynthesis

In this lab, you'll design an experiment to investigate what substances and conditions are needed for photosynthesis.

Problem

What raw materials and conditions are involved in photosynthesis?

Materials

Elodea plants	2 test tubes
water (boiled, then cooled)	2 wax pencils
wide-mouthed container	lamp (optional)
sodium bicarbonate solution	

Procedure

Part 1 Observing Photosynthesis

1. Use a wax pencil to label two test tubes *1* and *2*. Fill test tube 1 with sodium bicarbonate solution, which provides a source of carbon dioxide.
2. Fill the container about three-fourths full of sodium bicarbonate solution.
3. Hold your thumb over the mouth of test tube 1. Turn the test tube over, and lower the tube to the bottom of the container. Do not let in any air. If necessary, repeat this step so that test tube 1 contains no air pockets.
   CAUTION: *Glass test tubes are fragile. Handle the test tubes carefully. Do not touch broken glass.*
4. Fill test tube 2 with sodium bicarbonate solution. Place an *Elodea* plant in the tube with the cut stem at the bottom. Put your thumb over the mouth of the test tube, and lower it into the container without letting in any air. Wash your hands.

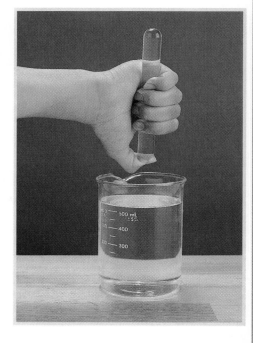

5. Place the container with the two test tubes in bright light. After a few minutes, examine both test tubes for bubbles.
6. If bubbles form in test tube 2, observe the *Elodea* stem to see if it is producing the bubbles. The bubbles are oxygen bubbles. The production of oxygen signals that photosynthesis is taking place.
7. Leave the setup in bright light for thirty minutes. Observe what happens to any bubbles that form. Record your observations.

Expected Outcome

Students should observe tiny bubbles forming along the stems or leaves of the plant in Part 1. These bubbles will grow larger with time. If no bubbles are present, review the variables and make a fresh cut in the *Elodea* stem. Make sure all variables, such as sunlight, are at their maximum.

Observations will support or reject students' hypotheses on whether a particular variable is important in photosynthesis.

Analyze and Conclude

1. photosynthesis
2. It was a control, to show whether the bubbles were really related to the plant.
3. Yes. Students' answers should reveal that no bubbles were formed when the plant was not exposed to a source of carbon dioxide.
4. Answers will depend on students' procedures, but students should realize that the most important factors for photosynthesis are light and the presence of CO_2.

Part 2 Is Carbon Dioxide Needed for Photosynthesis?

8. Your teacher will provide a supply of water that has been boiled and then cooled. Boiling drives off gases that are dissolved in the water, including carbon dioxide.

9. Based on what you learned in Part 1, design an experiment to show whether or not carbon dioxide is needed for photosynthesis. Obtain your teacher's approval before carrying out your experiment. Record all your observations.

Part 3 What Other Conditions Are Needed for Photosynthesis?

10. Make a list of other factors that may affect photosynthesis. For example, think about conditions such as light, the size of the plant, and the number of leaves.

11. Choose one factor from your list. Then design an experiment to show how the factor affects photosynthesis. Obtain your teacher's approval before carrying out your experiment. Record all your observations.

Analyze and Conclude

1. What process produced the bubbles you observed in Part 1?
2. In Part 1, what was the purpose of test tube 1?
3. Based on your results in Part 2, is carbon dioxide necessary for photosynthesis?
4. Explain what you learned about photosynthesis from the investigation you did in Part 3.
5. **Think About It** For the experiments you carried out in Parts 2 and 3, identify the manipulated variable and the responding variable. Explain whether or not your experiments were controlled experiments.

More to Explore

A small animal in a closed container will die, even if it has enough water and food. A small animal in a closed container with a plant, water, and food will not die. Use what you have learned from this experiment to explain those facts.

5. Sample answer: The manipulated variable was the presence or absence of sunlight. The responding variable was the production of oxygen. My experiment was controlled because I kept all other variables the same for both test tubes.

Extending the Inquiry

More to Explore Sample experiment: Place a candle securely in each of two identical jars. Place a small green plant in one jar. Light both candles and close the jars tightly. The candle in the jar without the plant will stop burning, but the other candle will continue to burn. Because candles need oxygen to burn, students will know that the oxygen being used in the first container is not being replaced. They should infer that the plant is producing oxygen.

Safety

Caution students to be careful with the glass test tube and container. Remind them to wash their hands thoroughly after the lab. Review the safety guidelines in Appendix A.

Program Resources

◆ **Teaching Resources** Chapter 4 Skills Lab, pp. 107–109
◆ **Inquiry Skills Activity Book** Provides teaching and review of all inquiry skills

SECTION 2 Photosynthesis and Light

Objectives

After completing the lesson, students will be able to
◆ explain what happens when light strikes a green leaf;
◆ describe the overall process of photosynthesis.

Key Term accessory pigment

1 Engage/Explore

Activating Prior Knowledge

Ask students to describe how colored lights affect the appearance of objects. Encourage students to think about neon lights, holiday lights, and even the difference between artificial lighting at night and natural daylight. *(Students should recognize that colors appear different under different lights.)*

········ **DISCOVER** ········

Skills Focus observing
Materials *shoebox, glue, white paper, hand mirror, prism*
Time 10 minutes
Tips If a sunny window or bright outside area is not available, students can use bright, narrow-beam flashlights to complete this activity. You may wish to demonstrate how to hold the prism so that it projects a rainbow.
Expected Outcome When students reflect sunlight into the shoebox with a mirror, they should see white light on the paper in the shape of the mirror. When the light passes through the prism, they should see a rainbow on the paper.
Think It Over White light is made up of different colors.
Extend Challenge students to use different colors of paper inside the shoebox and describe what they see.

SECTION 2 Photosynthesis and Light

DISCOVER ························· **ACTIVITY**

What Colors Make Up Sunlight?

1. Glue a piece of white paper onto the inside bottom of a shoebox.
2. Place the box on its side near a window or outside in a sunny area.
3. 🖐 Hold a mirror in front of the open side of the box. Adjust the mirror until it reflects sunlight onto the paper in the box. **CAUTION:** *Do not direct the sunlight into your eyes.*

4. Hold a prism between the mirror and the box as shown in the photo. Adjust the location of the prism so that sunlight passes through the prism.
5. Describe what you see on the paper in the box.

Think It Over
Observing What did you learn about light by carrying out this investigation?

GUIDE FOR READING

◆ **What happens when light strikes a green leaf?**

◆ **How do scientists describe the overall process of photosynthesis?**

Reading Tip As you read, make a list of the main ideas and the supporting details about photosynthesis.

The year was 1883. T. W. Engelmann, a German biologist, was at work in his laboratory. He peered into the microscope at some strands of algae on a slide. The microscope had a prism located between the light source and the algae. As Engelmann watched the algae, he saw gas bubbles forming in the water around some of the cells. Curiously, no gas bubbles formed around other cells. Although Engelmann did not know it at the time, his experiment provided a clue about how light is involved in photosynthesis. To understand what Engelmann observed, you need to know more about the nature of light.

The Nature of Light

The sun is the source of energy on Earth. If you take a walk outside on a sunny day, you feel the sun's energy as the sun heats your skin. You see the energy in the form of light on objects around you. The light that you see is called white light. But when white light passes through a prism, you can see that it is made up of the colors of the rainbow—red, orange, yellow, green, blue, and violet. Scientists refer to these colors as the visible spectrum.

Figure 6 When sunlight passes through a prism, it separates into its parts—the colors of the rainbow.

120 ◆ A

READING STRATEGIES

Reading Tip Remind students of these points as they read:
◆ Main ideas are the most important points in the paragraphs.
◆ Main ideas can often be found in section headings.
◆ A main idea is often stated in the first sentence of a paragraph.
◆ Supporting details include facts and examples.

Study and Comprehension Students can work with partners to create flowcharts that outline the stages of photosynthesis. A partial flowchart is shown.

Sunlight strikes plant leaves.
↓
Chlorophyll and accessory pigments absorb light energy.
↓
Energy is used to make sugar and oxygen from carbon dioxide and water.

In addition to prisms, white light strikes many other objects. Some objects such as glass and other transparent materials transmit light, or allow the light to pass through. Shiny surfaces such as mirrors reflect, or bounce back, light. Dark objects such as street pavements absorb, or take in and hold, light.

Most objects, however, reflect some colors of the visible spectrum while they absorb other colors. For example, when white light strikes a red shirt, the shirt absorbs most of the light's colors. However, the shirt reflects red light. The shirt looks red because your eyes see the reflected color.

☑ *Checkpoint* *What are the colors of the visible spectrum?*

Plants and Light

Like red shirts and most other objects around you, plants absorb some colors of the visible spectrum and reflect others. **When light strikes the green leaves of a plant, most of the green part of the spectrum is reflected. Most of the other colors of light are absorbed.**

Plant Pigments When light strikes a leaf, it is absorbed by pigments found in the chloroplasts of the cells. Chlorophyll, the most abundant pigment in plants, absorbs most of the blue and red light. Green light, on the other hand, is reflected rather than absorbed. This explains why chlorophyll appears green in color, and why plants appear green.

Other pigments, called **accessory pigments,** include yellow, orange, and red pigments. These pigments absorb colors of light that chlorophyll does not. Most accessory pigments are not visible in plants for most of the year because they are masked by the chlorophyll. However, in some areas during the fall season, cool temperatures break down the chlorophyll in many plants. The colors of the accessory pigments become visible and produce the beautiful orange, red, and yellow colors of fall leaves.

Figure 7 When chlorophyll breaks down in some trees in the fall, the accessory pigments in the leaves become visible. *Applying Concepts Which colors do the accessory pigments in leaves reflect?*

Program Resources

◆ **Teaching Resources** 4-2 Lesson Plan, p. 95; 4-2 Section Summary, p. 96
  Science Explorer Series *Chemical Interactions,* Chapter 1

Media and Technology

 Audiotapes English-Spanish Summary 4-2

Answers to Self-Assessment

Caption Question

Figure 7 Orange, red, and yellow

☑ *Checkpoint*

The colors of the visible spectrum are red, orange, yellow, green, blue, and violet.

2 Facilitate

The Nature of Light

Building Inquiry Skills: Observing

Materials *flashlight, 2 hand mirrors*
Time 15 minutes
Tips Dim the overhead lights. Challenge pairs of students to arrange the mirrors to direct the path of a flashlight beam around a corner. Ask: **What do you observe about the path of the light?** *(It bounces off the mirrors.)* Allow students to experiment, and then have two pairs challenge each other. Have them hold the flashlight in place, so that the beam shines in a straight line. Have one pair choose a point that is not on that line and challenge the other pair to direct the light to that point. Then have the second pair choose another point and challenge the first pair. **limited English proficiency**

Plants and Light

Using the Visuals: Figure 7

As students observe the photograph, ask them to name all of the colors that they see. *(Sample: green, yellow, orange, red, brown)* Ask: **What happens to the colors in the sunlight when it reaches the different-colored leaves? How does that affect what we see in the picture?** *(Some of the colors are absorbed and some are reflected. The reflected color is the color that we see.)* **learning modality: visual**

Ongoing Assessment

Oral Presentation Ask students to explain why the leaf of a tree looks green in the sunlight.

Plants and Light, continued

Capturing Energy Because light is a form of energy, a substance that absorbs light absorbs energy. Just as a car requires the energy in gasoline to move, the process of photosynthesis in plants requires energy in the form of light. Photosynthesis begins when light strikes the chlorophyll in the chloroplasts of the plant's cells. The light energy that is absorbed powers the process of photosynthesis.

☑ *Checkpoint* *What colors of light does chlorophyll absorb?*

SCIENCE & History

Unraveling the Mysteries of Photosynthesis

What do plants need to make their own food? What substances do plants produce in the process of photosynthesis? Over time, the work of many scientists has provided answers to these questions.

1771
Joseph Priestley

When Joseph Priestley, an English scientist, placed a burning candle in a covered jar, the flame went out. When he placed both a plant and a candle in a covered jar, the candle kept burning. Priestley concluded that the plant released something into the air that kept the candle burning. Today we know that plants produce oxygen, a product of photosynthesis.

1650 | **1750**

1643
Jean-Baptiste Van Helmont

A Dutch scientist, Jean-Baptiste Van Helmont, planted a willow tree in a tub of soil. After five years of adding only water, the tree gained 74 kilograms. Van Helmont concluded that trees need only water to grow. Today it is known that water is one of the raw materials of photosynthesis.

1779
Jan Ingenhousz

Jan Ingenhousz, a Dutch scientist, placed branches with leaves in water. In sunlight, the leaves produced oxygen bubbles. In the dark, the leaves produced no oxygen. Ingenhousz concluded that plants need sunlight to produce oxygen, a product of photosynthesis.

122 ◆ A

Background

Integrating Science Light moves in tiny packets of electromagnetic energy called photons. All photons travel at the speed of light, and they are found at all wavelengths of electromagnetic energy.

In photosynthesis, most of the photons that are absorbed are traveling at a wavelength of 700 or 680 nanometers. Both these wavelengths are within the visible spectrum of light. When a photon strikes chlorophyll, it excites an electron in the pigment's molecule. The electron moves from a lower-energy state to a higher-energy state on the pigment. When the electron moves back to its original state, it releases energy that causes chemical changes in a molecule called chlorophyll A. The energy from the photon is eventually converted into chemical energy, often stored in carbohydrates.

The Chemistry of Photosynthesis

 INTEGRATING CHEMISTRY Light energy is just one of the things that plants need to carry out photosynthesis. Just as you need flour and eggs to make cookies, a plant also needs raw materials to make its own food. Plants use carbon dioxide gas and water as raw materials for photosynthesis.

During photosynthesis, plants use the energy absorbed by the chlorophyll to power a series of complex chemical reactions.

In Your Journal

Find out more about the experiments conducted by one of these scientists. Then write a summary of one experiment as it might appear in a front-page newspaper story of the time. Be sure to give your story a headline.

1883
T. W. Engelmann

T. W. Engelmann studied how different colors of light affect photosynthesis in green algae. He found that cells bathed in blue and red light had the fastest rates of photosynthesis. Today scientists know that the chlorophyll in both green algae and plants absorbs mostly blue and red light.

1850

1950

1864
Julius Sachs

A German biologist, Julius Sachs, observed living leaf cells under a microscope. As he watched, he tested the cells for the presence of carbohydrates. Sachs discovered that plants produce carbohydrates during photosynthesis.

1948
Melvin Calvin

The American scientist Melvin Calvin traced the chemical path that the carbon from carbon dioxide follows during photosynthesis. By doing this, Calvin learned about the complex chemical reactions of photosynthesis.

Chapter 4 **A ◆ 123**

The Chemistry of Photosynthesis

Integrating Chemistry

Materials *2 small plants in pots, cardboard box, light source*

Time 5 minutes each day over 1 week

This activity will help students see how important light is in photosynthesis. Before the activity, ask: **What are the raw materials for photosynthesis?** *(Water and carbon dioxide)* Then ask: Is light considered a raw material? *(No. Light is a form of energy, not matter.)* Then challenge small groups to design experiments to find out what happens when a plant has the raw materials for photosynthesis, but lacks light as an energy source. Each student should have a specific task, such as head designer, data collector, and writer. Check student designs for accuracy and allow groups to carry out their experiments. Ask: **What happened to the plants that lacked light?** *(They did not have the energy to live because they could not carry out photosynthesis.)* **cooperative learning**

Ongoing Assessment

Skills Check Ask students to list everything that a plant needs for photosynthesis to occur and what is produced. *(Water, carbon dioxide, sunlight; oxygen, sugar)*

3 Assess

Section 2 Review Answers

1. When light strikes the green leaves of a plant, most of the green light is reflected and the other colors of light are mostly absorbed.

2. The overall equation for photosynthesis is

carbon dioxide + water

$$\xrightarrow{\text{light energy}}$$ sugar + oxygen.

Carbon dioxide and water combine in the presence of light to produce sugar and oxygen.

3. When light passes through a prism, you can see the colors of light. This shows that white light is made up of the colors of the visible spectrum.

4. The raindrops act as a prism to separate the colors of light.

Science at Home

Suggest students look at windows, plastic bags, shiny bowls, mirrors, and colored objects. Students should explain that white light is transmitted through clear objects and reflected off shiny or mirrored objects. Colored objects absorb all of the colors of light except the color that you see. The color that you see is reflected.

Performance Assessment

Drawing Have students use colored pencils to draw what happens when white light strikes different-colored objects. *(Students' drawings should show white light shining on an object of a certain color, with that color of light being reflected and all other colors being absorbed.)*

 Students can save their drawings in their portfolios.

124 ◆ A

Figure 8 In photosynthesis, the energy in sunlight is used to make sugar and oxygen from carbon dioxide and water. *Classifying Which substances are the raw materials of photosynthesis? Which are the products?*

In these reactions, carbon dioxide from the air and water from the soil combine to produce sugar, a type of carbohydrate. Another product, oxygen gas, is also produced. The events of photosynthesis are pictured in Figure 8.

One way that scientists describe chemical reactions is to write equations. A chemical equation shows the raw materials and the products. **The many chemical reactions of photosynthesis can be summarized by the following equation.**

$$\underset{(CO_2)}{\text{carbon dioxide}} + \underset{(H_2O)}{\text{water}} \xrightarrow{\text{light energy}} \underset{(C_6H_{12}O_6)}{\text{sugar}} + \underset{(O_2)}{\text{oxygen}}$$

Carbon dioxide and water combine in the presence of light to produce sugar and oxygen.

Like all organisms, plants need a steady supply of energy to grow and develop, respond, and reproduce. Some of the food made by plants supplies the energy for these activities. The excess food is stored by the plants in their roots, stems, or leaves. Carrot plants, for example, store excess food in their roots. When you eat a carrot, you are eating the plant's stored food.

Section 2 Review

1. Describe what happens when light strikes a green leaf.
2. What is the overall equation for photosynthesis? What information does the equation provide?
3. What happens when light passes through a prism? What does this reveal about white light?
4. **Thinking Critically** **Relating Cause and Effect** Sometimes you see a rainbow during a rain shower. What might act as a prism to separate the light into its colors?

Science at Home

With a family member, look around your kitchen for objects that transmit, reflect, and absorb white light. Explain to your family member what happens to white light when it strikes each type of object. Then use one object to explain why you see it as the color you do.

124 ◆ A

Program Resources

◆ **Teaching Resources** 4-2 Review and Reinforce, p. 97; Enrich, p. 98
◆ **Interdisciplinary Exploration Series** "Fate of the Rain Forest," pp. 20–21
◆ **Integrated Science Laboratory Manual** A-4, "Investigating Stomata"

Answers to Self-Assessment

Caption Question

Figure 8 The raw materials are carbon dioxide and water. The products are sugar and oxygen.

Media and Technology

 Interactive Student Tutorial CD-ROM A-4

SECTION 3 Mosses, Liverworts, and Hornworts

DISCOVER ·· ACTIVITY

Will Mosses Absorb Water?

1. Place 20 milliliters (mL) of sand into a plastic graduated cylinder. Place 20 mL of peat moss into a second plastic graduated cylinder.

2. Predict what would happen if you were to slowly pour 10 mL of water into each of the two graduated cylinders and then wait five minutes.

3. To test your prediction, use a third graduated cylinder to slowly add 10 mL of water to the sand. Then add 10 mL of water to the moss. After 5 minutes, record your observations.

Think It Over

Predicting How did your prediction compare with your results? What did you learn about moss from this investigation?

If you enjoy gardening, you know that a garden requires time, effort, and knowledge. Before you start to plant your garden, you need to know how much water and sun your plants will need. You also need to know whether the soil in your garden can supply the plants with the water and nutrients they need.

Many gardeners add peat moss to the soil in their gardens. Peat moss improves the texture of soil and increases the soil's ability to hold water. When peat moss is added to claylike soil, it loosens the soil so that the plant's roots can easily grow through it. When peat moss is added to sandy soil, the soil stays moist for a longer time after it is watered.

Characteristics of Nonvascular Plants

Peat moss contains one type of **nonvascular plant**. Some other nonvascular plants are liverworts and hornworts. **All nonvascular plants are low-growing plants that lack vascular tissue.**

> ### GUIDE FOR READING
> ◆ What characteristics do nonvascular plants share?
>
> *Reading Tip* As you read, make a table comparing and contrasting mosses, liverworts, and hornworts.

Chapter 4 **A ◆ 125**

A ◆ 125

2 Facilitate

Characteristics of Nonvascular Plants

Demonstration

Materials *plastic ice cube tray, paper towel, water, plastic dropper, food coloring*

ACTIVITY

Time 10 minutes

Model the way that materials pass through nonvascular plants. Tear off a 5-cm wide strip of paper towel and roll it tightly lengthwise. Fill a beaker with about 250 mL of water and 5–10 drops of food coloring. Using a dropper, carefully fill one section of an ice cube tray with colored water. Place one end of the rolled paper towel in the colored water and the other end in another section of the tray. Ask students to predict what will happen to the colored water. Then allow them to watch the movement of the water from one section to another. Ask: **How is this similar to the way that nonvascular plants transport materials?** *(Nonvascular plants move materials from one cell to the next through their bodies.)* **learning modality: visual**

Mosses

Using the Visuals: Figure 9

As they look at the figure, have students describe the life cycle of the moss. Ask: **How is the sporophyte created?** *(Gametophytes produce sperm cells and egg cells. When these are fertilized, a sporophyte develops.)* **What is the function of the sporophyte?** *(It contains spores which can develop into new gametophytes.)* **learning modality: visual**

Nonvascular plants do not have vascular tissue—a system of tubelike structures that transport water and other materials. Nonvascular plants can only pass materials from one cell to the next. That means that the materials do not travel very far or very quickly. Also, these plants have only their rigid cell walls to provide support. With this type of structure, these plants cannot grow very wide or tall. As a result, nonvascular plants are small and grow low to the ground.

Like all plants, nonvascular plants require water to survive. These plants lack roots, but they can obtain water and minerals directly from their surroundings. Many nonvascular plants live where water is plentiful. But even nonvascular plants that live in drier areas need enough water to let the sperm cells swim to the egg cells during reproduction.

Mosses

Have you ever seen mosses growing in the crack of a sidewalk, on a tree trunk, or on rocks that are misted by waterfalls? With over 10,000 species, mosses are by far the most diverse group of nonvascular plants.

The Structure of a Moss If you were to look closely at a moss, you would see a plant that looks something like the one in Figure 9. The familiar green fuzzy moss is the gametophyte generation of the plant. Structures that look like tiny leaves grow off a small stemlike structure. Thin rootlike structures called **rhizoids** anchor the moss and absorb water and nutrients from the soil. The sporophyte generation grows out of the gametophyte. It consists of a slender stalk with a capsule at the end. The capsule contains spores.

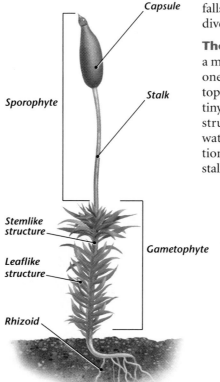

Figure 9 A moss gametophyte is low-growing and has structures that look like roots, stems, and leaves. The stalklike sporophyte generation remains attached to the gametophyte. *Interpreting Diagrams What structure anchors the gametophyte in the soil?*

Background

Integrating Science Peat moss, which can be used as a fuel, stores chemical energy from decaying plants and animals. This energy can be harnessed to provide fuel for people to use.

Before peat can be used as fuel, it must be cut into blocks and dried. The peat can also be compressed into bricks and made into high-quality charcoal. Peat burns easily and can produce about two-thirds as much heat

as the same amount of bituminous coal.

Between 286 and 360 million years ago, layers of rock and sand from the oceans repeatedly covered many thick peat beds. These layers increased the heat and pressure on the peat and caused it to harden into lignite, a low-grade form of coal. Even greater pressure, such as that exerted by the forces of mountain building, further transformed the lignite into hard, bituminous coal.

The Importance of Mosses Many people use peat moss in agriculture and gardening. The peat moss that gardeners use contains sphagnum (SFAG num) moss. Sphagnum moss grows in a type of wetland called a **bog.** The still water in a bog is so acidic that decomposing organisms cannot live in the water. Thus when the plants die, they do not decay. Instead, the dead plants accumulate at the bottom of the bog. Over time, the mosses become compressed into layers and form a blackish-brown material called **peat.** Large deposits of peat exist in North America, Europe, and Asia. In Europe and Asia, people use peat as a fuel to heat homes and to cook food.

 **INTEGRATING EARTH SCIENCE** Like the lichens you learned about in Chapter 3, many mosses are pioneer plants. They are among the first organisms to grow in areas destroyed by volcanoes or in burnt-out forests. Like lichens, mosses trap wind-blown soil. Over time, enough soil accumulates to support the growth of other plants whose spores or seeds are blown there.

 *Checkpoint* What does a moss sporophyte look like?

Figure 10 The sphagnum moss that grew in this bog is being harvested as peat.

Social Studies CONNECTION

Historians have found many items preserved in the acidic water of peat bogs. Weapons more than 1,600 years old have been recovered from bogs in northern Europe. In addition, about 700 human bodies have been found in bogs. Most are as well preserved as the body that you see in the photo. This man, who lived 2,000 years ago, was found in a bog in Denmark.

In Your Journal

Imagine that you have just recovered an old wooden tool from a bog. Write a letter to a natural history museum explaining why the tool is so well preserved.

Materials *hand lens, peat moss, white paper*
Time 10 minutes

Invite students to closely examine small clumps of peat moss. They should place a sample on white paper. Using a hand lens, students should examine the rhizoids, and the leaflike and stemlike structures. They should sketch their samples and label the parts.

portfolio Students can save their sketches in their portfolios. **limited English proficiency**

Social Studies CONNECTION

Help students recognize the historical importance of finding artifacts in bogs. Ask students: **What might be learned from studying these artifacts?** *(Sample: We can learn about the clothes that people wore, and about some of the tools and technology that they used.)*

In Your Journal Encourage students to provide a clear, concise explanation of the conditions found in a bog. Ask volunteers to share their letters with the class. **learning modality: verbal**

Integrating Earth Science

Tell students that moss not only traps soil but also traps water that might wash the soil away otherwise. Ask: **What traits does moss have that would help other plants grow?** *(Sample: It traps water so it helps to keep the ground moist.)*
learning modality: verbal

Program Resources

. **Science Explorer Series**
  Environmental Science, Chapter 3
◆ **Interdisciplinary Exploration Series**
  "Fate of the Rain Forest," pp. 12–13

Answers to Self-Assessment

Caption Question

Figure 9 Rhizoids anchor the gametophyte in the soil.

Checkpoint

A moss sporophyte consists of a thin brownish stalk with a spore-containing capsule at the end. It grows out of the gametophyte.

Ongoing Assessment

Writing Have students write one or two sentences to describe the function of rhizoids.

Liverworts and Hornworts

Using the Visuals: Figure 11

Have students identify the parts of the plants shown in the photos. Ask: **What part of the liverwort is the gametophyte?** *(The liver-shaped leaflike structures)* **What part of the hornwort is the sporophyte?** *(The horn-shaped structures)* **learning modality: visual**

3 Assess

Section 3 Review Answers

1. Nonvascular plants are low growing and lack vascular tissue. They do not have vascular tissue for support and movement of materials and therefore are low growing.

2. A moss gametophyte has rhizoids, a stemlike part, and leaflike parts. The sporophyte grows out of the top of the gametophyte.

3. Peat forms from dead moss plants in a bog. The layers of dead moss do not decompose because the water is so acidic; they become compressed and form peat.

4. Mosses, liverworts, and hornworts are all nonvascular plants. Moss grows in soil and on rocks and trees. Liverworts live in very moist areas near streams. Hornworts live on moist soil.

Check Your Progress

Check students' observation records on a regular basis. Students should record observations daily and include details about changes in the size of the moss and the growth of new structures.

Performance Assessment

Organizing Information Have students make Venn diagrams to compare and contrast the three types of nonvascular plants. *(Venn diagrams should show the similarities between mosses, liverworts, and hornworts, as well as the specific characteristics of each.)*

Figure 11 Like mosses, liverworts and hornworts are nonvascular plants. **A.** Liverworts grow flat along the ground on moist soil and rocks. **B.** Hornworts grow only in soil and are often found growing among grasses.

Liverworts and Hornworts

Figure 11 shows examples of two other groups of nonvascular plants—liverworts and hornworts. There are more than 8,000 species of liverworts. This group of plants is named for the shape of the plant's body, which looks somewhat like a human liver. *Wort* is an old English word for "plant." Liverworts are often found growing as a thick crust on moist rocks or soil along the sides of a stream. Unlike mosses, most liverworts grow flat along the ground. In Figure 11, you can see the gametophyte generation of one type of liverwort.

There are fewer than 100 species of hornworts. At first glance, these plants resemble liverworts. But if you look closely, you can see slender, curved structures that look like horns growing out of the gametophytes. These hornlike structures, which give these plants their names, are the sporophytes. Unlike mosses or liverworts, hornworts are seldom found on rocks or tree trunks. Instead, hornworts live in moist soil, often mixed in with grass plants.

Section 3 Review

1. Describe two characteristics that nonvascular plants share. Explain how the two characteristics are related.
2. Describe the structure of a moss plant.
3. How does peat form?
4. **Thinking Critically Comparing and Contrasting** In what ways are mosses, liverworts, and hornworts similar? How do they differ?

Check Your Progress

You should now be caring for your moss, and providing the best conditions for its survival and growth. Be sure to keep in mind how mosses differ from other familiar kinds of plants. (*Hint:* Keep your terrarium warm, but not hot, and make sure it remains moist.)

Program Resources

◆ **Teaching Resources** 4-3 Review and Reinforce, p. 101; Enrich, p. 102

Media and Technology

 Interactive Student Tutorial CD-ROM A-4

Masses of Mosses

I n this lab, you will look closely at some tiny members of the plant kingdom.

Problem

How is a moss plant adapted to carry out its life activities?

Materials

clump of moss	hand lens
metric ruler	toothpicks
plastic dropper	water

Procedure

1. Your teacher will give you a clump of moss. Examine the clump from all sides. Draw a diagram of what you see. Measure the size of the overall clump and the main parts of the clump. Record your observations.

2. Using toothpicks, gently separate five individual moss plants from the clump. Be sure to pull them totally apart so that you can observe each plant separately. If the moss plants appear to dry up as you are working, moisten them with a few drops of water.

3. Measure the length of the leaflike, stemlike, and rootlike structures on each plant. If brown stalks and capsules are present, measure them. Find the average length of each structure.

4. Make a life-size drawing of a moss plant. Label the parts, give their sizes, and record the color of each part. When you are finished observing the moss, return it to your teacher. Wash your hands thoroughly.

5. Obtain class averages for the sizes of the structures you measured in Step 3. Also, if the moss that you observed had brown stalks and capsules, share your observations about those structures.

Analyze and Conclude

1. Describe the typical size of the leaflike portion of moss plants, the typical height of the stemlike portion, and the typical length of the rootlike portion.

2. In which part(s) of the moss does photosynthesis occur? How do you know?

3. Why are mosses unable to grow very tall?

4. **Think About It** What did you learn by observing a moss up close and in detail?

More to Explore

Select a moss plant with stalks and capsules. Use toothpicks to release some of the spores, which can be as small as dust particles. Examine the spores under a microscope.

Safety

Students should wash their hands thoroughly after finishing the lab. If students use microscopes, review all relevant safety procedures. Review the safety guidelines in Appendix A.

Program Resources

◆ **Teaching Resources** Chapter 4 Skills Lab, pp. 110–111
◆ **Inquiry Skills Activity Book** Provides teaching and review of all inquiry skills

---

Masses of Mosses

Preparing for Inquiry

Key Concept Students will observe a moss and describe its structures.

Skills Objective Students will be able to
◆ make detailed observations of a moss and communicate their observations;
◆ measure the structures of a moss and calculate class averages.

Time 45 minutes

Advance Planning Provide a variety of species of mosses. If possible, obtain some moss clumps with sporophytes present.

Alternative Materials If you have microscopes available, allow students to use them.

Guiding Inquiry

Troubleshooting the Experiment
Clumps of moss obtained from nature may contain more than one type. You may wish to have a field guide to the mosses available for students to consult.

Expected Outcome
◆ Students should be able to identify all the parts of the plant.
◆ Measurements will vary, depending on the type of moss.

Analyze and Conclude

1. Leaflike: a few millimeters long, by a fraction of a millimeter thick; stemlike: up to 15-cm high, often much shorter; rootlike: very short. Some mosses are only a few millimeters tall.

2. The green parts (leaflike and stemlike); only the green parts, which contain chlorophyll, can carry out photosynthesis.

3. Mosses cannot transport water quickly over long distances.

4. Sample: You can see that a moss is made of many small plants.

Extending the Inquiry

More to Explore Show students how to gently crush the moss capsules to release the spores. Students can then observe these structures with a microscope.

Objective

After completing the lesson, students will be able to
◆ name some seedless vascular plants and list the characteristics that they share;
◆ describe the structure of a fern plant.

Key Terms vascular plant, frond

1 Engage/Explore

Activating Prior Knowledge

Ask students to draw and label a picture of a plant that includes leaves, stems, and roots. Then show students a potted fern and ask them to point out the leaves, stems, and roots on the fern.

········ DISCOVER ········

Skills Focus inferring
Materials goggles, plastic petri dish, narrow glass tube, water, food coloring, dropper
Time 10 minutes
Tips Caution students to handle the glass tube gently. If they roughly push the glass tube onto the bottom of the petri dish, the tube may shatter.
Expected Outcome The colored water should move quickly up the glass tube.
Think It Over Students should infer that a tubelike arrangement of cells will help water move quickly up the plant.

DISCOVER ·············· ACTIVITY····

How Quickly Can Water Move Upward?

1. Put on your goggles. Your teacher will give you a plastic petri dish as well as a narrow glass tube that is open at both ends.

2. Fill the petri dish half full of water. Add a drop of food coloring to the water.

3. Stand the tube on end in the water and hold it upright. Observe what happens. Record your observations.

Think It Over
Inferring Why might it be an advantage for the transporting cells of plants to be arranged in a tubelike way?

GUIDE FOR READING

◆ What are the main characteristics of seedless vascular plants?

Reading Tip As you read, create a table comparing ferns, club mosses, and horsetails.

The time is 340 million years ago—long before the dinosaurs lived. The place is somewhere in the forests that covered most of Earth's land. If you could have walked through one of these ancient forests, it would have looked very strange to you. You might have recognized the mosses and liverworts that carpeted the moist soil. But overhead you would have seen odd-looking trees, some towering 25 meters above the ground. Among the trees were ancient ferns—huge versions of the ferns you find in today's florist shops. Other trees resembled giant stick figures with leaves up to one meter long. The huge leaves hugged the branches, looking something like the scales that cover a fish.

130 ◆ A

READING STRATEGIES

Reading Tip Have students work with learning partners to create their tables. Partners can use the information in the table to quiz each other on the section.

Study and Comprehension Before students begin reading, have them preview the section by looking at the pictures and reading the headings, subheadings, and captions. Ask students to list questions they have as they preview the section. Write the questions on the board. After students have read the section, challenge them to answer the questions.

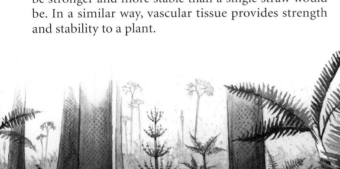

 As the trees and other plants died, they formed thick layers and partially decomposed. Over millions of years, the layers became compressed under the weight of the layers above them. Eventually, these layers became the coal deposits that we use for fuel today.

Characteristics of Seedless Vascular Plants

The odd-looking plants in the ancient forests were the ancestors of three groups of plants that are alive today—ferns, club mosses, and horsetails. **Ferns and their relatives share two characteristics. They have vascular tissue and use spores to reproduce.**

Vascular Tissue What adaptations allowed plants to grow very tall? Unlike the mosses, the ancient trees were **vascular plants**—plants that have vascular tissue. Vascular plants are better suited to life on land than are nonvascular plants. This is because vascular tissue solves the problems of support and transportation. Vascular tissue transports water quickly and efficiently throughout the plant's body. It also transports the food produced in the leaves to other parts of the plant, including the roots.

In addition, vascular tissue strengthens the plant's body. Imagine a handful of drinking straws bundled together with rubber bands. The bundle of straws would be stronger and more stable than a single straw would be. In a similar way, vascular tissue provides strength and stability to a plant.

Figure 12 Ferns and their relatives dominated the ancient forests on Earth.

Chapter 4 • **A** ◆ **131**

Program Resources

◆ **Teaching Resources** 4-4 Lesson Plan, p. 103; 4-4 Section Summary, p. 104

Media and Technology

 Audiotapes English-Spanish Summary 4-4

2 Facilitate

Integrating Earth Science

Ask students to explain where the energy in coal comes from. *(The plants that eventually become coal contained energy that they received from the sun.)* **learning modality: verbal**

Characteristics of Seedless Vascular Plants

Including All Students

Students who are visually impaired and those who need extra help may benefit from exploring the structure of vascular tissue by feeling a bunch of celery. Ask: **What do you feel on the outside of the stalks?** *(Narrow ridges)* Explain that these are bundles of vascular tissue. Have students hold the base of the celery bunch in one hand and apply pressure to the top of the stalks with the other. Ask: **Why couldn't you crush the bunch of celery?** *(The vascular tissue is strong enough to resist the force of a hand pressing down on it.)* **learning modality: kinesthetic**

Ongoing Assessment

Skills Check Have students list two functions of vascular tissue. *(Transports food and transports water through the plant's body, provides support)*

A ◆ **131**

Ferns

Skills Focus inferring
Materials *fern plant, hand lens, plastic dropper, water*
Time 20 minutes
Tips Students should observe the fronds, the stem, and the roots. They should notice that the upper surface of a frond is smooth and shiny compared to the lower surface. Spore cases may be visible on the underside of the blade. Water dropped onto the upper surface of the frond should run off.
Inferring The roots anchor the plant on land and absorb water. The cuticle on the upper surface reduces water loss.
Extend Suggest students closely examine a spore case, then release the spores from the case with a dissecting knife and examine them with a hand lens. **learning modality: visual**

Visual Arts Connection

Rubbings of fern fronds are attractive to look at and can be useful for making scientific observations. To make a rubbing, students can place tracing paper on top of a frond and rub the tracing paper with charcoal. Have students examine the rubbings to see if they can identify any features that were difficult to see on the plant. Keep rubbings for classroom display. **learning modality: kinesthetic**

Students can save their rubbings in their portfolios.

Examining a Fern

1. Your teacher will give you a fern plant to observe.
2. Draw a diagram of the plant and label the structures that you see.
3. Use a hand lens to observe the top and lower surfaces of the leaf. Run a finger over both surfaces.
4. With a plastic dropper, add a few drops of water to the top surface of the leaf. Note what happens.

Inferring Use your observations to explain how ferns are adapted to life on land.

Spores for Reproduction Ferns, club mosses, and horsetails still need to grow in moist surroundings. This is because the plants release spores into their surroundings, where they grow into gametophytes. When the gametophytes produce egg cells and sperm cells, there must be enough water available for fertilization to occur.

☑ *Checkpoint* **What adaptation allowed plants to grow tall?**

Ferns

Fossil records indicate that ferns first appeared on land about 400 million years ago. There are over 12,000 species of ferns alive today. They range in size from tiny plants about the size of this letter "M" to large tree ferns that grow up to 5 meters tall in moist, tropical areas.

The Structure of Ferns Like other vascular plants, ferns have true stems, roots, and leaves. The stems of most ferns are underground. Leaves grow upward from the top side of the stems, and roots grow downward from the bottom of the stems. Roots are structures that anchor the fern to the ground and absorb water and nutrients from the soil. These substances enter the root's vascular tissue and travel through the tissue into the stems and leaves. In Figure 13 you can see the fern's structure.

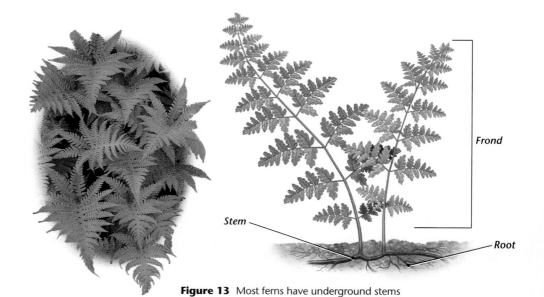

Figure 13 Most ferns have underground stems in addition to underground roots. The leaves, or fronds, grow above ground.

Background

Facts and Figures The small aquatic fern mentioned on page 133 is called *Azolla*. Its benefit as a fertilizer is due to the mutualistic relationship it shares with a cyanobacterium (blue-green alga) called *Anabaena azollae*. Filaments of *Anabaena* live inside ovoid cavities within the leaves of *Azolla*. The cyanobacterium provides the *Azolla* with a source of usable nitrogen in the form of ammonia. Nitrogen fixation makes nitrogen available to autotrophic plants, such as rice. *Azolla* and its partner *Anabaena* have been used to fertilize rice paddies in China and other Asian countries for centuries. Some reports suggest that *Azolla* can increase rice yields by as much as 158 percent per year. Because the soil is not depleted of nutrients, rice can be grown in the same fields year after year with no loss of productivity.

Figure 14 Spores are produced on the undersides of mature fronds. *Applying Concepts What happens to spores that are released?*

Look closely at the fern's leaves, or **fronds.** Notice that the frond is divided into many smaller parts that look like small leaves. Many other ferns have a similar divided-leaf structure. The upper surface of each frond is coated with a cuticle that helps the plant retain water. In many types of ferns, the developing leaves are coiled at first. Because they resemble the top of a violin, these young leaves are often called fiddleheads. As they mature, the fiddleheads uncurl.

Reproduction in Ferns The familiar fern with its visible fronds is the sporophyte stage of the plant. On the underside of mature fronds, spores develop in tiny spore cases. When the spores are released, wind and water can carry them great distances. If a spore lands in moist, shaded soil, it develops into a gametophyte. Fern gametophytes are tiny plants that grow low to the ground.

The Importance of Ferns Ferns are useful to people in many ways. They are popular houseplants because they are attractive and easy to grow. Ferns are also used to grow other kinds of houseplants. For example, orchids are often grown on the tangled masses of fern roots.

People eat some ferns. During the spring, fiddleheads are sold in supermarkets and farm stands. Fiddleheads make a nutritious vegetable dish. But because some ferns are not safe to eat, you should never gather wild fiddleheads for food.

In Southeast Asia, farmers grow a small aquatic fern alongside rice plants in their rice fields. Tiny pockets in the fern's leaves provide a home for some bacteria. The bacteria produce a natural fertilizer that helps the rice plants grow.

Figure 15 Fiddleheads are the developing leaves of a fern.

Chapter 4 **A ◆ 133**

Building Inquiry Skills: Drawing Conclusions

Describe the reproductive cycle of ferns to students: the mature plant releases spores that grow into gametophytes; the gametophytes develop egg cells and free-swimming sperm that fertilize the egg cells. The fertilized egg cells develop into mature fern plants. Have students discuss the importance of water to this cycle. Ask: **During which part of the cycle does the fern plant require water?** (*The free-swimming sperm must have water to swim in.*) **How would a fern plant survive in a climate that was mostly arid with only seasonal rains?** (*Plants could have evolved a cycle that was synchronized with the seasons so liquid water was available for the free-swimming sperm.*) **learning modality: logical/mathematical**

Club Mosses and Horsetails

Building Inquiry Skills: Classifying

Materials *samples of ferns, club mosses, moss, liverworts or hornworts, and horsetails*

ACTIVITY

Time 10 minutes

Provide samples for students to examine. Have students work in pairs to compare the plants and identify structures. Challenge each pair to classify these plants according to their similarities. Then have students diagram the plants and explain their classifications. **learning modality: visual**

Program Resources

- **Science Explorer Series** *Earth's Changing Surface,* Chapter 2
- ◆ **Interdisciplinary Exploration Series** "Fate of the Rain Forest," pp. 6–9, 17–19

Answers to Self-Assessment

Caption Question

Figure 14 Spores that are released are carried by wind and water. If they land in a suitable spot, the spore develops into a gametophyte.

☑ *Checkpoint*
Vascular tissue allowed plants to grow tall.

Ongoing Assessment

Writing Have students write brief paragraphs to describe the life cycle of a fern.

3 Assess

Section 4 Review Answers

1. Ferns and their relatives have two common characteristics: vascular tissue and the use of spores to reproduce. Mosses do not have vascular tissue.
2. The leaves, or fronds, of ferns have vascular tissue and a cuticle that helps prevent water loss. The stems have vascular tissue and are underground. Leaves grow upward and roots grow downward from the stems.
3. Any three: People use some ferns as house plants. Some ferns are eaten. Some ferns help rice grow. The remains of ancient ferns are used as fuel in the form of coal.
4. Ferns need to live in moist, shady places in order to reproduce.

CHAPTER PROJECT 4

Check Your Progress

Tell students that their brochures should outline the steps needed to construct a terrarium and summarize the growth requirements for mosses, based on their observations. The directions must be clear enough that an individual from another class could set up a terrarium and successfully grow mosses using only the brochure. Students should also describe the general characteristics and life cycle of mosses.

Performance Assessment

Organizing Information Ask students to create Venn diagrams that compare ferns, club mosses, and horsetails. (*Venn diagrams should indicate that all three have vascular tissue and reproduce without seeds. Ferns have fronds and underground stems. Club mosses have needlelike leaves. Horsetails have jointed stems with branches growing in a circle around each joint.*)

Figure 16 Club mosses and horsetails are other seedless vascular plants. **A.** This club moss looks like a tiny pine tree. **B.** These horsetail plants have jointed stems. Needle-like branches grow out of each joint.

Club Mosses and Horsetails

Two other groups of seedless, vascular plants are the club mosses and horsetails. Like ferns, club mosses and horsetails have true leaves, stems, and roots. They also have a similar life cycle. However, there are relatively few species of club mosses and horsetails alive today.

Unlike their larger ancestors, today's club mosses are small. Do not be confused by the name *club mosses*. Unlike the true mosses, the club mosses have vascular tissue. You may be familiar with the club moss you see in Figure 16. The plant, which looks like the small branch of a pine tree, is sometimes called ground pine or princess pine. It grows in moist woodlands and near streams.

There are 30 species of horsetails on Earth today. As you can see in Figure 16, the stems of horsetails are jointed. Long, coarse, needlelike branches grow in a circle around each joint. Small leaves grow flat against the stem just above each joint. The stems contain silica, a gritty substance also found in sand. During colonial times, Americans called horsetails "scouring rushes" because they used the plants to scrub their pots and pans.

Section 4 Review

1. What two characteristics do ferns, club mosses, and horsetails share? How do these characteristics differ from those of mosses?
2. Describe the structure of a fern plant. What do its leaves, stems, and roots look like?
3. List three ways that ferns are useful to people today.
4. **Thinking Critically** **Applying Concepts** Although ferns have vascular tissue, they still must live in moist, shady environments. Explain why this is true.

134 ◆ A

CHAPTER PROJECT 4

Check Your Progress

Begin planning your brochure as you continue caring for your moss. What's the best way to give clear directions for making a terrarium? What must you say about the amount of light, water, and other conditions that mosses need to survive? (*Hint:* Be sure to include important information about mosses, such as how tall they grow and how they reproduce.)

Program Resources

◆ **Teaching Resources** 4-4 Review and Reinforce, p. 105; 4-4 Enrich, p. 106

Media and Technology

 Interactive Student Tutorial CD-ROM A-4

SECTION 1 The Plant Kingdom

Key Ideas

◆ Plants are autotrophs. All plants are also multicellular eukaryotes.

◆ Plant cells have cell walls that are made mostly of cellulose. Plant cells contain chloroplasts, in which food is made, and vacuoles that store water, food, and other substances.

◆ All plants have complex life cycles. In the sporophyte stage, plants produce spores. In the gametophyte stage, plants produce sperm cells and egg cells.

◆ For plants to survive on land, they need ways to obtain water and other materials from their surroundings, retain moisture, support their bodies, transport materials throughout the plant, and reproduce successfully.

Key Terms

photosynthesis	cuticle	sporophyte
cell wall	vascular tissue	gametophyte
cellulose	fertilization	gamete
chloroplast	zygote	
vacuole		
tissue		
chlorophyll		

SECTION 2 Photosynthesis and Light

INTEGRATING PHYSICS

Key Ideas

◆ White light is made up of the different colors of the rainbow—red, orange, yellow, green, blue, and violet.

◆ Most of the light that strikes a leaf is absorbed by pigments in the chloroplasts of the cells. Chlorophyll, the main pigment, absorbs red and blue light. Light energy powers the process of photosynthesis.

◆ In photosynthesis, carbon dioxide and water are converted into sugars and oxygen using the light energy.

Key Term

accessory pigment

SECTION 3 Mosses, Liverworts, and Hornworts

Key Ideas

◆ Nonvascular plants are small, low-growing plants that lack vascular tissue. Most nonvascular plants transport materials by passing them from one cell to the next. They live in areas where there is enough moisture for them to survive.

◆ Mosses, liverworts, and hornworts are three types of nonvascular plants.

Key Terms

nonvascular plant	bog
rhizoid	peat

SECTION 4 Ferns and Their Relatives

Key Ideas

◆ Seedless vascular plants have vascular tissue and use spores to reproduce. These plants include ferns, club mosses, and horsetails.

◆ Although seedless vascular plants grow taller than nonvascular plants, they still need to live in moist places. The plants' spores are released into the environment, where they grow into gametophytes.

Key Terms

vascular plant	frond

USING THE INTERNET

ACTIVITY

www.science-explorer.phschool.com

Program Resources

◆ **Teaching Resources** Chapter 4 Project Scoring Rubric, p. 90; Chapter 4 Performance Assessment Teacher Notes, p. 177; Chapter 4 Chapter 4 Performance Assessment Student Worksheets, pp. 178–179; Chapter 4 Test, pp. 180–183

Reviewing Content:
Multiple Choice
1. d **2.** c **3.** a **4.** c **5.** c

True or False
6. true **7.** true **8.** Sugar and oxygen
9. nonvascular **10.** ferns

Checking Concepts

11. Cell wall—boundary that surrounds the cell membrane and separates the cell from the environment; chloroplasts—look like "green jelly beans" and are structures where food is made; vacuoles—large, sacklike storage areas where many substances including water, wastes, and food are stored.

12. Vascular tissue enables a plant to efficiently transport water and food to all its cells and supports plants so they can grow large.

13. Plants have complex life cycles in which a sporophyte generation produces spores that develop into a gametophyte. The gametophyte plant produces egg cells and sperm cells. Fertilization occurs when a sperm cell fuses with an egg cell to form a zygote. The zygote develops into a new sporophyte plant.

14. The bus appears yellow because the paint on its body contains pigments that reflect the yellow part of visible light.

15. Chlorophyll absorbs the red and blue colors of light so the energy in these colors can be used to power photosynthesis.

16. Mosses are nonvascular plants; club mosses are vascular. Both mosses and club mosses need to grow in moist environments because they use spores for reproduction.

17. Students' descriptions should indicate that when the beam strikes the leaf, most of the green light is reflected. Pigments in the leaf absorb the other colors. The energies in the red and blue light fuel photosynthesis.

Thinking Visually

18. a. Small and low **b.** Moist **c.** Fronds, stems, and roots **d.** Gametophyte **e.** No **f.** Yes; Characteristics of Mosses and Ferns

---

Reviewing Content

 For more review of key concepts, see the Interactive Student Tutorial CD-ROM.

Multiple Choice
Choose the letter of the best answer.

1. Mosses and ferns are both
  a. vascular plants.
  b. nonvascular plants.
  c. seed plants.
  d. plants.

2. The ancestors of plants were probably
  a. fungi.
  b. brown algae.
  c. green algae.
  d. bacteria.

3. When visible light strikes a green leaf, green light is
  a. reflected.
  b. absorbed.
  c. transmitted.
  d. stored.

4. The familiar green, fuzzy moss is the
  a. frond.
  b. rhizoid.
  c. gametophyte.
  d. sporophyte.

5. The leaves of ferns are called
  a. rhizoids.
  b. sporophytes.
  c. fronds.
  d. cuticles.

True or False
If the statement is true, write true. If it is false, change the underlined word or words to make the statement true.

6. Plants are <u>autotrophs</u>.

7. In the fall, leaves turn colors because <u>accessory pigments</u> become visible as the chlorophyll breaks down.

8. <u>Carbon dioxide and water</u> are the products of photosynthesis.

9. Mosses are <u>vascular</u> plants.

10. The young leaves of <u>liverworts</u> are known as fiddleheads.

Checking Concepts

11. Describe three structures that characterize the eukaryotic cells of plants. Explain the role of each structure.

12. In what two ways is vascular tissue important to a plant?

13. Briefly describe the life cycle of a typical plant.

14. Explain why a yellow school bus appears yellow.

15. What role does chlorophyll play in photosynthesis?

16. In what ways do mosses and club mosses differ from each other? In what ways are they similar?

17. Writing to Learn Imagine that you are a beam of white light traveling through the air. Write a paragraph to explain what happens to you when a green leaf gets in your way.

Thinking Visually

18. Compare/Contrast Table Copy the table comparing mosses and ferns onto a separate sheet of paper. Complete the table by filling in the missing information. Then add a title. (For more on compare/contrast tables, see the Skills Handbook.)

Characteristic	Moss	Fern
Size	**a.** _?_	Can be tall
Environment	Moist	**b.** _?_
Body parts	Rootlike, stemlike, and leaflike	**c.** _?_
Familiar generation	**d.** _?_	sporophyte
Vascular tissue present?	**e.** _?_	**f.** _?_

Applying Skills

19. Graphs should show the percentage of light absorbed on the vertical axis, in increments of five or ten percentage points. The colors of light should be placed along the horizontal axis. The height of each color's bar should correspond to the number in the table.

20. Red, blue, and violet are the three colors of light that were most absorbed by the plant and therefore are probably the most important for photosynthesis.

21. Students should predict that little photosynthesis would occur if the plant were exposed only to yellow light. Without photosynthesis, the plant would starve to death.

22. A plant with reddish leaves would reflect more red light. The value of absorbed red light would be lower.

Thinking Critically

23. Students should indicate that their friend is probably mistaken. Mosses are nonvascular

Applying Skills

A scientist exposed a green plant to different colors of light. She then measured how much of each light the plant absorbed. Use the data to answer Questions 19–22.

Absorption of Light by a Plant

Color of Light	Percentage of Light Absorbed
Red	55
Orange	10
Yellow	2
Green	1
Blue	85
Violet	40

19. Graphing Construct a bar graph using the information in the data table. (For information on constructing bar graphs, see the Skills Handbook.)

20. Drawing Conclusions List the three colors of light that are most important for photosynthesis in this plant.

21. Predicting If the plant were exposed only to yellow light, how might the plant be affected? Explain.

22. Inferring If a plant with reddish leaves were used in a similar experiment, how might the results differ? Explain.

Thinking Critically

23. Applying Concepts A friend tells you that he has seen moss plants that are about 2 meters tall. Is your friend correct? Explain.

24. Comparing and Contrasting How does the sporophyte generation of a plant differ from the gametophyte generation?

25. Relating Cause and Effect People have observed that mosses tend to grow on the north side of a tree rather than the south side. Why do you think this is so?

plants and cannot grow tall. They can neither support, nor transport material through, large bodies.

24. The sporophyte generation produces spores. The spore develops into the gametophyte stage. The gametophyte generation produces two kinds of gametes—sperm cells and egg cells.

25. The north sides are cooler and get less sunlight. Therefore, the north sides of trees should be more moist and provide the moisture mosses need to grow.

Performance Assessment

Wrap Up

CHAPTER PROJECT 4

Present Your Project Students' brochures should be well organized and should contain detailed pictures and/or drawings of mosses. Students' presentations should include what they learned about growing mosses and how mosses compare with other plants.

Reflect and Record As students give their reports, have their classmates take brief notes. After all the reports have been given, encourage students to discuss any differences that were apparent among the groups. Have students evaluate their own brochures. Encourage them to decide whether they would change the information presented in their brochure or whether they would present information differently.

Performance Assessment

Wrap Up

CHAPTER PROJECT 4

Present Your Project It's time to share your "How to Raise Mosses" brochure with your classmates and with your chosen audience. Be prepared to explain any of the information in your brochure. Also be sure to ask other students about their work. What did you discover about growing mosses? How do mosses compare with other plants?

Reflect and Record What did you learn by keeping the terrarium and making the brochure? Did you discover new ideas from brochures made by others? If you were to do this project again, how could you improve your work?

Getting Involved

In Your Community Spend some time in a park or other outdoor area in your community. Draw a map of the area. Look closely for mosses, ferns, and other plants you learned about in this chapter. Plot the locations of all the plants you find in the area. Record information about how much sun and water each location receives. Create a data table of the information on poster board. As a class, display the maps and posters so that others can see the diversity of plants in your community.

Program Resources

◆ **Inquiry Skills Handbook** Provides teaching and review of all inquiry skills

Getting Involved

In Your Community This activity would work well as a class field trip because all students would be given the opportunity to observe these plants in nature. Information about the amount of sun and water that a location receives could be general, or students could choose smaller areas within the park. Display students' posters in a school hallway or at a local library.

Sections	Time	Student Edition Activities	ACTIVITY Other Activities		
CHAPTER PROJECT 5 **Cycle of a Lifetime** p. 139	Ongoing (2½ weeks)	Check Your Progress, pp. 149, 161, 170 Wrap Up, p. 173	TE	Chapter 5 Project Notes, pp. 138–139	
1 The Characteristics of Seed Plants pp. 140–149 ◆ List the characteristics that seed plants share. ◆ Name the main parts of a seed, identify the function of each part of the seed, and describe how seeds disperse and germinate. ◆ Describe the functions of leaves, stems, and roots.	5 periods/ 2½ blocks	**Discover** Which Plant Part Is It?, p. 140 **Try This** The In-Seed Story, p. 142 **Sharpen Your Skills** Calculating, p. 146	TE TE TE TE	Building Inquiry Skills: Observing, pp. 141, 147 Inquiry Challenge, p. 143 Building Inquiry Skills: Classifying, p. 144 Demonstrations, pp. 146, 148	
2 Gymnosperms pp. 150–155 ◆ Give examples of gymnosperms and list the characteristics they share. ◆ Describe how gymnosperms reproduce.	3 periods/ 1½ blocks	**Discover** Are All Leaves Alike?, p. 150 **Try This** The Scoop on Cones, p. 153	TE	Social Studies Connection, p. 151	
3 Angiosperms pp. 156–163 ◆ Name types of angiosperms and list the characteristics that they all share. ◆ Describe the life cycle of angiosperms. ◆ Compare monocots and dicots.	4 periods/ 2 blocks	**Discover** What Is a Fruit?, p. 156 **Real-World Lab: How It Works** A Close Look at Flowers, pp. 162–163	TE TE TE PTA	Building Inquiry Skills: Comparing and Contrasting, p. 159 Including All Students, p. 160 Integrating Health, p. 160 Testing Jeans, pp. 1–8	
4 Plant Responses and Growth pp. 164–167 ◆ Identify three stimuli that produce plant responses. ◆ List the functions that plant hormones control.	2 periods/ 1 block	**Discover** Can a Plant Respond to Touch?, p. 164 **Skills Lab: Developing Hypotheses** Which Way Is Up?, p. 167	TE TE ISLM	Demonstration, p. 165 Inquiry Challenge, p. 165 A-5, "Investigating Hormones That Control Germination"	
5 _INTEGRATING TECHNOLOGY_ **Feeding the World** pp. 168–170 ◆ Describe some methods that might help farmers produce more crops.	1½ periods/ ½–1 block	**Discover** Will There Be Enough to Eat?, p. 168	IES IES	"Riddles of the Pharaohs," pp. 26–27 "Fate of the Rain Forest," p. 42	
Study Guide/Chapter Review pp. 171–173	1 period/ ½ block		ISAB	Provides teaching and review of all inquiry skills	

 For Standard or Block Schedule The Resource Pro® CD-ROM gives you maximum flexibility for planning your instruction for any type of schedule. Resource Pro® contains Planning Express®, an advanced scheduling program, as well as the entire contents of the Teaching Resources and the Computer Test Bank.

CHAPTER PLANNING GUIDE

Program Resources	Assessment Strategies	Media and Technology
TR Chapter 5 Project Teacher Notes, pp. 112–113 **TR** Chapter 5 Project Overview and Worksheets, pp. 114–117 **TR** Chapter 5 Project Scoring Rubric, p. 118	**SE** Performance Assessment: Chapter 5 Project Wrap Up, p. 173 **TE** Check Your Progress, pp. 149, 161, 170 **TE** Performance Assessment: Chapter 5 Project Wrap Up, p. 173 **TR** Chapter 5 Project Scoring Rubric, p. 118	Science Explorer Internet Site
TR 5-1 Lesson Plan, p. 119 **TR** 5-1 Section Summary, p. 120 **TR** 5-1 Review and Reinforce, p. 121 **TR** 5-1 Enrich, p. 122 **SES** Book I, *Weather and Climate*, Chapter 3	**SE** Section 1 Review, p. 149 **TE** Ongoing Assessment, pp. 141, 143, 145, 147 **TE** Performance Assessment, p. 149 **TR** 5-1 Review and Reinforce, p. 121	Exploring Life Science Videodisc, Unit 2 Side 2, "Xeriscape" Audiotapes: English-Spanish Summary 5-1 Transparencies 15, "The Structure of Seeds"; 16, "Exploring a Leaf"; 17, "The Parts of a Woody Stem" Interactive Student Tutorial CD-ROM, A-5
TR 5-2 Lesson Plan, p. 123 **TR** 5-2 Section Summary, p. 124 **TR** 5-2 Review and Reinforce, p. 125 **TR** 5-2 Enrich, p. 126 **SES** Book E, *Environmental Science*, Chapter 3	**SE** Section 2 Review, p. 155 **TE** Ongoing Assessment, pp. 151, 153 **TE** Performance Assessment, p. 155 **TR** 5-2 Review and Reinforce, p. 125	Audiotapes: English-Spanish Summary 5-2 Transparency 18, "Exploring the Life Cycle of a Gymnosperm" Interactive Student Tutorial CD-ROM, A-5
TR 5-3 Lesson Plan, p. 127 **TR** 5-3 Section Summary, p. 128 **TR** 5-3 Review and Reinforce, p. 129 **TR** 5-3 Enrich, p. 130 **TR** Chapter 5 Real-World Lab, pp. 139–141 **SES** Book D, *Human Biology and Health*, Chapter 6	**SE** Section 3 Review, p. 161 **SE** Analyze and Conclude, p. 163 **TE** Ongoing Assessment, pp. 157, 159 **TE** Performance Assessment, p. 161 **TR** 5-3 Review and Reinforce, p. 129	Audiotapes: English-Spanish Summary 5-3 Transparencies 19, "The Structure of a Flower"; 20, "Exploring the Life Cycle of an Angiosperm" Interactive Student Tutorial CD-ROM, A-5
TR 5-4 Lesson Plan, p. 131 **TR** 5-4 Section Summary, p. 132 **TR** 5-4 Review and Reinforce, p. 133 **TR** 5-4 Enrich, p. 134 **TR** Chapter 5 Skills Lab, pp. 142–143	**SE** Section 4 Review, p. 166 **SE** Analyze and Conclude, p. 167 **TE** Ongoing Assessment, p. 165 **TE** Performance Assessment, p. 166 **TR** 5-4 Review and Reinforce, p. 133	Exploring Life Science Videodisc, Unit 2 Side 2, "Fertilizers" Audiotapes: English-Spanish Summary 5-4 Interactive Student Tutorial CD-ROM, A-5
TR 5-5 Lesson Plan, p. 135 **TR** 5-5 Section Summary, p. 136 **TR** 5-5 Review and Reinforce, p. 137 **TR** 5-5 Enrich, p. 138 **SES** Book E, *Environmental Science*, Chapter 1	**SE** Section 5 Review, p. 170 **TE** Ongoing Assessment, p. 169 **TE** Performance Assessment, p. 170 **TR** 5-5 Review and Reinforce, p. 137	Exploring Life Science Videodisc, Unit 1 Side 2, "Can We Still Get What We Need?" Audiotapes: English-Spanish Summary 5-5 Interactive Student Tutorial CD-ROM, A-5
TR Chapter 5 Performance Assessment, pp. 184–186 **TR** Chapter 5 Test, pp. 187–190	**SE** Chapter Review, pp. 171–173 **TR** Chapter 5 Performance Assessment, pp. 184–186 **TR** Chapter 5 Test, pp. 187–190 **CTB** Test A-5	Computer Test Bank, Test A-5 Interactive Student Tutorial CD-ROM, A-5

Key: **SE** Student Edition   **TE** Teacher's Edition   **TR** Teaching Resources
CTB Computer Test Bank   **SES** Science Explorer Series Text   **ISLM** Integrated Science Laboratory Manual
ISAB Inquiry Skills Activity Book   **PTA** Product Testing Activities by *Consumer Reports*   **IES** Interdisciplinary Explorations Series

Meeting the National Science Education Standards and AAAS Benchmarks

National Science Education Standards	Benchmarks for Science Literacy	Unifying Themes
Science as Inquiry (Content Standard A) ◆ **Think critically and logically to make the relationships between evidence and explanations** Students examine plant responses to gravity. *(Skills Lab)* **Life Science** (Content Standard C) ◆ **Structure and function in living systems** Seed plants have specialized tissues, such as xylem and phloem, that carry out specific functions. *(Section 1)* Gymnosperms and angiosperms have different structures involved in reproduction. *(Sections 2, 3; Real-World Lab)* Hormones are chemicals that govern growth and development. *(Section 4; Skills Lab)* ◆ **Reproduction** Seeds are specialized structures for reproduction. *(Section 1)* Most gymnosperms sexually reproduce using cones. *(Section 2)* Angiosperms sexually reproduce using flowers and fruit. *(Section 3; Chapter Project; Real-World Lab)* **Science in Personal and Social Perspectives** (Content Standard F) ◆ **Populations, resources, and environments** Overpopulation may lead to a food shortage. *(Section 5)*	**3C Issues in Technology** Technological advances in food production may reduce world hunger. *(Section 5)* **5A Diversity of Life** Seed plants have vascular tissue and seeds. Gymnosperms and angiosperms are two types of seed plants with different reproductive structures. *(Sections 1, 2, 3; Chapter Project; Real-World Lab)* **5C Cells** Pollen releases male sperm cells that unite with a female egg cell to form a seed. *(Section 1, 2, 3; Chapter Project)* Actively dividing cells are found in the root cap and cambium of a seed plant. *(Section 1)* **8A Agriculture** Many varieties of angiosperms produce edible food for humans. *(Section 3)* Agricultural technology, such as genetic engineering, hydroponics, and precision farming can improve crop growth. *(Section 5)* **11C Constancy and Change** Seed plants have predictable life cycles. *(Sections 1, 2, 3; Chapter Project)* Tropisms are predictable responses plants have to stimuli, such as light, gravity, and touch. Angiosperms may have annual, biennial, or perennial life spans. *(Section 4; Skills Lab)*	◆ **Energy** Plants use light energy to change water and carbon dioxide into carbohydrates and oxygen. Plants store energy in their roots, stems, leaves, fruits, and seeds. *(Section 1)* ◆ **Evolution** Gymnosperms were the first group of seed plants to evolve. Angiosperms first appeared about 100 million years ago. Seed plants have evolved adaptations to many different environments. *(Sections 2, 3)* ◆ **Patterns of Change** The life cycle of seed plants involves pollination, fertilization, seed development, dispersal of seeds, and growth of a new plant. Angiosperms have different life spans. *(Sections 1, 2, 3, 4; Chapter Project)* ◆ **Scale and Structure** All seed plants have vascular tissue and seeds that allow seed plants to grow tall and survive in many different environments. *(Sections 1, 2, 3; Real-World Lab)* ◆ **Unity and Diversity** While all seed plants share specific characteristics and responses to stimuli, many different species of seed plants exist. *(Sections 1, 2, 3, 4; Chapter Project; Skills Lab; Real-World Lab)* ◆ **Systems and Interactions** Many angiosperms rely on animals for pollination and seed dispersal. *(Section 1)* ◆ **Stability** Photosynthesis helps to maintain the atmospheric balance of oxygen and carbon dioxide. *(Section 1)*

Media and Technology

Exploring Life Science Videodisc

◆ **Section 1** "Xeriscape" demonstrates the landscaping technique of Xeriscaping as a way to conserve water.

◆ **Section 4** "Fertilizers" describes the use of nitrogen, phosphorus, and potassium in plant fertilizers.

◆ **Section 5** "Can We Still Get What We Need?" integrates ecology, social studies, and current events as the demands of the global population are examined.

Interactive Student Tutorial CD-ROM

◆ **Chapter Review** Interactive questions help students to self-assess their mastery of key chapter concepts.

Student Edition Connection Strategies

◆ **Section 1** Integrating Earth Science, p. 148

◆ **Section 2** Integrating Environmental Science, p. 155

◆ **Section 3** Visual Arts Connection, p. 158
Integrating Health, p. 161

◆ **Section 5** Integrating Technology, p. 168
Integrating Environmental Science, p. 170

USING THE INTERNET

www.science-explorer.phschool.com

Visit the Science Explorer Internet site to find an up-to-date activity for Chapter 5 of *From Bacteria to Plants*.

ACTIVITY	**Time** (minutes)	**Materials** Quantities for one work group	**Skills**
Section 1			
Discover, p. 140	10	**Nonconsumable** foods such as carrots, parsnips, broccoli, cabbage, lettuce, celery, parsley, potato, onion	Classifying
Try This, p. 142	10	**Nonconsumable** hand lens; dried kidney, lima, or black beans; dried yellow or green peas; shelled peanuts	Observing
Sharpen Your Skills, p. 146	15 min, plus 20 min after 2 h for observation	**Consumable** water, food coloring, celery stalk **Nonconsumable** plastic container, dropper, spoon, metric ruler, clock or stopwatch, lab apron	Calculating
Section 2			
Discover, p. 150	10	**Consumable** 2 or 3 leaves from different angiosperms, such as an oak tree, maple tree, day lily, and rose; 2 or 3 leaves from different gymnosperms, such as pine, yew, and spruce **Nonconsumable** hand lens, metric ruler	Classifying
Try This, p. 153	10	**Nonconsumable** mature female pine cone, hand lens, piece of white paper	Inferring
Section 3			
Discover, p. 156	15	**Nonconsumable** hand lens; metric ruler; three different fruits, such as apples, cherries, peaches, plums, tomatoes, or peppers	Forming Operational Definitions
Real-World Lab, pp. 162–163	40	**Consumable** paper towels, tape, large flower, water, lens paper **Nonconsumable** hand lens, slide, cover slip, metric ruler, plastic dropper, microscope, scalpel	Observing, Measuring, Inferring
Section 4			
Discover, p. 164	10	**Nonconsumable** sensitive plant such as a Venus' flytrap or mimosa, common house plant such as a geranium or impatiens	Inferring
Skills Lab, p. 167	30 min, plus a few minutes each day for a week	**Consumable** 4 corn seeds, paper towels, water, masking tape **Nonconsumable** marking pencil, plastic petri dish, scissors, clay	Developing Hypotheses
Section 5			
Discover, p. 168	20	**Consumable** cooked rice, peanuts, or cereal **Nonconsumable** bag, tags	Predicting

A list of all materials required for the Student Edition activities can be found on pages T14–T16. You can order Materials Kits by calling 1-800-828-7777 or by accessing the Science Explorer Internet site at **www.science-explorer.phschool.com.**

Cycle of a Lifetime

Although most students are aware that plants grow from seeds, they may never have observed each stage in the life of a seed plant. This project will allow students to observe a plant's growing cycle.

Purpose In this project, students will grow plants from seeds and make detailed observations of the plant's life cycle from germination through growth, flowering, and pollination.

Skills Focus After completing the Chapter 5 Project, students will be able to
◆ pose questions about how plants grow and reproduce;
◆ observe different parts of the seed plant life cycle;
◆ communicate their findings about seed plants to their classmates.

Project Time Line This project will take 4–5 weeks to complete. Students should plant their seeds as soon as possible; germination will take several days. During this time, students should discuss the life cycle of plants and what they expect to observe. They should set up their data tables and prepare to take measurements. Around week three, the plants should have flowers that are ready for pollination. Students should be able to collect new seeds by the fourth week. At this time they should prepare their displays and work on their class presentations. Before beginning the project, see Chapter 5 Project Teacher Notes on pages 112–113 in Teaching Resources for more details on carrying out the project. Also, distribute the students' Chapter 5 Project Overview, Worksheets, and Scoring Rubric on pages 114–118 in Teaching Resources.

Possible Materials Students will need basic gardening supplies: fast-growing seeds (seeds that germinate in about 28 days, such as seeds from fast-growing plants from biological suppliers or from tomatoes, peas, etc.), potting trays, potting soil, water, and cotton swabs for transferring pollen.

Launching the Project To introduce the project and to stimulate student interest, ask: **How do we get more**

CHAPTER
5 Seed Plants

WHAT'S AHEAD

SECTION 1 The Characteristics of Seed Plants

Discover **Which Plant Part Is It?**
Try This **The In-Seed Story**
Sharpen Your Skills **Calculating**

SECTION 2 Gymnosperms

Discover **Are All Leaves Alike?**
Try This **The Scoop on Cones**

SECTION 3 Angiosperms

Discover **What Is a Fruit?**
Real-World Lab **A Close Look at Flowers**

138 ◆ A

plants? (*Discussion should lead to the answer "seeds."*) Then ask: **How do we get seeds?** This should lead to a discussion of seed production.

Allow time for students to read the description of the project in their text and the Chapter Project Overview on pages 114–115 in Teaching Resources. Then encourage discussions on the life cycle of seed plants and the materials that students will use. Make sure students understand that the most important activity in this project is caring for the plant so that it will grow well and provide useful information for

their observations. Answer any initial questions students may have, and distribute copies of the Chapter 5 Project Worksheets on pages 116–117 in Teaching Resources for students to review.

You may want to have students work in small groups as a cooperative learning task. To ensure that every student will have ample opportunity to care for the plants, each group should consist of no more than three students.

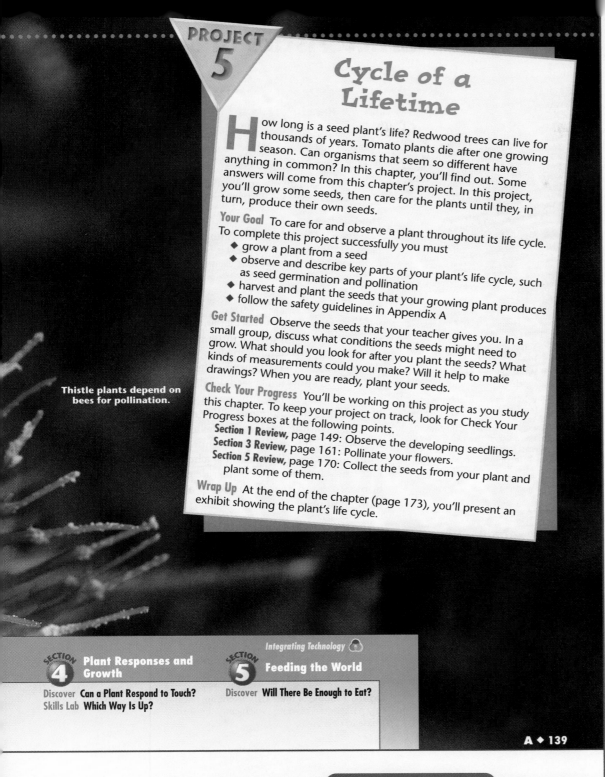

Cycle of a Lifetime

How long is a seed plant's life? Redwood trees can live for thousands of years. Tomato plants die after one growing season. Can organisms that seem so different have anything in common? In this chapter, you'll find out. Some answers will come from this chapter's project. In this project, you'll grow some seeds, then care for the plants until they, in turn, produce their own seeds.

Your Goal To care for and observe a plant throughout its life cycle. To complete this project successfully you must

◆ grow a plant from a seed
◆ observe and describe key parts of your plant's life cycle, such as seed germination and pollination
◆ harvest and plant the seeds that your growing plant produces
◆ follow the safety guidelines in Appendix A

Get Started Observe the seeds that your teacher gives you. In a small group, discuss what conditions the seeds might need to grow. What should you look for after you plant the seeds? What kinds of measurements could you make? Will it help to make drawings? When you are ready, plant your seeds.

Check Your Progress You'll be working on this project as you study this chapter. To keep your project on track, look for Check Your Progress boxes at the following points.

Section 1 Review, page 149: Observe the developing seedlings.
Section 3 Review, page 161: Pollinate your flowers.
Section 5 Review, page 170: Collect the seeds from your plant and plant some of them.

Wrap Up At the end of the chapter (page 173), you'll present an exhibit showing the plant's life cycle.

Thistle plants depend on bees for pollination.

SECTION 4 **Plant Responses and Growth**
Discover **Can a Plant Respond to Touch?**
Skills Lab **Which Way Is Up?**

Integrating Technology
SECTION 5 **Feeding the World**
Discover **Will There Be Enough to Eat?**

A ◆ 139

SECTION
1 The Characteristics of Seed Plants

Objectives

After completing the lesson, students will be able to
◆ list the characteristics that seed plants share;
◆ name the main parts of a seed, identify the function of each part of the seed, and describe how seeds disperse and germinate;
◆ describe the functions of leaves, stems, and roots.

Key Terms phloem, xylem, seed, embryo, cotyledon, germination, stomata, transpiration, cambium, root cap

1 Engage/Explore

Activating Prior Knowledge

Have students brainstorm a list of plants they encounter everyday and classify each plant on the board under the headings *Have Seeds* and *No Seeds*. Note that most of the plants they encounter have seeds.

DISCOVER

Skills Focus classifying **ACTIVITY**
Materials *foods such as carrots, parsnips, broccoli, cabbage, lettuce, celery, parsley, potato, onion (do not use fruits—they form from flowers)*
Time 10 minutes
Tips Mention that underground plant parts are not necessarily roots. For example, potatoes and onions are underground stems. Celery is not a true stem but a petiole, a leaf stalk.
Expected Outcome Students should identify carrots and parsnips as roots, lettuce and cabbage as leaves, and broccoli as stems.
Think It Over Students should classify foods from roots, stems, and leaves in separate categories.

DISCOVER

Which Plant Part Is It?

1. With a partner, carefully observe the items of food your teacher gives you.
2. Make a list of the food items.
3. For each food item, write the name of the part of the plant—root, stem, or leaf—from which you think the food is obtained.

Think It Over
Classifying Classify the items into groups depending on the plant part from which the food is obtained. Compare your groupings with those of your classmates.

GUIDE FOR READING

◆ What characteristics do seed plants share?
◆ What are the main parts of a seed?
◆ What are the functions of leaves, stems, and roots?

Reading Tip As you read, make a list of the boldfaced terms. Write a definition for each term in your own words.

Chances are you've seen dandelions. But how much do you know about these common plants? For example, do you know that dandelion blossoms open only in sunlight? Or that each blossom is made up of hundreds of tube-shaped flowers? Do you know that a seed develops in each of these tiny flowers? And that, just like apple seeds, dandelion seeds are enclosed in structures that biologists call fruits?

The next time you see a dandelion's fluffy "seed head," examine it closely. It is made up of hundreds of individual fruits, each containing a seed. Each fruit has a hooklike structure at one end. Like tiny parachutes, the fruits ride in currents of air. When one hooks into moist soil, the seed inside can grow into a new dandelion plant.

What Is a Seed Plant?

Dandelions are seed plants. So are most of the other plants on Earth. In fact, seed plants outnumber seedless plants by more than ten to one. You eat many seed plants—rice, tomatoes, peas, and squash, for example. You may also eat the meat of animals that eat seed plants. You wear clothes made from seed plants, such as cotton and flax. You may even live in a home built from seed plants—oak, pine, or maple trees. In addition, seed plants produce much of the oxygen you breathe.

Figure 1 Some of these dandelions are releasing tiny parachute-like fruits, which carry the seeds inside to new areas.

140 ◆ A

READING STRATEGIES

Reading Tip As students write definitions for the boldfaced terms, encourage them to add sketches or examples that will help them remember the meanings of the words. Have students work in pairs to quiz each other on the key terms using their definitions.

Study and Comprehension After students read the section, have them work in small groups to write ten questions about characteristics of seed plants. Suggest that they write a mixture of short-answer, fill-in-the-blank, and matching questions. Remind them to create answer keys. Then have groups exchange worksheets and questions and complete them. Instruct students to check their answers against the answer keys.

All seed plants share two characteristics. They have vascular tissue and use seeds to reproduce. In addition, they all have body plans that include leaves, stems, and roots. Like seedless plants, seed plants have complex life cycles that include the sporophyte and the gametophyte. In seed plants, the plants that you see are the sporophytes. The gametophytes are microscopic.

Vascular Tissue

Most seed plants live on land. Recall from Chapter 4 that land plants face many challenges, including standing upright and supplying all their cells with water and food. Like ferns, seed plants meet these two challenges with vascular tissue. The thick walls of the cells in the vascular tissue help support the plants. In addition, water, food, and nutrients are transported throughout the plants in vascular tissue.

There are two types of vascular tissue. **Phloem** (FLOH um) is the vascular tissue through which food moves. When food is made in the plant's leaves, it enters the phloem and travels to the plant's stems and roots. Water and nutrients, on the other hand, travel in the vascular tissue called **xylem** (ZY lum). The plant's roots absorb water and nutrients from the soil. These materials enter the root's xylem and move upward into the plant's stems and leaves.

☑ *Checkpoint* *What material travels in phloem? What materials travel in xylem?*

Figure 2 Seed plants are diverse and live in many environments. **A.** Wheat is an important food for people. **B.** Organpipe cacti, here surrounded by other flowering plants, live in deserts. **C.** Lodgepole pines thrive in the mountains of the western United States.
Applying Concepts *What two roles does vascular tissue play in these plants?*

Answers to Self-Assessment

Caption Question

Figure 2 Vascular tissue provides transportation and support, making it possible for plants to grow large.

☑ *Checkpoint*

Food travels in phloem. Water and nutrients travel in xylem.

2 Facilitate

What Is a Seed Plant?

Building Inquiry Skills: Comparing and Contrasting

Have students discuss similarities and differences among some seed plants—real ones or photos from magazines and other sources. Ask: **How are these plants all alike?** *(They all have leaves, stems, and roots.)* Then ask: **How are they different?** *(Samples: Appearance, uses, life span, seed dispersal method)* **learning modality: verbal**

Vascular Tissue

Building Inquiry Skills: Observing

Materials *large tree leaf, scissors or lab knife, food coloring, large test tube, water*
Time 5 minutes on each of 4 days

Have students carefully cut the end of the stem of the leaf. They should fill a large test tube with water, add 15 drops of food coloring, and put the stem in the water. Ask students to observe the stem over 3 days, looking for uptake of dye. If the water level drops, students can add small amounts of colored water to the test tube. Ask: **Is the dye moving through the xylem or the phloem? Explain.** *(The dye moves through the xylem with the water.)* **learning modality: visual**

Ongoing Assessment

Organizing Information Have students make flowcharts showing the movement of food, water, and nutrients through a vascular plant. *(Phloem—food moves from the leaves to the roots and stem; xylem—water and nutrients travel from the roots into the stems and leaves.)*

A ◆ 141

Seeds

Using the Visuals: Figure 3

As students study the visual, ask them to compare and contrast the seeds. *(Samples: The seed coat covers the exterior of each seed. The cotyledon in the bean stores food.)* **learning modality: visual**

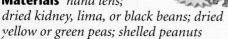

Skills Focus observing
Materials *hand lens; dried kidney, lima, or black beans; dried yellow or green peas; shelled peanuts*
Time 10 minutes
Tips Soak the beans in water for 2 hours before the activity. Soak the peas for 24 hours. Remove peanuts from their shells 3 or 4 days before the activity, and store them in a moist place so the cotyledons will open.
Expected Outcome Students should notice that each of these seeds is composed of two sections that can be easily separated. After they separate the seed, students should see the tiny leaves and root (and possibly the miniature stem) of the embryo plant.
Observing Students' sketches should include the seed coat, which protects the embryo and food from drying out; the cotyledons, which contain stored food; and the embryo, which will develop into a mature plant.
Extend Challenge students to repeat the activity with other kinds of seeds.
learning modality: visual

Portfolio Students can save their drawings in their portfolios.

The In-Seed Story

1. Your teacher **ACTIVITY** will give you a hand lens and two different seeds that have been soaked in water.
2. Carefully observe the outside of each seed. Draw what you see.
3. Gently remove the coverings of the seeds. Then carefully separate the parts of each seed. Use a hand lens to examine the inside of each seed. Draw what you see.

Observing Based on your observations, label the parts of each seed. Then describe the function of each part next to its label.

Seeds

One reason why seed plants are so numerous is that they produce seeds. **Seeds** are structures that contain a young plant inside a protective covering. As you learned in Chapter 4, seedless plants need water in the surroundings for fertilization to occur. Seed plants do not need water in the environment to reproduce. This is because the sperm cells are delivered directly to the regions near the eggs. After sperm cells fertilize the eggs, seeds develop and protect the young plant from drying out.

If you've ever planted seeds in a garden, you know that seeds look different from each other. Despite their differences, however, all seeds have a similar structure. **A seed has three important parts—an embryo, stored food, and a seed coat.**

The young plant that develops from the zygote, or fertilized egg, is called the **embryo.** The embryo already has the beginnings of roots, stems, and leaves. In the seeds of most plants, the embryo stops growing when it is quite small. When the embryo begins to grow again, it uses the food stored in the seed until it can make its food. In some plants, food is stored inside one or two seed leaves, or **cotyledons** (kaht uh LEED unz). You can see the cotyledons in the seeds in Figure 3.

The outer covering of a seed is called the seed coat. Some familiar seed coats are the "skins" on lima beans, peanuts, and peas. The seed coat acts like plastic wrap, protecting the embryo and its food from drying out. This allows a seed to remain inactive for a long time. For example, after finding some 10,000-year-old seeds in the Arctic, scientists placed them in warm water. Two days later, the seeds began to grow!

✓ *Checkpoint* *What is the function of the seed coat?*

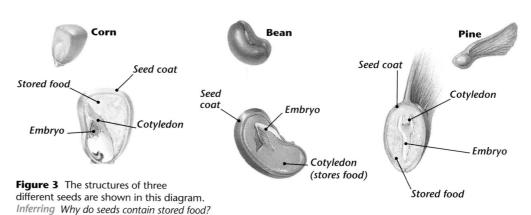

Figure 3 The structures of three different seeds are shown in this diagram. *Inferring* Why do seeds contain stored food?

Seed Dispersal

To develop into a new plant, a seed needs light, water, and nutrients. After seeds have formed, they are usually scattered, sometimes far from where they were produced. When seeds land in a suitable area, they can sprout, or begin to grow.

The scattering of seeds is called seed dispersal. Seeds, or the fruits that enclose the seeds, are dispersed in many ways. One method involves animals. Some animals eat fruits, such as cherries and grapes. The seeds inside pass through the animal's digestive system and are deposited in new areas. Other seeds are enclosed in barblike structures that hook onto an animal's fur or a person's clothes. The structures then fall off in a new area. Water disperses other seeds when the seeds float in oceans, rivers, and streams. The seeds inside a coconut, for example, are carried from one area to another by ocean currents.

A third dispersal method involves wind. Wind disperses lightweight seeds, such as those of milkweed plants and pine trees. Finally, some plants shoot out their seeds, in a way that might remind you of popping popcorn. For example, the seedpods of wisteria and impatiens plants burst suddenly. The force scatters the seeds away from the pods in many directions.

Figure 4 Plants have different ways of dispersing their seeds. **A.** Both grass seeds and spiny parsley seeds are hitching a ride on this dog's fur. **B.** Water transports coconut palm seeds to new areas. **C.** The wind carries milkweed seeds through the air. **D.** Witch hazel plants shoot out seeds when their pods explode.

Seed Dispersal

Inquiry Challenge

Time 25 minutes

Materials *modeling materials such as tissue paper, modeling clay, plastic foam balls, plastic spoons, cotton swabs, table tennis balls, hook-and-loop fastener strips*

This activity allows students to examine seed shapes and different forms of seed dispersal. Have students work together to build model seeds that can be dispersed by wind, water, or by sticking to clothes or animal fur. Groups should choose the materials for the models, collaborate on seed design, and assign roles for testing the seeds. Ask students to predict how far their model seeds will travel. After they test their predictions, have students identify how their model seeds are similar to real seeds and how their models could be improved. **cooperative learning**

Building Inquiry Skills: Predicting

Have students examine Figure 4 and predict which method would distribute seeds farthest. What characteristic would be important for seeds distributed by each method? (*Dog's fur—stick to fur; water—seed floats; wind—light weight; mechanical—small, dense seed*)

Answers to Self-Assessment

Caption Question

Figure 3 The stored food provides the energy needed for the embryo's early growth.

 Checkpoint

The seed coat protects the seed from temperature and moisture extremes until the seed grows.

Ongoing Assessment

Drawing Have students draw a seed and label the embryo, stored food, and seed coat. Then have students describe the labeled parts.

Portfolio Students can save their drawings and descriptions in their portfolios.

Germination

Real-Life Learning

In 1982, plant physiologist Jane Shen-Miller obtained seven lotus seeds that had been found at the site of an ancient lotus lake. Shen-Miller took four seeds and filed through their seed coats. Three sprouted into tiny plants. When Shen-Miller used radiocarbon dating to determine how old the seeds were, she discovered that they ranged in age from 684 to 1,288 years old! In 1994, she dated the remaining seeds, then planted one 332-year-old seed at her house. It sprouted vigorously and looked like a modern lotus plant. Ask students: **How could having seeds that can remain inactive for so long benefit a plant?** *(Sample: Travelers could carry seeds with them to new places. The seeds may survive for an extended time in a harsh environment even if the plant cannot.)* **learning modality: verbal**

Leaves

Building Inquiry Skills: Classifying

Materials *magazines or catalogs that contain pictures of plants; scissors, poster board, glue*

Time 20 minutes

Ask students to find pictures of plants with different shapes of leaves, then cut out the pictures and group them by leaf shape. Students can glue the groups of pictures onto poster board, then label them with explanations of how each leaf's shape benefits the plant. Then have students speculate on the type of environment each plant is best suited for. *(Sample: broad leaves to capture as much light as possible—rain forest)* **limited English proficiency**

Figure 5 The embryo in this peanut seed uses stored food to germinate. **A.** The peanut's root is the first structure to begin growing. **B.** After the root anchors the germinating plant, the peanut's stem and first two leaves emerge from the seed.

Germination

After seeds are dispersed, they may remain inactive for a while, or they may begin to grow immediately. **Germination** (jur muh NAY shun) is the early growth stage of the embryo. Germination begins when the seed absorbs water from the environment. Then the embryo uses its stored food to begin to grow. First, the embryo's roots grow downward, then its leaves and stem grow upward.

Seeds that are dispersed far away from the parent have a better chance of survival. This is because these young plants do not have to compete with their parent for light, water, and nutrients as they begin to grow.

☑ *Checkpoint* *What must happen before germination can begin?*

Leaves

The most numerous parts on many plants are their leaves. Plant leaves vary greatly in size and shape. Pine trees, for example, have needle-shaped leaves. Birch trees have small rounded leaves with jagged edges. Yellow skunk cabbages, which grow in the northwestern United States, have oval leaves that can be more than one meter wide. No matter what their shape, leaves play an important role in a plant. **Leaves capture the sun's energy and carry out the food-making process of photosynthesis.**

The Structure of a Leaf If you were to cut through a leaf and look at the edge under a microscope, you would see the structures in *Exploring a Leaf.* The leaf's top and bottom surface layers protect the cells inside. Between the layers of cells inside the leaf are veins that contain xylem and phloem. The underside of the leaf has small openings, or pores, called **stomata** (STOH muh tuh) (singular *stoma*). The Greek word *stoma* means "mouth"—and stomata do look like tiny mouths. The stomata open and close to control when gases enter and leave the leaf. When the stomata are open, carbon dioxide enters the leaf and oxygen and water vapor exit.

The Leaf and Photosynthesis The structure of a leaf is ideal for carrying out photosynthesis. Recall from Chapter 4 that photosynthesis occurs in the chloroplasts of plant cells. The cells that contain the most chloroplasts are located near the leaf's upper surface, where they are exposed to the sun. The chlorophyll in the chloroplasts traps the sun's energy.

Background

Facts and Figures The leaves of house plants can reveal information about the plants' native climates.

Many house plants come from the rain forest and require special care when kept inside. The Zebra plant, an evergreen from Brazil, has large leaves. The large leaves are well suited to the high humidity and bright indirect light in the rain forest. Zebra plants must be kept warm and moist in the home,

or they will lose their leaves.

Other house plants originally come from very dry climates. Plants from dry climates tend to have very small leaves or no leaves at all. The reduced area of the leaf restricts the amount of water that the plant can lose to the dry desert air. In many cactuses, the stems carry out photosynthesis and perform all the functions that both the stems and leaves of other plants perform.

Carbon dioxide enters the leaf through open stomata. Water, which is absorbed by the plant's roots, travels up the stem to the leaf through the xylem. During photosynthesis, sugar and oxygen are produced from the carbon dioxide and water. Oxygen passes out of the leaf through the open stomata. The sugar enters the phloem and then travels throughout the plant.

EXPLORING a Leaf

A leaf is a well-adapted food factory. Each structure helps the leaf produce food.

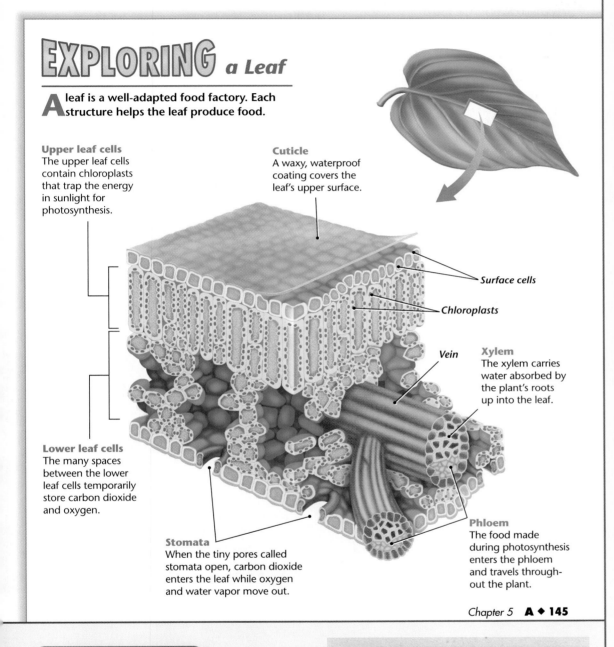

Upper leaf cells
The upper leaf cells contain chloroplasts that trap the energy in sunlight for photosynthesis.

Cuticle
A waxy, waterproof coating covers the leaf's upper surface.

Surface cells

Chloroplasts

Vein

Xylem
The xylem carries water absorbed by the plant's roots up into the leaf.

Lower leaf cells
The many spaces between the lower leaf cells temporarily store carbon dioxide and oxygen.

Stomata
When the tiny pores called stomata open, carbon dioxide enters the leaf while oxygen and water vapor move out.

Phloem
The food made during photosynthesis enters the phloem and travels through-out the plant.

Chapter 5 **A ◆ 145**

Answers to Self-Assessment

✓ *Checkpoint*
The seed must absorb water from the environment.

Language Arts Connection
Point out that the terms *chloroplast* and *chlorophyll* share the prefix *chloro*, which comes from the Greek word for "greenish-yellow." Have students use a good dictionary to find out what the Greek words *phyll* and *plast* mean. (*Phyll comes from the word for "leaf," and* plast *comes from the word for "molded."*) Challenge students to define *chloroplast* and *chlorophyll* using the Greek root words. **learning modality: verbal**

EXPLORING

a Leaf

Materials *large leaf, hand lens*
Time 20 minutes

As students examine the visual essay, encourage them to locate some of the labeled structures on a real leaf. Have students wash their hands thoroughly after handling the leaves. First, direct them to feel the cuticle on the leaf's upper surface and compare the cuticle to the drawing. Then have students look at the leaf with a hand lens. When they have identified the external structures, such as the cuticle and veins, call students' attention back to the visual. Ask: **How does it benefit the plant to have upper leaf cells that are long, rather than round?** (*The long cells provide more surface area and thus more exposure to the sun for photosynthesis.*)
Extend Obtain prepared slides from a biological supply house showing tissue from the underside of a leaf, the top side of a leaf, and a cross section of a leaf. Students can view the slides with a microscope and draw and label the structures they see. **learning modality: visual**

Ongoing Assessment

Writing Ask students to choose a structure found in a leaf and explain the function of that structure.

Leaves, continued

Demonstration

Materials *large potted plant such as a geranium*

Time 15 minutes setup; 10 minutes on each of two subsequent days

Allow the class to observe evidence of transpiration. Place a clear plastic bag over a cluster of leaves attached to the same stem of the plant. Seal the bag around the stem with masking tape. Students should observe the plant over 2 days. After the second day, remove the bag. Ask: **What formed on the inside of the bag?** *(Water droplets)* Have students explain how the water droplets got into the sealed plastic bag. *(As the plant carried out transpiration, it released water through its leaves, and the water formed droplets inside the bag.)* **learning modality: visual**

Stems

Sharpen your *Skills*

Calculating

Materials *plastic container, water, food coloring, dropper, spoon, celery stalk, metric ruler, clock or stopwatch, lab apron*

Time 15 minutes, plus 20 minutes after 2 hours for observation

Tips Choose stalks that are 15–30 cm tall. Before the activity, cut the ends of each stalk, and strip a thin layer of tissue off the back of each.

Answers In 20 minutes, the water should rise about 30 mm.

Speed = 30 mm ÷ 20 min = 1.5 mm/min
After 2 hours, the water should rise 180 mm:
(120 min)(1.5 mm/min) = 180 mm
(or 18 cm)

Extend Have students repeat the activity with another plant, such as a green onion or a leek. **learning modality: logical/mathematical**

Sharpen your Skills

Calculating

In this activity you will calculate the speed at which fluid moves up a celery stalk.

1. Put on your apron. Fill a plastic container halfway with water. Stir in a drop of red food coloring.

2. Place the freshly cut end of a celery stalk in the water. Lean the stalk against the container's side.

3. After 20 minutes, remove the celery. Use a metric ruler to measure the height of the water in the stalk.

4. Use the measurement and the following formula to calculate how fast the water moved up the stalk.

$$\text{Speed} = \frac{\text{Height}}{\text{Time}}$$

Based on your calculation, predict how far the water would move in 2 hours. Then test your prediction.

Figure 6 This road in Madagascar is called Baobab Avenue. Tall, fat stems and stubby branches give baobab trees an unusual appearance.

Controlling Water Loss Because such a large area of a leaf is exposed to the air, water can quickly evaporate, or be lost, from a leaf into the air. The process by which water evaporates from a plant's leaves is called **transpiration.** A plant can lose a lot of water through transpiration. A corn plant, for example, can lose as much as 3.8 liters of water on a hot summer day. Without a way to slow down the process of transpiration, a plant would shrivel up and die.

Fortunately, plants have ways to slow down transpiration. One way that plants retain water is by closing the stomata. The stomata often close when the temperature is very hot.

✓ *Checkpoint* *How does carbon dioxide get into a leaf?*

Stems

The stem of a plant has two important functions. **The stem carries substances between the plant's roots and leaves. The stem also provides support for the plant and holds up the leaves so they are exposed to the sun.** In addition, some stems, such as those of asparagus, also store food.

Stems vary in size and shape. Some stems, like those of the baobab trees in Figure 6, are a prominent part of the plant. Other stems, like those of cabbages, are short and hidden.

The Structure of a Stem Stems can be either herbaceous (hur BAY shus) or woody. Herbaceous stems are soft. Dandelions, dahlias, peppers, and tomato plants have herbaceous stems.

Background

Integrating Science Wood is used to construct many things, such as bridges, buildings, playgrounds, and furniture. Before choosing which type of wood to use, engineers must consider how well a wood beam resists compression—a pushing force—and shearing—a twisting force. The strength of a wood beam depends on many factors, including the structure of its woody stem, the density of the wood, and its water content. To determine the strength of a piece of wood, engineers use small pieces of wood to test how well the wood bears weight and other forces. The laboratory results are analyzed to reveal how much force the wood could bear in a real-world situation. Engineers, architects, and designers use this information to choose the best wood for their project.

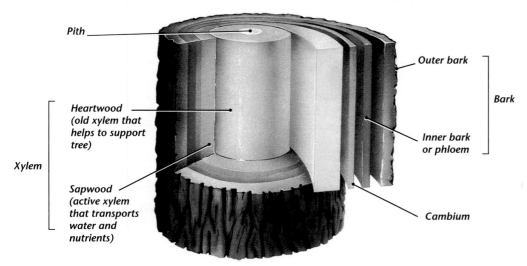

Pith

Heartwood
(old xylem that
helps to support
tree)

Xylem

Sapwood
(active xylem
that transports
water and
nutrients)

Outer bark

Bark

Inner bark
or phloem

Cambium

Figure 7 A typical woody stem is made up of many cell layers. *Interpreting Diagrams Where is the cambium located? What is the function of this layer of cells?*

In contrast, woody stems are hard and rigid. Maple trees, pine trees, and roses all have woody stems.

Herbaceous and woody stems consist of phloem and xylem tissue as well as many other supporting cells. However, unlike herbaceous stems, woody stems have an outer layer of material called bark, which helps protect the cells inside it, and inner layers of heartwood for additional support.

In Figure 7 you can see the inner structure of a woody stem. Bark covers the outer part of the stem. Just inside the bark is the phloem. Inside the phloem is a layer of cells called the **cambium** (KAM bee um). The cells of the cambium divide to produce new phloem and xylem. This process increases the stem's width. Just inside the cambium is a layer of active xylem that transports water and nutrients. Inside that layer is a layer of xylem cells that no longer carries water and nutrients. This layer, which is called heartwood, strengthens the stem, providing it with additional support. In the center of the stem is a material called the pith. In young trees, the pith stores food and water.

Annual Rings Have you ever looked at a tree stump and seen a pattern of circles that looks something like a target? These circles are called annual rings because they represent one year of a tree's growth. Annual rings are made of xylem. Xylem cells that form in the spring are large and have thin walls because they grow rapidly. They produce a wide, light brown ring. Xylem cells that form in the summer grow slowly and, therefore, are small and have thick walls. They produce a thin, dark ring. One pair of

Using the Visuals: Figure 7

Have students place a finger in the center of the woody stem shown in the visual. As they move their finger slowly from the figure's center to its outer edge, have them state the functions of each layer in the stem. *(Sample: Pith—stores food and water in young trees)* Then ask them to list *cambium, phloem,* and *xylem* in the order they appear from the pith outward. *(Xylem, cambium, phloem)* **learning modality: visual**

Including All Students

Ask students who speak Spanish to translate the English verb *to change* into Spanish. *(cambiar)* Point out that *cambiar* and *cambium* share similar roots; both come from the Latin word for "exchange." Have students discuss how the function of a stem's cambium relates to its Latin root. *(The cells in the cambium change by dividing to produce new xylem and phloem.)* **limited English proficiency**

Building Inquiry Skills: Observing

Materials *cross-sectional slice of tree trunk; hand lens*
Time 15 minutes

Have students carefully examine the rings in the trunk and sketch what they see. Challenge students to find three pairs of dark and light rings of different widths. Ask students to infer which pair of rings represents the year of heaviest rainfall and which pair of rings represents the year of lightest rainfall. *(The ring with the greatest width is from the year of heaviest rainfall. The ring with the smallest width is from the year of lightest rainfall.)* **learning modality: visual**

Answers to Self-Assessment

Caption Question

Figure 7 The cambium is inside the inner bark or phloem. It divides to produce new xylem and phloem cells.

☑ *Checkpoint*

Carbon dioxide enters the leaf through the open stomata.

Ongoing Assessment

Drawing Have students sketch and label the layers in a woody stem.

Stems, continued

Addressing Naive Conceptions

Students may not realize that trees grow by adding layers to the outside of the stem, so that the outer rings are newer than the inner rings. Point out that the heartwood, the old xylem, is at the center of the trunk. Contrast this with the apical growth that causes trees to increase in height: A nail driven into the bark of a tree will not move up as the tree grows, but will remain at the same height as the tree grows upward above it.
learning modality: verbal

Integrating Earth Science

Have students calculate the average number of years between the droughts in the southwestern United States.
$(227 + 312 + 253) \div 3 = 264$ *years*
Then have them calculate the average time between droughts if the next severe drought were to occur in 2022. *(298)*
learning modality: logical/mathematical

Roots

Demonstration

Materials *small potted plant with a fibrous root system such as a geranium*
Time 10 minutes

Gently loosen the plant from the container. Hold the plant over newspapers or paper towels, so that spilled dirt can be removed easily. Gently tap or shake the soil around the roots until the root system is clearly visible. Show students the roots and ask: **What kind of root system do you see?** *(fibrous)* Have students sketch the root system and label where the root cap and root hairs can be found. After the activity, carefully return the plant to its container and wash your hands thoroughly. **learning modality: visual**

148 ◆ A

Figure 8 Tree rings tell more than just the age of a tree. For example, thick rings that are far apart indicate years in which growing conditions were favorable.
Interpreting Photographs What was the weather like during the early years of this locust tree's life?

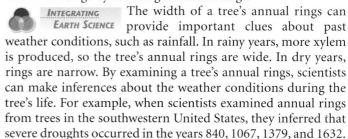

light and dark rings represents one year's growth. You can estimate a tree's age by counting its annual rings.

INTEGRATING EARTH SCIENCE The width of a tree's annual rings can provide important clues about past weather conditions, such as rainfall. In rainy years, more xylem is produced, so the tree's annual rings are wide. In dry years, rings are narrow. By examining a tree's annual rings, scientists can make inferences about the weather conditions during the tree's life. For example, when scientists examined annual rings from trees in the southwestern United States, they inferred that severe droughts occurred in the years 840, 1067, 1379, and 1632.

☑ *Checkpoint* **What function does bark perform?**

Roots

Have you ever tried to pull a dandelion out of the soil? It's not easy, is it? That is because most roots are good anchors. **Roots anchor a plant in the ground and absorb water and nutrients from the soil.** The more root area a plant has, the more water and nutrients it can absorb. The roots of an oak tree, for example, may be twice as long as the aboveground tree. In addition, for plants such as carrots and beets, roots function as a storage area for food.

Types of Roots As you can see in Figure 9, there are two types of root systems: taproot and fibrous. A taproot system consists of a long, thick main root. Thin, branching roots grow off the main root. Turnips, radishes, dandelions, and cacti have taproots. In contrast, fibrous root systems consist of several main roots that branch

Figure 9 A plant's roots anchor the plant and absorb substances from the soil. **A.** A taproot grows deep into the soil. The plant is hard to pull out of the ground. **B.** Fibrous roots consist of several main roots that repeatedly branch. They take soil with them when you pull them out of the ground.

148 ◆ A

Background

Facts and Figures A traditional Polynesian dish called *poi* is made from the root of the taro plant. Poi is made by pounding cooked taro root and mixing it with water until it forms a thin, starchy, bluish paste. In Hawaii, taro root is usually the main ingredient in poi, but on other Pacific Islands poi often contains mashed pineapple or banana mixed with coconut cream in addition to the taro root.

When European settlers arrived in the northeastern United States, Native American healers shared their knowledge of local plants with the colonists. The roots of milkweed plants were boiled to produce an extract believed to help bowel and kidney disorders. The roots of a poisonous plant called green false hellebore were applied to snakebite wounds.

repeatedly to form a tangled mass. Lawn grass, corn, and most trees have fibrous roots.

The Structure of a Root In Figure 10 you see the structure of a typical root. Notice that the tip of the root is rounded and is covered by a structure called the **root cap.** The root cap, which contains dead cells, protects the root from injury from rocks and other material as the root grows through the soil.

Behind the root cap are the cells that divide to form new root cells. These dividing cells cause the root to lengthen. Root hairs grow out of the root's surface. These hairs increase the surface area of the root that touches the soil. When more surface area is in contact with the soil, more water and nutrients can be absorbed. The root hairs also help to anchor the plant.

Locate the vascular tissue in the center of the root. The water and nutrients that are absorbed from the soil quickly move into the xylem. From there, these substances are transported upward to the plant's stems and leaves.

Phloem tissue transports food manufactured in the leaves to the root. The root tissues may then use the food for growth or store it for future use by the plant. The root also contains a layer of cambium, which produces new xylem and phloem.

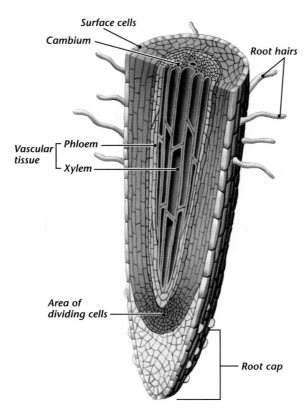

Surface cells
Cambium
Root hairs
Vascular tissue — Phloem
— Xylem
Area of dividing cells
Root cap

Figure 10 The root cap protects the root as it grows into the soil. Root hairs absorb water and nutrients, which are transported through the root's vascular tissue.

Section 1 Review

1. What two characteristics do all seed plants share?
2. List the three main parts of a seed. Describe the function of each part in producing a new plant.
3. What are the main functions of a plant's leaves, stems, and roots?
4. **Thinking Critically** **Predicting** Predict what would happen to a plant if you were to coat the underside of each leaf with wax. Explain your prediction.

Check Your Progress

CHAPTER PROJECT 5

If your seeds haven't germinated yet, they soon will. For the next few days keep a close watch on your young plants to see how they grow. How do they change in height? How do the leaves appear and grow? (*Hint:* Consider using drawings or photographs as part of your record keeping.)

3 Assess

Section 1 Review Answers

1. All seed plants have vascular tissue and use seeds to reproduce.
2. Seed coat—protects seed from unfavorable conditions in the environment; embryo plant—grows into new plant; stored food—used by embryo to grow until it can make its own food.
3. Leaves—capture the sun's energy and carry out photosynthesis; stems—carry substances between roots and leaves, provide support for plant; roots—anchor plant, absorb water and nutrients from soil.
4. Coating the underside of a leaf with wax would clog the stomata. Carbon dioxide could not get into the plant for photosynthesis and oxygen could not escape. The plant would be unable to make food and would die.

Check Your Progress

CHAPTER PROJECT 5

By now, seeds should have germinated and students should be making their observations. If some seeds have not germinated, allow students to start over or to observe seeds that have germinated. Make sure students make detailed diagrams, drawings, or photographs of their observations.

Program Resources

◆ **Teaching Resources** 5-1 Review and Reinforce, p. 121; 5-1 Enrich, p. 122

Media and Technology

Interactive Student Tutorial CD-ROM A-5

Answers to Self-Assessment

Caption Question

Figure 8 The narrow inner rings indicate dry years and the wider rings indicate wetter years. Both conditions existed during the tree's early years.

✓ *Checkpoint*

Bark protects the inner cells of woody plants.

Performance Assessment

Oral Presentation Have groups of students make posters showing how leaves, stems, or roots function to produce or transport food and water. Then have them present their posters to the class.

A ◆ 149

Objectives

After completing the lesson, students will be able to
♦ give examples of gymnosperms and list the characteristics they share;
♦ describe how gymnosperms reproduce.

Key Terms gymnosperm, cone, pollen, ovule, pollination

1 Engage/Explore

Activating Prior Knowledge

Ask students to name trees they know that stay green during the winter. *(Sample: Pine and fir)* Have students compile a list of the trees' additional characteristics. *(Sample: Cones, leaves like needles)*

DISCOVER

Skills Focus classifying
Materials *hand lens; metric ruler; 2 or 3 leaves from different angiosperms, such as an oak tree, maple tree, day lily, and rose; 2 or 3 leaves from different gymnosperms, such as pine, yew, and spruce*
Time 10 minutes
Tips Encourage students to include a detailed description of the leaves' features beneath their sketches. Instruct students to wash their hands thoroughly after handling the leaves.
Expected Outcome Students should observe differences in size, length, width, and thickness.
Think It Over Students should group the leaves into needlelike shapes and broad leaves. Their reasons may include the marked difference in thickness and broadness of the leaves.

150 ◆ A

SECTION

2 Gymnosperms

DISCOVER

Are All Leaves Alike?

1. Your teacher will give you a hand lens, a ruler, and the leaves from some seed plants.
2. Using the hand lens, examine each leaf. Sketch each leaf in your notebook.
3. Measure the length and width of each leaf. Record your measurements in your notebook.

Think It Over
Classifying Divide the leaves into two groups on the basis of your observations. Explain why you grouped the leaves as you did.

GUIDE FOR READING

♦ What are the characteristics of gymnosperms?

♦ How do gymnosperms reproduce?

Reading Tip Before you read, preview *Exploring the Life Cycle of a Gymnosperm* on page 154. List any unfamiliar terms. As you read, write definitions for the terms.

Have you ever seen a tree that has grown wider than a car? Do trees this huge really exist? The answer is yes. Some giant sequoia trees, which grow almost exclusively in central California, are over ten meters wide. You can understand why giant sequoias are commonly referred to as "big trees." It takes a long time for a tree to grow so big. Scientists think that the largest giant sequoias may be about 2,000 years old. One reason they live so long is because their bark is fire-resistant.

What Are Gymnosperms?

The giant sequoia trees belong to the group of seed plants known as gymnosperms. A **gymnosperm** (JIM nuh spurm) is a seed plant that produces naked seeds. The seeds of gymnosperms are "naked" because they are not enclosed by any protective covering.

Every gymnosperm produces naked seeds. In addition, many gymnosperms also have needlelike or scalelike leaves, and deep-growing root systems. Although a few kinds of gymnosperms are shrubs or vines, most are trees.

◀ A giant sequoia in California

150 ◆ A

READING STRATEGIES

Reading Tip As students preview *Exploring the Life Cycle of a Gymnosperm*, have them write each unfamiliar term on the front of a card and its definition on the back. Then direct students to quiz partners on the terms, using the cards as flashcards.

Study and Comprehension Have students write brief summaries of the information under each heading. Remind students to include only main ideas and key details in their summaries. Students can then use the summaries as study guides for the section.

Types of Gymnosperms

Gymnosperms are the oldest type of seed plant. According to fossil evidence, gymnosperms first appeared on Earth about 360 million years ago. Fossils also indicate that there were many more species of gymnosperms in the past than today. Today, gymnosperms are classified into four groups—the cycads, the ginkgo, the gnetophytes, and the conifers.

Cycads About 175 million years ago, the majority of plants on Earth were cycads (SY kadz). Today, cycads are found only in tropical areas. As you can see in Figure 11, cycads look like palm trees with cones. A cycad cone can grow as large as a football. In Mexico people grind seeds from the cones of one cycad to make a type of flour for tortillas.

Ginkgo Like cycads, ginkgoes (GING kohz) are also hundreds of millions of years old. Only one species of ginkgo, *Ginkgo biloba*, exists today. It probably survives only because the Chinese and Japanese cared for the species in their gardens. Ginkgoes can grow as tall as 25 meters. Today, ginkgo trees are planted along many city streets because they can tolerate the air pollution produced by city traffic.

Gnetophytes Gnetophytes (NEE tuh fyts) are the gymnosperms that you are least likely to see. These gymnosperms live only in the hot, dry deserts of southern Africa, the deserts of the western United States, and the tropical rain forests. Some gnetophytes are trees, some are shrubs, and others are vines.

Figure 11 Gymnosperms are the oldest seed plants. **A.** Cycads, similar to this sago palm, were quite common during the age of dinosaurs. **B.** Only one kind of ginkgo, *Ginkgo biloba*, lives today. **C.** Gnetophytes, such as *Welwitschia mirabilis* shown here, grow in the very dry deserts of west Africa.

What Are Gymnosperms?

Building Inquiry Skills: Making Models

Have students draw a picture of a gymnosperm based on the description in the text. (*Students' drawings should include needlelike or scalelike leaves, deep-growing root systems, and an indication that the seeds produced are not protected.*) Encourage each student to include something in their drawings that will help them remember the main characteristics. (*Samples: A needle for needlelike leaves, a marble for unprotected seeds, a ladder for deep-growing root systems*) **learning modality: visual**

Types of Gymnosperms

Social Studies Connection

Materials *state map, map pins*
Time 15 minutes

To help students visualize the geographical distribution of gymnosperms in your state, allow them to first research gymnosperms in the library or on the Internet. Then have students place pins on the map (one color for each type of gymnosperm) as they locate the areas where each type grows. Ask: **Which type of gymnosperm is the most common in your state?** (*Answers will vary.*) **learning modality: visual**

Program Resources
◆ **Teaching Resources** 5-2 Lesson Plan, p. 123; 5-2 Section Summary, p. 124

Media and Technology
🎧 **Audiotapes** English-Spanish Summary 5-2

Ongoing Assessment

Writing Have students describe three types of gymnosperms and state their common characteristics.

Types of Gymnosperms, continued

Figure 12 Ponderosa pines (**A**) are conifers that grow in the Rocky Mountains. Both male cones (**B**) and female cones (**C**) are produced on a single tree. *Comparing and Contrasting How do the male and female cones differ?*

Conifers Conifers (KAHN uh furz), or cone-bearing plants, are the largest and most diverse group of gymnosperms on Earth today. Most conifers, such as pines, redwoods, cedars, hemlocks, and junipers, are evergreen plants. Evergreen plants keep their leaves, or needles, year round. Old needles drop off and are replaced by new ones throughout the life of the plant.

If someone were to write a Book of Records for plants, conifers would get many awards. As you already know, giant sequoia trees would win the widest tree on Earth award. New Zealand pygmy pines, in contrast, are among the shortest trees on Earth. They grow only 8 centimeters tall. A bristlecone pine tree in Nevada holds the record for being the oldest organism on Earth. Its annual rings indicate that the tree is about 4,900 years old!

Reproduction

Most gymnosperms have reproductive structures called **cones.** Cones are covered with scales. Most gymnosperms produce two types of cones: male cones and female cones. Usually, a single plant produces both male and female cones. In some types of gymnosperms, however, individual trees produce either male cones or female cones. A few types of gymnosperms produce no cones at all.

Figure 12 shows the male and female cones of a Ponderosa pine. Notice that the male cones are smaller than the female cones. Male cones produce tiny grains of pollen. **Pollen** contains the microscopic cells that will later become sperm cells. Male cones produce so many pollen grains that they can overflow the spaces between the cone's scales.

Female cones contain at least one ovule at the base of each scale. An **ovule** (OH vyool) is a structure that contains an egg cell. After fertilization occurs, the ovule develops into a seed.

You can learn how gymnosperms reproduce in *Exploring the Life Cycle of a Gymnosperm* on the next page. **First, pollen falls from a male cone onto a female cone. In time, a sperm cell and an egg cell join together in an ovule on the female cone.** After fertilization occurs, the zygote develops into the embryo part of the seed.

Pollination and Fertilization The transfer of pollen from a male reproductive structure to a female reproductive structure is called **pollination.** In gymnosperms, wind often carries the pollen from the male cones to the female cones. The pollen collects in a sticky substance produced by each ovule. The scales of the female cone close and seal in the pollen. Inside the closed scale, fertilization occurs. The seed then develops on the scale.

Female cones stay on the tree until the seeds mature. It can take up to two years for the seeds of some gymnosperms to mature. Male cones, however, usually fall off the tree after they have shed their pollen.

Seed Dispersal As the seeds develop, the female cone increases in size. The cone's position on the branch may change as well. Cones that contain immature seeds point upward, while cones that contain mature seeds point downward. When the seeds are mature, the scales open. The wind shakes the seeds out of the cone and carries them away. Only a few seeds will land in a suitable place and grow into new plants.

✓ *Checkpoint* *What is pollen and where is it produced?*

The Scoop on Cones

In this activity, you will observe the structure of a female cone.

1. Use a hand lens to look closely at the female cone. Gently shake the cone over a piece of white paper. Observe what happens.
2. Break off one scale from the cone. Examine its base. If the scale contains a seed, remove the seed.
3. With a hand lens, examine the seed from Step 2, or examine a seed that fell on the paper in Step 1.
4. Wash your hands.

Inferring How does the structure of the cone protect the seeds?

Skills Focus inferring
Materials *mature female pine cone, hand lens, piece of white paper*
Time 10 minutes
Tips Make sure the cones still have some seeds inside the scales. Check for allergies before allowing students to perform this lab. Remind students to wash their hands after the activity.
Expected Outcome The scales of the cone provide some protection for the seeds that develop inside them. For example, the scales probably protect developing seeds from wind, rain, and very cold temperatures.
Extend Have students compare, then sketch, male and female pine cones. Sketches should indicate differences in size, shape, and structure of the scales.
learning modality: visual

 Students can save their sketches in their portfolios.

Program Resources

Science Explorer Series
Environmental Science, Chapter 3

Answers to Self-Assessment

Caption Question

Figure 12 Male cones are smaller than female cones and produce tiny grains of pollen. Female cones have an ovule at the base of each scale.

✓ *Checkpoint*

Pollen contains the cells that mature into sperm cells. It is produced in male cones.

Ongoing Assessment

Writing Have students use the following words in paragraphs to describe gymnosperm reproduction: ovule, pollen, fertilization, seed, and scales. *(Sample: Pollen falls from a male cone onto a female cone. The scales of the female cone close. Fertilization occurs when a sperm cell and an egg cell join inside the ovule on the female cone. This develops into the embryo part of the seed.)*

A ◆ 153

Reproduction, continued

EXPLORING
the Life Cycle of a Gymnosperm

Direct students to carefully study the diagram of the pine tree's life cycle. As they read through the descriptions on the visual essay, ask students to think about how the shape and size of each structure is suited to its function. For example, note the structure of the seed. Ask students: **How do you think the shape of the seed affects its motion in the wind?** *(The shape of the seed allows the wind to carry the seed and prevents the seed from falling directly under the tree.)* Discuss other adaptations that enhance the tree's ability to produce seeds, such as the position of the male cones at the tips of branches *(for efficient pollen distribution)* and growth of male and female cones on the same tree *(increases the probability of fertilization).*
Extend Have students toss a pine seed into the air to see how it travels when released from the female cone. **learning modality: visual**

Gymnosperms and the Living World

Integrating Environmental Science

Tell students that one alternative to clear cutting, *sustained yield,* allows foresters to harvest timber year after year indefinitely. Based on the time it takes a tree to grow to maturity and other factors, the trees managed by sustained yield are cut down no faster than they can be replaced by new trees. For example, pines take about 20 years to mature, so one twentieth (5 percent) of the pine trees in a forest can be cut every year. Ask students to infer how much of a forest could be cut if the trees required 100 years to grow. *(One-hundredth, or 1 percent)* **learning modality: logical/mathematical**

EXPLORING the Life Cycle of a Gymnosperm

Pine trees have a typical life cycle for a gymnosperm. Follow the steps of pollination, fertilization, and seed development in the pine tree.

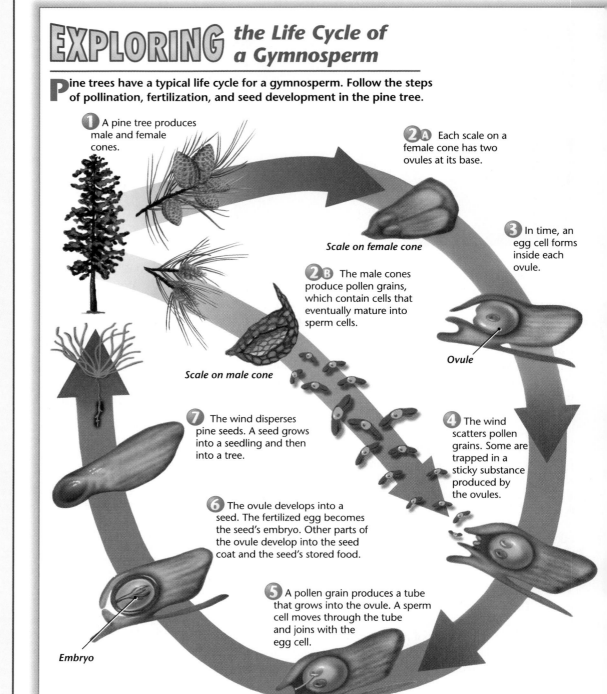

1 A pine tree produces male and female cones.

2A Each scale on a female cone has two ovules at its base.

Scale on female cone

3 In time, an egg cell forms inside each ovule.

2B The male cones produce pollen grains, which contain cells that eventually mature into sperm cells.

Ovule

Scale on male cone

4 The wind scatters pollen grains. Some are trapped in a sticky substance produced by the ovules.

7 The wind disperses pine seeds. A seed grows into a seedling and then into a tree.

6 The ovule develops into a seed. The fertilized egg becomes the seed's embryo. Other parts of the ovule develop into the seed coat and the seed's stored food.

5 A pollen grain produces a tube that grows into the ovule. A sperm cell moves through the tube and joins with the egg cell.

Embryo

154 ◆ A

Background

Facts and Figures Some of the most important products obtained from gymnosperms are resins, used for everything from art supplies to the production of medicine. Natural resin is a thick, yellowish liquid that is exuded from trees. Pine and fir trees are the source of most natural resin. Resin forms when the bark of the tree is injured, such as when it is affected by severe winds, fire, or lightning.

Turpentine is one form of resin. Oil of turpentine is used in the production of oil pastels, and artists use it to clean their paintbrushes. It is used extensively in the manufacture of chemical products such as insecticides, camphor, and synthetic resins, and in the production of plastic.

Gymnosperms and the Living World

Paper and other wood products, such as the lumber used to build homes, come from conifers. Conifers are also used to make the rayon fibers in clothes as well as the cellophane wrappers on some food products. Other products, such as turpentine and the rosin used by baseball pitchers and musicians, are made from the sap produced by some conifers.

INTEGRATING ENVIRONMENTAL SCIENCE Because conifers are so useful to humans, they are grown in large forests in many regions of the United States. One method that is sometimes used to obtain lumber is called clear cutting. In this method all of the trees in a large area of a forest are cut down at once. This practice can leave forest animals homeless and cause the soil to be washed away by rains. Sometimes, other less-damaging cutting methods are used. For example, loggers may cut down trees in a long, narrow strip and then plant new trees in the strips. This method allows forests to regrow more quickly without the loss of soil and homes for wildlife.

Figure 13 Conifers provided the lumber for this playground.

Section 2 Review

1. What are three characteristics of many gymnosperms?
2. Describe how gymnosperms reproduce.
3. List four products that are produced from gymnosperms. Which group of gymnosperms are used to make the products in your list?
4. **Thinking Critically** Comparing and Contrasting Compare the functions of male and female cones.

Science at Home

With a family member, make a list of things in your home that are made from gymnosperms. Then describe the characteristics of gymnosperms to your family member. What gymnosperms grow where you live?

Program Resources

◆ **Teaching Resources** 5-2 Review and Reinforce, p. 125; 5-2 Enrich, p. 126

Media and Technology

Interactive Student Tutorial CD-ROM A-5

Transparencies "Exploring the Life Cycle of a Gymnosperm," Transparency 18

3 Assess

Section 2 Review Answers

1. All produce unprotected seeds; many have needlelike or scalelike leaves and grow deep root systems
2. Pollen falls from a male cone onto a female cone. In time, the sperm cell and egg cell join together in the ovule and eventually develop into the embryo of the seed. When the seed is mature, it falls out and is carried by the wind.
3. Samples: paper, lumber, rayon fibers, cellophane, turpentine, and rosin. All of these products are produced by conifers.
4. The function of both types of cones is to produce reproductive cells. Male cones produce pollen grains while female cones have ovules in which eggs are produced.

Science at Home

Ask students to review the characteristics of gymnosperms. As a class, compile a list of gymnosperms that grow in your area of the country. Then guide students to look for gymnosperm products such as furniture, cellophane, and turpentine. Have students bring their lists to class to compare with those of others. Encourage students to name any unusual products that they found.

Performance Assessment

Oral Presentation Have students work in groups to make presentations about gymnosperms that grow in their area. Suggest students show a photograph or videotape of a gymnosperm in its natural environment as they explain what type of gymnosperm it is, how it reproduces, and what products are made from it.

Portfolio Students can save their photographs or videotapes in their portfolios.

Objectives

After completing the lesson, students will be able to
◆ name types of angiosperms and list the characteristics that they all share;
◆ describe the life cycle of angiosperms;
◆ compare monocots and dicots.

Key Terms angiosperm, ovary, flower, petal, sepal, stamen, pistil, fruit, monocot, dicot

1 Engage/Explore

Activating Prior Knowledge

Ask students to describe how the flowering plants or trees they are familiar with change throughout the year. Encourage students to use specific examples, such as a tree in the schoolyard, a house plant, or a cactus on the bus route. Have students describe the changes in chronological order. Prompt students to include times of increased insect or animal activity in their descriptions, if applicable.

········ **DISCOVER** ········

Skills Focus forming operational definitions
Materials *hand lens; metric rule; three different fruits, such as apples, cherries, peaches, plums, tomatoes, or peppers*
Time 15 minutes
Tips Students may not think that vegetables such as tomatoes or peppers are fruits. Begin by challenging students to determine why scientists consider the foods they are examining to be fruits.
Think It Over Sample definition: Fruits contain seeds and have a fleshy edible part. They vary in color, shape, and the number of seeds they contain.

SECTION 3 Angiosperms

DISCOVER ••••••••••••••••••••••••••••••••••• **ACTIVITY**

What Is a Fruit?

1. Your teacher will give you three different fruits that have been cut in half.

2. Use a hand lens to carefully observe the outside of each fruit. For each fruit, record its color, shape, size, and external features. Record your observations in your notebook.

3. Carefully observe the structures inside the fruit. Record your observations.

Think It Over
Forming Operational Definitions Based on your observations, how would you define the term *fruit*?

GUIDE FOR READING

◆ What characteristics do angiosperms share?

◆ How do angiosperms reproduce?

Reading Tip Before you read, preview the photographs in this section. Predict how angiosperms differ from gymnosperms.

Americans who visited the Japanese pavilion at the United States Centennial Exhibition in 1876 were introduced to kudzu, an attractive Asian vine. Soon, many Americans began planting kudzu in their communities. Little did they know that this creeping vine would become a huge problem.

Kudzu is one of the world's fastest-growing plants. Although it is nicknamed the "mile-a-minute vine," kudzu really does not grow that fast. But it can grow as much as 30 centimeters a day. In the southern United States, kudzu now covers an area twice the size of Connecticut. Unfortunately, there is no effective way to control the growth of this fast-growing plant.

What Are Angiosperms?

Kudzu is a type of seed plant known as an angiosperm. An **angiosperm** (AN jee uh spurm) is a plant that produces seeds that are enclosed in a fruit. The word *angiosperm* comes from two Greek words that mean "seed in a vessel." The protective "vessel"

▼ Kudzu vines

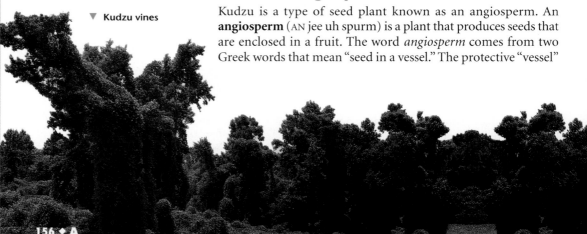

156 ◆ A

READING STRATEGIES

Reading Tip As students preview the photographs, suggest they read the captions. Have them divide a sheet of paper into two columns. Direct students to write their predictions in the first column. Encourage them to add any questions they have as they preview the photographs. After they read, have students confirm their predictions and write answers to the questions in the second column.

Organizing Information Have students use concept maps to organize information about angiosperms. Begin the map for students by writing the main concepts in the section (such as *flower, fruit, monocot,* and *dicot*) on the board. Have students add additional concepts and linking words that connect concepts on one branch of the map to those on other branches.

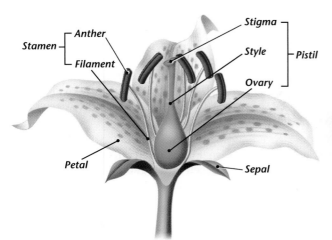

Stamen — Anther, Filament
Petal
Stigma, Style, Ovary — Pistil
Sepal

Figure 14 Like most flowers, this lily contains both male and female reproductive structures. *Interpreting Photographs What structures in the diagram can you find in the photograph?*

where seeds develop is called the **ovary.** The ovary is located within an angiosperm's **flower**—the reproductive structure of an angiosperm. **Two characteristics of angiosperms are that they produce flowers and fruits.**

Most of the familiar plants around you are angiosperms. Angiosperms live almost everywhere on Earth. They grow in frozen areas in the Arctic, tropical jungles, and barren deserts. A few angiosperms, such as mangrove trees and some sea grasses, even live in the oceans.

The Structure of Flowers

Like the plants that produce them, flowers come in all sorts of shapes, sizes, and colors. But all flowers have the same function—reproduction. Look at Figure 14 to see the parts of a typical flower. As you read about the parts, keep in mind that the description does not apply to all flowers. For example, some flowers have only male reproductive parts, and some flowers lack **petals**—the colorful structures that you see when flowers open.

When a flower is still a bud, it is enclosed by leaflike structures called **sepals** (SEE pulz). Sepals protect the developing flower. After the sepals fold back, the petals are revealed. The colors and shapes of the petals and the odors produced by the flower attract insects and other animals. These organisms ensure that pollination occurs.

Within the petals are the flower's male and female reproductive parts. Locate the thin stalks topped by small knobs inside the flower in Figure 14. These are the **stamens** (STAY munz), the male reproductive parts. The thin stalk is called the filament. Pollen is produced in the knob, or anther, at the top of the stalk.

Media and Technology

 Transparencies "The Structure of a Flower," Transparency 19

 Audiotapes English-Spanish Summary 5-3

Program Resources

◆ **Teaching Resources** 5-3 Lesson Plan, p. 127; 5-3 Section Summary, p. 128

Answers to Self-Assessment
Caption Question
Figure 14 Petals, stamens, sepals, pistil

2 Facilitate

What Are Angiosperms?

Building Inquiry Skills: Inferring

Make sure students understand the relationship between the flowers and fruit in an angiosperm. Ask: **If you have an apple tree that has not flowered in over a year, would you expect to be able to get fruit from it?** *(No, because the fruit develops from the ovary, and the flower contains the ovaries.)* **learning modality: verbal**

The Structure of Flowers

Using the Visuals: Figure 14

As students examine the figure, ask them to identify the reproductive parts as male or female. Point out the different parts of the pistil and stamen. Tell students that while most flowers contain both male and female reproductive parts, some flowers contain only one or the other. Ask: **What role do the nonreproductive parts (such as sepals and petals) play?** *(Attract insects)* **learning modality: visual**

Ongoing Assessment

Drawing Have students sketch a flower and label the sepal, petals, stamens, and pistil.

 Students can save their sketches in their portfolios.

A ◆ 157

Reproduction

Visual Arts CONNECTION

The American artist Georgia O'Keeffe (1887–1986) is best known for her paintings of the landscape and wildlife in the western United States. Below you see an O'Keeffe painting of a red poppy. O'Keeffe painted the flower with accurate detail. Look carefully at the red poppy. At first it may not appear to have a lot of detail. But if you look more closely, you can see such structures as petals and reproductive parts.

In Your Journal

Write a paragraph describing the red poppy's adaptations for attracting animals for pollination.

The female parts, or **pistils** (PIS tulz), are usually found in the center of the flower. Some flowers have two or more pistils; others have only one. The sticky tip of the pistil is called the stigma. A slender tube, called a style, connects the stigma to a hollow structure at the base of the flower. This hollow structure is the ovary, which contains one or more ovules.

Reproduction

You can learn how angiosperms reproduce in *Exploring the Life Cycle of an Angiosperm*. **First, pollen falls on a stigma. In time, the sperm cell and egg cell join together in the flower's ovule. The zygote develops into the embryo part of the seed.**

Pollination and Fertilization A flower is pollinated when a grain of pollen falls on the stigma. Like gymnosperms, some angiosperms are pollinated by the wind. But most angiosperms rely on birds, bats, or insects for pollination. Nectar, a sugar-rich food, is located deep inside a flower. When an animal enters a flower to obtain the nectar, it brushes against the anthers and becomes coated with pollen. Some of the pollen can drop onto the flower's stigma as the animal leaves the flower. The pollen can also be brushed onto the sticky stigma of the next flower the animal visits. If the pollen falls on the stigma of a similar plant, fertilization can occur. The zygote then begins to develop into the seed's embryo. Other parts of the ovule develop into the rest of the seed.

Seed Dispersal As the seed develops, the ovary changes into a **fruit**—a ripened ovary and other structures that enclose one or more seeds. Apples and cherries are fruits. So are many foods you usually call vegetables, such as tomatoes and squash. For an angiosperm, a fruit is a way to disperse its seeds. Animals that eat fruits help to disperse their seeds.

Checkpoint What attracts pollinators to angiosperms?

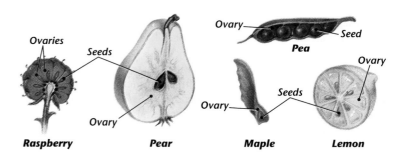

Figure 15 The seeds of angiosperms are enclosed within fruits, which protect and disperse the seed.

Raspberry — Ovaries, Seeds, Ovary

Pear — Seeds, Ovary

Pea — Ovary, Seed

Maple — Ovary, Seeds

Lemon — Ovary

EXPLORING the Life Cycle of an Angiosperm

All angiosperms have a similar life cycle. Follow the steps of pollination, fertilization, and fruit development in this typical angiosperm.

1 The angiosperm produces flowers.

2A Inside the ovary, an egg cell is produced in each ovule.

2B The cells in the anther produce pollen grains.

Anther

Ovule

Ovary

3 Pollen grains are trapped on the stigma.

7 A seed grows into a new plant.

6 The ovary and other structures develop into a fruit that encloses the seeds. The fruit helps in seed dispersal.

5 The ovule develops into a seed. The fertilized egg becomes the seed's embryo. Other parts of the ovule develop into the seed coat and the seed's stored food.

Embryo

Pollen tube

4 The pollen grain produces a pollen tube that grows into the ovule. A sperm cell moves through the pollen tube and joins with the egg cell.

Answers to Self-Assessment

☑ *Checkpoint*

The colors and shapes of the petals and the fragrance of the flowers

EXPLORING

the Life Cycle of an Angiosperm

Explain to students that different parts of an angiosperm produce the different structures needed for reproduction. As students review the steps in the visual, have them record what each of these structures produces and its role in the life cycle: anther *(pollen grains)*, ovule *(egg cell, seed)*, pollen grain *(pollen tube, etc.)*, ovule's wall *(seed coat)*, and ovary *(fruit)*. Make sure students can identify the ovary and anther in the figure at step 1. Ask: **What is the relationship between step 1 and steps 2A and 2B?** *(The ovary in step 2A is shown in the center of step 1; the anther in step 2B is the circled structure.)*

Extend Have students find local examples of an angiosperm, then explain its life cycle in a diagram similar to that in the visual essay. **learning modality: visual**

Building Inquiry Skills: Comparing and Contrasting

Materials *fruits from different plants*
Time 5 minutes

Encourage students to feel the shape, weight, and texture of several fruits, such as grapes, coconuts, apples, bananas, tomatoes, etc. Ask them to infer how the physical characteristics of each fruit are related to the way its seeds are dispersed. CAUTION: *Check for allergies before conducting the activity.* **learning modality: kinesthetic**

Ongoing Assessment

Oral Presentation Have students describe the roles of an orange blossom and an orange in the reproduction of an orange tree. *(Students should describe the orange blossom as containing anthers that produce pollen and an ovary that contains ovules in which egg cells are produced. The fertilized eggs develop into seeds in the ovary. When the fruit develops, it contains the seeds; when the fruit is eaten, the seeds are dispersed.)*

Types of Angiosperms

Including All Students

Materials *cuttings or* *cut flowers from several plants, including monocots (corn, wheat, grasses, lilies, tulips) and dicots (roses, violets, dandelions, oak, maple, apples, bean plants), dissecting knife, hand lens*

Time 20 minutes

Students with limited English proficiency may benefit from comparing real plants to the description in the text. Have small groups compare different plants and classify them as monocots or dicots. Students should sketch the parts of the plants they examine and compare them to the diagrams shown in Figure 16. Caution students to be careful when using the knife. **limited English proficiency**

Angiosperms and the Living World

Real-Life Learning

Have students brainstorm a list of items in the classroom that are made from angiosperms. Encourage students to think about items in different categories, such as food, furniture, clothing, school supplies. Write responses on the board. Ask: **Which items are you surprised come from angiosperms?** (*Students may mention paper, dyes, or chemicals in household products.*) **learning modality: logical/mathematical**

Integrating Health

Students may believe that **ACTIVITY** only "natural" or "herbal" medicines are made from plants. Point out that the text includes examples of prescription medications that are made from angiosperms. Interested students may want to research other medicines to find out whether they are made from angiosperms. **learning modality: verbal**

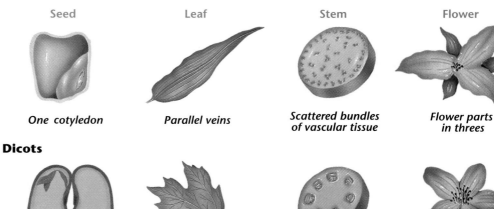

Monocots

Seed — One cotyledon

Leaf — Parallel veins

Stem — Scattered bundles of vascular tissue

Flower — Flower parts in threes

Dicots

Two cotyledons

Branching veins

Circle of vascular tissue

Flower parts in fours or fives

Figure 16 Monocots and dicots are the two groups of angiosperms. The groups differ in the number of cotyledons, the arrangement of veins and vascular tissue, and the number of petals. *Classifying Would a plant whose flowers have 20 petals be a monocot or a dicot?*

Types of Angiosperms

Angiosperms are divided into two major groups: monocots and dicots. "Cot" is short for *cotyledon*. Recall from Section 1 that the cotyledon, or seed leaf, provides food for the embryo. *Mono* means "one" and *di* means "two". **Monocots** are angiosperms that have only one seed leaf. **Dicots,** on the other hand, produce seeds with two seed leaves. Look at Figure 16 to compare the characteristics of monocots and dicots.

Monocots Grasses, including corn, wheat, and rice, and plants such as lilies and tulips are monocots. The flowers of a monocot usually have either three petals or a multiple of three petals. Monocots usually have long, slender leaves with veins that run parallel to one another like train rails. The bundles of vascular tissue in monocot stems are usually scattered randomly throughout the stem.

Dicots Dicots include plants such as roses and violets, as well as dandelions. Both oak and maple trees are dicots, as are food plants such as beans and apples. The flowers of dicots often have either four or five petals or multiples of these numbers. The leaves are usually wide, with veins that branch off from one another. Dicot stems usually have bundles of vascular tissue arranged in a circle.

☑ *Checkpoint How do the petals of monocots and dicots differ in number?*

Background

Facts and Figures Some of the most unusual angiosperms are insect-eating plants. These plants generally live in nitrogen-poor soils and receive vital nutrients from their prey.

The bogs of North Carolina house the well-known Venus flytrap. Each plant grows several kidney-shaped leaves with sensitive inner bristles. When a moving insect touches a bristle, the leaf halves snap together.

Enzymes flood the inside of the trap and slowly digest the prey. Special glands absorb the nutrients. When the insect is fully digested, the trap opens again.

The pitcher plant uses a narrow, juglike structure to lure and trap insects. The pitcher has a strong scent and attractive color. Insects slip down the side of the pitcher and fall into a bath of water and digestive juices.

Angiosperms and the Living World

Angiosperms are an important source of food, clothing, and medicine for other organisms. Plant-eating animals, such as cows, elephants, and beetles, eat flowering plants such as grasses as well as the leaves of trees. People eat vegetables, fruits, and cereals, all of which are angiosperms.

People also produce clothing and other products from angiosperms. For example, the seeds of cotton plants, like the ones you see in Figure 17, are covered with cotton fibers. The stems of flax plants provide linen fibers. The sap of tropical rubber trees is used to make rubber for tires and other products. Furniture is often made from the wood of maple, cherry, and oak trees.

 INTEGRATING HEALTH Some angiosperms are used in the making of medicine. For example, aspirin was first made from a substance found in the leaves of willow trees. Digitalis, a heart medication, comes from the leaves of the foxglove plant. Cortisone is a medicine made from the roots of the Mexican yam. It is used to treat arthritis and other joint problems. These medicines have helped improve the health of many people.

Figure 17 Cotton seeds, which develop in structures called bolls, are covered with fibers that are manufactured into cotton fabric.

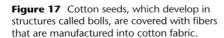

Section 3 Review

1. What two characteristics do all angiosperms share? Explain the importance of those characteristics.
2. Give a brief description of how reproduction occurs in angiosperms.
3. List the parts of a typical flower. What is the function of each part?
4. **Thinking Critically Inferring** A certain plant has small, dull-colored flowers with no scent. Do you think the plant is pollinated by animals or by the wind? Explain.

> **Check Your Progress** CHAPTER PROJECT 5
>
> Your plants should now have, or will soon have, flowers. Make a diagram of the flower's structure. When the flowers open, you'll have to pollinate them. This work is usually done by insects or birds. After pollination, watch how the flower changes. (*Hint:* Discuss with your teacher and classmates how to pollinate the flowers.)

Answers to Self-Assessment

Caption Question

Figure 16 A dicot

☑ *Checkpoint*

Monocot petals are in multiples of three. Dicot petals are in multiples of four or five.

---

3 Assess

Section 3 Review Answers

1. All angiosperms produce flowers and fruits. Both are important in reproduction.
2. First, pollen falls on a stigma. In time, the sperm cell and egg cell join together in the flower's ovule. The zygote develops into the embryo part of the seed.
3. Sepals—protect the developing flower; petals—attract pollinators; stamen—consists of an anther and filament, produces pollen; pistil—consists of a stigma, a style, and an ovary that contains one or more ovules; ovule—egg cells are made in ovule
4. The plant is probably pollinated by the wind. If it had to be pollinated by animals, its flowers would probably have an odor and bright colors that attract animals.

> *Check Your Progress* CHAPTER PROJECT 5
>
> Check the growth of the plants. If you observe that some of the plants are dying, discuss their care with students. When the plants flower, help students pollinate them. The two best methods are to use the bee parts that come in a seed-growing kit, or to tap the flower gently and collect the pollen on a piece of paper. The pollen can then be placed on the stigma. A third method is to use cotton swabs, but this may not be as successful. Discuss with students how these methods compare to the ways plants are pollinated in nature.

Performance Assessment

Organizing Information Have students draw flowcharts showing the processes involved in the reproduction of angiosperms.

A Close Look at Flowers

Preparing for Inquiry

Key Concept Flowers contain several distinct parts whose structures can be studied for a more complete understanding of their functions.

Skills Objectives Students will be able to

- observe the structures of a flower;
- measure petal size, and the heights of the pistil and stamen;
- infer the method of pollination and whether the plant is a monocot or dicot.

Time 40 minutes

Advance Planning Provide a variety of flowers so that students can observe more than one type. Use large- or medium-sized flowers that have all the essential structures, such as tulips, lilies, gladiolas, daffodils, petunias, and others. Find out in advance of doing the lab which students may be allergic to pollen. Provide a substitute activity for these students and make any other necessary arrangements.

Guiding Inquiry

Invitation Angiosperms are seed plants that produce flowers. Ask: **What is the function of the flower?** (*reproduction*) Ask students to think about how each structure of the flower relates to the two stages of reproduction in angiosperms—pollination and fertilization.

Introducing the Procedure

- Teach students how to use a scalpel safely. Scissors can be substituted for a scalpel in some steps.
- Introduce or review the use of a microscope and how to make a wet mount. Remind students that slides and cover slips are fragile and they should alert you immediately if anything breaks in the lab.
- To obtain pollen samples, students can simply tap the stamen if the flower is sufficiently developed. If the flower has just opened, demonstrate how to crush the stamen against the slide.

A Close Look at Flowers

In this lab, you will examine a flower in order to understand how it works.

Problem

What is the function of a flower, and what roles do its different parts play?

Skills Focus

observing, measuring, inferring

Materials

paper towels	plastic dropper
hand lens	microscope
slide	large flower
coverslip	scalpel
tape	water
metric ruler	lens paper

Procedure

Part 1 The Outer Parts of the Flower

1. Tape 4 sheets of paper towel on your work area. Obtain a flower from your teacher. While handling the flower gently, observe its shape and color. Use the ruler to measure it. Notice whether the petals have any spots or other markings. Does the flower have a scent? Record your observations with sketches and descriptions.
2. Observe the sepals. How many are there? How do they relate to the rest of the flower? (*Hint:* The sepals are often green, but not always.) Record your observations.

3. Use a scalpel to carefully cut off the sepals without damaging the structures beneath them. **CAUTION:** *Scalpels are sharp. Cut in a direction away from yourself and others.*
4. Observe the petals. How many are there? Are all the petals the same, or are they different? Record your observations.

Part 2 The Male Part of the Flower

5. Carefully pull off the petals to examine the male part of the flower. Try not to damage the structures beneath the petals.
6. Observe the stamens. How many are there? How are they shaped? How tall are they? Record your observations.
7. Use a scalpel to carefully cut the stamens away from the rest of the flower without damaging the structures beneath them. Lay the stamens on the paper towel.

Troubleshooting the Experiment

If pollen begins to fall off as students handle the flowers, they can collect it on a piece of paper and put it aside for Steps 8–9.

Expected Outcome

- The top of the pistil (the stigma) may be rough, smooth, sticky, branched, or feathery.
- The number of chambers in the ovary is equal to or is a multiple of the number of petals and stamens.

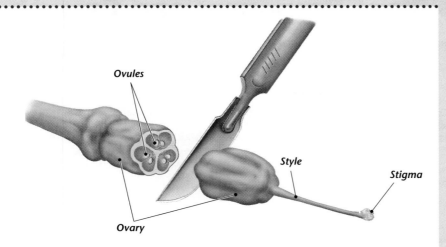

Ovules

Style

Stigma

Ovary

8. Obtain a clean slide and coverslip. Hold a stamen over the slide, and gently tap some pollen grains from the anther onto the slide. Add a drop of water to the pollen. Then place the coverslip over the water and pollen.

9. Observe the pollen under both the low-power objective and the high-power objective of a microscope. Draw and label a pollen grain.

Part 3 The Female Part of the Flower

10. Use a scalpel to cut the pistil away from the rest of the flower. Measure the height of the pistil. Examine its shape. Observe the top of the pistil. Determine if that surface will stick to and lift a tiny piece of lens paper. Record your observations.

11. Lay the pistil on the paper towel. Holding it firmly at its base, use a scalpel to cut the pistil in half at its widest point, as shown in the diagram above. **CAUTION:** *Cut away from your fingers.* How many compartments do you see? How many ovules do you see? Record your observations.

Analyze and Conclude

1. Based on your observations, describe how the petals, pistils, sepals, and stamens of a flower are arranged.

2. What is the main function of a flower? How are the sepals, petals, stamens, and pistil involved in that function?

3. How does a flower produce seeds?

4. Did your flower show any patterns in the number of sepals, petals, stamens, or other structures? If so, describe that pattern. Is your flower a monocot or a dicot?

5. **Apply** How do you think the flower you examined is pollinated? Use your observations, including the heights of the pistil and stamens, to support your answer.

More to Explore

Some kinds of flowers do not have all the parts found in the flower in this lab. Obtain a different flower. Find out which parts this flower has, and which parts are missing. Get your teacher's approval before carrying out this investigation.

Analyze and Conclude

1. In circles, in this order: sepals on the outside, then petals, then stamens, then the pistil at the center.

2. The main function of a flower is reproduction. The sepals protect the flower as it develops and support the base of the flower. The petals may attract the attention of animals by color or scent. Stamens produce pollen, which releases sperm cells. Pistils hold the egg cells.

3. The flower produces seeds when sperm cells from pollen fertilize egg cells inside the ovary.

4. Flower parts of monocots are usually in threes or multiples of threes. Flower parts of dicots are usually in fives or fours, or in multiples of those numbers.

5. Answers will vary. For example, colorful petals suggest the flower is pollinated by organisms with color vision. A pistil that is taller than the stamens may suggest that the flower does not self-pollinate. A flower structure in which the anthers and stigma are located deep within the flower suggests pollination by small pollinators, such as insects or hummingbirds.

Extending the Inquiry

More to Explore Make sure students' second flower is different from the first flower they dissected. Students should compare flowers and discover that flowers vary greatly in structure. For example, some plants have separate male and female flowers. Students should make sketches and should point out the differences between the flowers they studied.

Safety

Provide a substitute activity for any student who is allergic to pollen. Make sure all students wash their hands immediately after this activity. Teach scalpel safety. Substitute scissors for scalpels whenever possible. Students should take care not to drop the glass microscope slides. Review the safety guidelines in Appendix A.

Program Resources

◆ **Teaching Resources** Chapter 5 Real-World Lab, pp. 139–141

SECTION
4 Plant
Responses
and Growth

Objectives

After completing the lesson, students will be able to
◆ identify three stimuli that produce plant responses;
◆ list the functions that plant hormones control.

Key Terms tropism, hormone, auxin

1 Engage/Explore

Activating Prior Knowledge

Ask students to describe the usual direction of root and stem growth for plants on Earth. *(Roots point down; stems point up.)* Tell students that scientists and astronauts are studying how plants grow in space, particularly in the apparent weightless conditions in the orbiting space shuttle. Challenge them to speculate how the absence of Earth's gravity might affect plant growth. *(Sample: Without Earth's gravity, plants might not be able to achieve the same orientation.)*

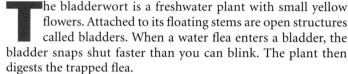

········ DISCOVER ········

Skills Focus inferring
Materials *sensitive plant such as a Venus' flytrap or mimosa; common houseplant such as a geranium or impatiens*
Time 10 minutes
Tips If you have difficulty finding sensitive plants, contact a biological supply house or specialty gardening shop. Remind students to wash their hands after touching the plants.
Expected Outcome The leaf of the sensitive plant closes after it is touched. The leaf of the houseplant does not respond.
Think It Over Students might infer that having sensitive leaves helps to protect a plant from predators and environmental conditions.

DISCOVER ···························· ACTIVITY

Can a Plant Respond to Touch?

1. Your teacher will give you two plants. Observe the first plant. Gently touch a leaf and observe what happens over the next three minutes. Record your observations.

2. Repeat Step 1 with the second plant. Record your observations.

3. Wash your hands with soap and water.

Think It Over
Inferring What advantage might a plant have if its leaves responded to touch?

GUIDE FOR READING

◆ What are three stimuli that produce plant responses?
◆ What functions do plant hormones control?

Reading Tip As you read, use the headings to make an outline about plant responses and growth.

▼ A floating bladderwort

The bladderwort is a freshwater plant with small yellow flowers. Attached to its floating stems are open structures called bladders. When a water flea enters a bladder, the bladder snaps shut faster than you can blink. The plant then digests the trapped flea.

A bladderwort responds quickly—faster than many animals respond to a similar stimulus. You may be surprised to learn that some plants have lightning-quick responses. In fact, you might have thought that plants do not respond to stimuli at all. But plants do respond to some stimuli, although they usually do so more slowly than the bladderwort.

Tropisms

Animals usually respond to stimuli by moving. Unlike animals, plants commonly respond by growing either toward or away from a stimulus. A plant's growth response toward or away from a stimulus is called a **tropism** (TROH pihz uhm). If a plant grows toward the stimulus, it is said to show a positive tropism. If a plant grows away from a stimulus, it shows a negative tropism. **Touch, light, and gravity are three important stimuli to which plants respond.**

Touch Some plants, such as bladderworts, show a response to touch called thigmotropism. The term *thigmo* comes from a Greek word that means "touch." The stems of many vines, such as grapes and morning glories, show a positive thigmotropism. As the vines grow, they coil around any object that they touch.

Light All plants exhibit a response to light called phototropism. The leaves, stems, and flowers of plants grow toward light, showing a positive phototropism. For example, sunflower plants

READING STRATEGIES

Reading Tip As a class, outline the information under the first section heading, incorporating headings in complete sentences.

I. Plants grow toward or away from stimuli (tropism).
  A. Plants respond to touch (thigmotropism).
  B. Plants respond to light (phototropism).
  C. Plants respond to gravity (gravitropism).

Study and Comprehension After students read the section, have them use the outlines they created to generate questions about plant response and growth. Instruct students to write five questions on a sheet of paper. Then have partners use the questions to quiz each other on the information in the section.

exhibit a strong positive phototropism. As the sun's position changes during the day, sunflowers move on their stalks so that they are always facing the sun.

Gravity Plants also respond to gravity. This response is called gravitropism. Roots show positive gravitropism—they grow downward, with the pull of gravity. Stems, on the other hand, show negative gravitropism—they grow upward.

Plant Hormones

Plants are able to respond to light, gravity, and touch because they produce hormones. A **hormone** produced by a plant is a chemical that affects how the plant grows and develops. **In addition to tropisms, plant hormones also control germination, the formation of flowers, stems, and leaves, the shedding of leaves, and the development and ripening of fruit.**

One important plant hormone is named **auxin** (AWX sin). Auxin speeds up the rate at which a plant's cells grow. Auxin controls a plant's response to light. When light shines on one side of a plant's stem, auxin moves to the shaded side of the stem. The cells on that side begin to grow faster. Eventually, the cells on the stem's shady side are longer than those on its sunny side. So the stem bends toward the light.

☑ *Checkpoint* *What role does the hormone auxin play in a plant?*

Life Spans of Angiosperms

If you've ever planted a garden, you know that many flowering plants grow, flower, and die in a single year. Flowering plants that complete a life cycle within one growing season are called annuals. The word annual comes from the Latin word *annus,* which means "year." Most annuals have herbaceous stems. Annuals include many garden plants, such as marigolds, petunias, and pansies. Wheat, tomatoes, and cucumbers are also annuals.

Angiosperms that complete their life cycle in two years are called biennials (by EN ee ulz). The Latin prefix *bi* means "two."

Figure 18 The face of this sunflower turns on its stalk throughout the day so that it always faces the sun.
Making Generalizations How does a positive phototropism help a plant survive?

Program Resources

◆ **Teaching Resources** 5-4 Lesson Plan, p. 131; 5-4 Section Summary, p. 132

Media and Technology

 Audiotapes English-Spanish Summary 5-4

Answers to Self-Assessment

Caption Question

Figure 18 Positive phototropism keeps a plant facing toward light so that it gets enough energy to make its food.

☑ *Checkpoint*

Auxin speeds up the rate at which plant cells grow.

2 Facilitate

Tropisms

Demonstration

Materials *small potted plant, such as a bean plant; materials to support the pot*
Time 10 minutes, with observations one week later

Students who are mastering English will benefit from this dramatic presentation. Place the plant on a ledge near a window or light. Ask: **In what direction is the plant growing? Why?** *(The stem is growing upward, toward the light and away from the pull of gravity.)* Support the pot on its side so the stem is parallel to the floor. Ask students to predict what the plant will look like in a week. After one week, the plant's new growth should be pointing up, with a bend between the old and new growth. Ask the students to explain what happened in terms of the plant's tropisms. *(The plant's positive phototropism and negative gravitropism caused it to grow upward.)* **limited English proficiency**

Plant Hormones

Inquiry Challenge

Materials *coiled spring toy*
Time 5 minutes

Students may have difficulty understanding how auxin's effect on plant cells controls how a plant responds to light. Have them model this by holding a coiled spring toy and causing one side to elongate, or "grow." The spring toy will bend away from the elongated side. Ask students: **Which side represents the shaded side of the plant?** *(The elongated side)* **learning modality: kinesthetic**

Ongoing Assessment

Writing Have students explain how plants exhibit positive phototropism and positive and negative gravitropism.

A ◆ 165

Life Spans of Angiosperms

Language Arts Connection
Students may be familiar with the word *perennial* from phrases such as "the perennial favorite." Ask students to think of other phrases using *annual*, *biennial*, *perennial*, or similar words. Have students compose sentences using these words. Groups can share their sentences, then work as a class to come up with three phrases that help them remember the life spans of each type of plant.
cooperative learning

3 Assess

Section 4 Review Answers
1. Light, gravity, and touch
2. A plant hormone is a chemical that affects how a plant grows and develops. Hormones control tropisms, germination, the formation of flowers, stems, and leaves, the shedding of leaves, and the development of fruit.
3. The plant's leaves and flowers show a positive phototropism, so they grow toward the light.
4. The grass that grows in most lawns is a perennial; it lives through many years.

Science at Home

Materials *corn kernels or lima bean seeds, water, soil, paper cup*
Tips Students should explain that the plants respond with positive phototropism because they grew toward the light. Ask: **What part of the seedling demonstrated positive gravitropism?** *(The roots)*

Performance Assessment

Drawing Have students draw a series of pictures showing a plant responding to stimuli. Each example should be labeled with the appropriate tropism.

Figure 19 A flowering plant is classified as an annual, biennial, or perennial depending on the length of its growing season. **A.** These morning glories are annuals. **B.** Foxglove, like this *Digitalis purpurea*, is a biennial. **C.** This peony, a perennial, will bloom year after year.

In the first year, biennials germinate and grow roots, very short stems, and leaves. During their second year, biennials grow new stems and leaves and then produce flowers and seeds. Once the flowers produce seeds, the plant dies. Parsley, celery, and foxglove are biennials.

Flowering plants that live for more than two years are called perennials. The Latin word *per* means "through." Perennials usually live through many years. Some perennials, such as peonies and asparagus, have herbaceous stems. The leaves and stems above the ground die each winter. New ones are produced each spring. Most perennials, however, have woody stems. Bristlecone pines, oak trees, and honeysuckle are examples of woody perennials.

Section 4 Review

1. Name three stimuli to which plants respond.
2. What is a plant hormone? List four processes that a plant's hormones control.
3. Suppose you are growing a plant on a windowsill. After a few days, you notice that the plant's leaves and flowers are facing the window. Explain why this has occurred.
4. **Thinking Critically** **Applying Concepts** Is the grass that grows in most lawns an annual, a biennial, or a perennial? Explain.

Science at Home
With a family member, soak some corn seeds or lima bean seeds in water overnight. Then push them gently into some soil in a paper cup until they are just covered. Keep the soil moist. When you see the stems break through the soil, place the cup in a sunny window. After a few days, explain to your family member why the plants responded the way they did.

Media and Technology

Interactive Student Tutorial CD-ROM A-5

Exploring Life Science Videodisc Unit 2, Side 2, "Fertilizers"
Chapter 6

Program Resources

- **Teaching Resources** 5-4 Review and Reinforce, p. 133; 5-4 Enrich, p. 134
- **Integrated Science Laboratory Manual** A-5, "Investigating Hormones That Control Germination"

Which Way is Up?

Skills Lab

In this lab, you will develop and test a hypothesis about how seedlings respond to gravity.

Problem

How is the growth of a seed affected by gravity?

Materials

4 corn seeds   plastic petri dish
paper towels   scissors
water   masking tape
marking pencil   clay

Procedure

1. Read over the entire procedure. Then, with your group, develop a hypothesis about the direction in which the seedlings will grow in response to gravity.
2. Arrange four seeds that have been soaked in water for 24 hours in a petri dish. The pointed ends of the seeds should face the center of the dish, as shown in the illustration.
3. Place a circle cut from a paper towel over the seeds. Moisten one or more paper towels with water so that they are wet but not dripping. Pack them in the dish to hold the seeds firmly in place. Cover the dish, and seal it with tape.
4. Lay the dish upside-down so the seeds show. Use a marking pencil to draw a small, outward-facing arrow over one of the seeds, as shown in the illustration. Turn the dish over and write your name and the date on it.
5. Use clay to stand up the petri dish so that the arrow points upward. Put the petri dish in a dark place.

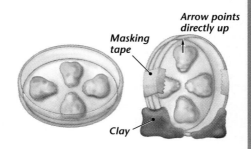

Masking tape

Arrow points directly up

Clay

6. Once a day for a week, remove the petri dish and check it. Do not open the dish. Observe and sketch the seeds. Note the seeds' direction of growth. Then return the dish, making sure that the arrow points upward.

Analyze and Conclude

1. What new structures emerged as the seeds developed? How did the direction of growth compare from seed to seed?
2. Did your results confirm your hypothesis? If not, describe any differences between your hypothesis and your results.
3. Why was it necessary to grow these seeds in the dark?
4. **Think About It** What evidence or ideas did you consider when you wrote your hypothesis? Did any of your ideas change as a result of this experiment? Explain.

Design an Experiment

How will your seedlings respond if you now allow them to grow in the light? Design an experiment to find out. Obtain your teacher's approval before carrying out your experiment.

---

variable so the direction of growth was affected only by gravity. The dark also simulates the underground environment in which seeds usually germinate.
4. Answers will vary. Students should realize that the results show that the direction of growth is influenced by gravity, not the direction in which the seeds are planted.

Extending the Inquiry

Design an Experiment Students may want to place their petri dish so that it is exposed to

light on only one side to observe any differences in the growth of the four plants. Remind them to take gravity into account.

Program Resources

◆ **Teaching Resources** Chapter 5 Skills Lab, pp. 142–143
◆ **Inquiry Skills Activity Book** Provides teaching and review of all inquiry skills

---

Skills Lab

Developing Hypotheses

Which Way Is Up?

Preparing for Inquiry

Key Concept When the new root emerges from a germinating seed, it always grows downward; the new stem always grows upward.
Skills Objective Students will be able to
◆ develop hypotheses that explain how the growth of a seed is affected by gravity.
Time 30 minutes, plus a few minutes each day for a week
Advance Planning Make sure there are enough corn seeds for you to give four seeds to each student or group. Soak the seeds in water for 24 hours before the lab.
Alternative Materials Other seeds that can be used include lima beans, sunflowers, squash, oats, and cucumbers. If you use glass petri dishes, remind students to follow all the safety procedures associated with the use of glass.

Guiding Inquiry

Invitation Ask students to imagine what the world would be like if gravity did not influence the growth of plants. Ask: **If you planted a seed in the ground, would the plant always grow up out of the ground?** (*The plant might sometimes grow up, other times grow in other directions.*)

Introducing the Procedure

Make sure students understand that the seeds must be kept in exactly the same position throughout the experiment. Show two sample petri dishes, one in which the positions of the seeds can shift and one that is properly packed.

Analyze and Conclude

1. Roots grew from the pointed tip of the seed, while the stem grew from the rounded part. The roots always grew downward, and the stems always grew upward, bending if necessary.
2. Students should be able to use what they learned in this lab to explain any inconsistencies between their hypotheses and the evidence.
3. Plants usually grow toward light; it was necessary to exclude light as a

SECTION 5 Feeding the World

Objective
After completing the lesson, students will be able to
◆ describe some methods that might help farmers produce more crops.

Key Terms genetic engineering, hydroponics

1 Engage/Explore

Activating Prior Knowledge
Ask students to describe a typical farm from 100 years ago. *(Most will say small, one family worked on it, only grew enough food for the family.)* Then have students describe a farm today. *(Large, may be run by a company, grows enough food for many people.)* Then ask students to imagine what a farm will be like 100 years from now.

DISCOVER

Skills Focus predicting
Materials *bag, tags, cooked rice, peanuts, or cereal*
Time 20 minutes
Tips For a class of 30, create three number 1 tags, five number 2 tags, and twenty-two number 3 tags. Divide the food into three equal portions, and present one portion to each student, depending on the group. Group 1 should have the largest portion. Group 3 should have the smallest portion. Check for food allergies among students. Encourage but don't require students to eat their portion.
Expected Outcome Students may feel guilt, self-righteousness, pity, envy, anger, resentment, or gratefulness.
Think It Over Food is already scarce in some countries. If the world's population increases, there will be even less food in many places.

SECTION 5 Feeding the World

DISCOVER   ACTIVITY

Will There Be Enough to Eat?
1. Choose a numbered tag from the bag that your teacher provides. If you pick a tag with the number 1 on it, you're from a wealthy country. If you pick a tag with the number 2, you're from a middle-income country. If you pick a tag with the number 3, you're from a poor country.
2. Find classmates that have the same number on their tag. Sit down as a group.
3. Your teacher will serve your group a meal. The amount of food you receive will depend on the number on your tag.
4. As you eat, observe the people in your group and in the other groups. After you eat, record your observations. Also, record how you felt and what you were thinking during the meal.

Think It Over
Predicting Based on this activity, predict what effect an increase in the world's population would have on the world's food supply.

GUIDE FOR READING
◆ What methods may help farmers produce more crops?

Reading Tip As you read, make a list of the technologies being used to increase Earth's food supply.

Today, about six billion people live on Earth. Some scientists predict that by the year 2050 the population will grow to ten billion people. Think about how much additional food will be needed to feed the growing population. How will farmers be able to grow enough food?

Fortunately, both scientists and farmers are already hard at work trying to find answers to this question. **In laboratories, scientists are developing plants that are more resistant to insects, disease, and drought. They are also developing plants that produce more food per plant. On farms, new, efficient, "high-tech" farming practices are being used.**

READING STRATEGIES

Reading Tip Before students begin reading, encourage them to preview the section by reading the headings, captions, and boldfaced terms and looking at the photographs. Then have students make their lists of technologies as they read, summarizing each one in their own words.

Study and Comprehension Arrange students in groups of three or four. Have students in each group use the information in the section to write a list of questions about feeding the world's population. Encourage students to read the section to find the answers to their questions. Students may want to do additional research in the school media center.

Producing Better Plants

Wheat, corn, rice, and potatoes are the major sources of food for people on Earth today. To feed more people, then, the production, or yields, of these crops must be increased. This is not an easy task. One challenge facing farmers is that these crops grow only in certain climates. Another challenge is that the size and structure of these plants limit how much food they can produce.

Today scientists are using new technologies to address these challenges. Recall from Chapter 2 that scientists can manipulate the genetic material of certain bacteria to produce human insulin. The process that these scientists use is called genetic engineering. In **genetic engineering,** scientists alter an organism's genetic material to produce an organism with qualities that people find useful.

Scientists are using genetic engineering to produce plants that can grow in a wider range of climates. They are also engineering plants to be more resistant to damage from insects. For example, scientists have inserted genetic material from a bacterium into corn and tomato plants. The new genetic material enables the plants to produce substances that kill insects. Caterpillars or other insects that bite into the leaves of these plants are killed. Today, many kinds of genetically engineered plants are grown on experimental farms. Some of these plants may produce the crops of the future.

☑ *Checkpoint* *What are the four crops on which people depend?*

Improving the Efficiency of Farms

On the farms of the future, satellite images and computers will be just as important as tractors and harvesters. These new tools will allow farmers to practice "precision farming"—knowing just how much water and fertilizer different fields require. First, satellite images of the farmer's fields are taken. Then, a computer analyzes the images to determine the makeup of the soil in different fields on the farm. The computer uses the data to prepare a watering and fertilizing plan for each field. Precision farming benefits farmers because it saves time and money. It also increases crop yields by helping farmers maintain ideal conditions in all fields.

Figure 20 In this high-tech greenhouse, scientists control the environmental conditions as they develop new types of plants. *Applying Concepts How might new plant types lead to increased crop yields in the future?*

Program Resources

◆ **Teaching Resources** 5-5 Lesson Plan, p. 135; 5-5 Section Summary, p. 136
◆ **Interdisciplinary Exploration Series** *Riddles of the Pharaohs,* pp. 26–27

Media and Technology

 Audiotapes English-Spanish Summary 5-5

Answers to Self-Assessment

Caption Question

Figure 20 New plant types that were resistant to pests or disease and able to grow in a variety of climates would result in higher crop yields.

☑ *Checkpoint*

Wheat, corn, rice, and potatoes

2 *Facilitate*

Producing Better Plants

Building Inquiry Skills: Making Judgments

Inform students that scientists have genetically engineered rice plants, using genes from the potato to make the rice resist insects and genes from barley plants to make it salt—and drought—tolerant. The scientists decided to give this technology to developing countries for free, but to sell it to developed countries such as Japan and the United States. Use this information to stimulate class discussion. Encourage the class to make judgments about the scientists' decision. **learning modality: verbal**

Improving the Efficiency of Farms

 Integrating Environmental Science

If possible, visit a local farm or invite a farmer or farm manager to talk to the class. Direct students to prepare questions about the size and layout of the farm, the crops produced, the quality of the soil, and the methods used to protect plants from disease and pests. After the visit, ask students: **How could precision farming both improve the efficiency of this farm and protect the environment?** *(Sample: Precision farming could keep farmers from using more water and fertilizer than necessary.)* **learning modality: verbal**

Ongoing Assessment

Oral Presentation Ask students to explain why it is necessary to produce better plants and increase the efficiency of farms. *(Answers should include that the world's population is growing and more food will be needed.)*

Hydroponics

Building Inquiry Skills: Inferring

Ask students to infer some benefits of growing food crops hydroponically. *(Hydroponics allows plants to be grown in conditions where it would be difficult to grow plants in soil.)* **learning modality: logical/mathematical**

3 Assess

Section 5 Review Answers

1. Genetic engineering, precision farming, and hydroponics
2. It can produce plants that are resistant to disease, insects, and drought; can produce more food; and can grow in a wider range of climates.
3. It saves time and money and helps improve crop yields. It benefits the environment because less fertilizer is used.
4. They can survive without soil because they absorb water and nutrients directly from the nutrient-rich water that bathes their roots.

Check Your Progress
CHAPTER PROJECT 5

Help students collect seeds. Collect data from each student or group and find the average number of seeds produced per plant. If time permits, have students plant these seeds to begin the life cycle again. Emphasize that this second cycle should be similar to the one they just observed. Check student's data tables for completeness and make sure their diagrams are labeled appropriately.

Performance Assessment

Oral Presentation Have students work in groups to make displays to show how genetic engineering, precision farming, or hydroponics can help farmers increase food production.

Figure 21 The map on the computer screen of this tractor shows the makeup of the soil in a farm's fields. The map was obtained by satellite imaging.

 INTEGRATING ENVIRONMENTAL SCIENCE Precision farming also benefits the environment because farmers use only as much fertilizer as the soil needs. When less fertilizer is used, fewer nutrients wash off the land into lakes and rivers. As you read in Chapter 3, reducing the use of fertilizers is one way to prevent algal blooms from damaging bodies of water.

Hydroponics

In some areas of the world, poor soil does not support the growth of crops. For example, on some islands in the Pacific Ocean, the soil contains large amounts of salt from the surrounding ocean. Food crops will not grow in the salty soil.

On these islands, people can use hydroponics to grow food crops. **Hydroponics** (hy druh PAHN iks) is a method by which plants are grown in solutions of nutrients instead of in soil. Usually, the plants are grown in containers in which their roots are anchored in gravel or sand. The nutrient-rich water is pumped through the gravel or sand. Unfortunately, hydroponics is a costly method of growing food crops. But, the process allows people to grow crops in areas with poor farmland to help feed a growing population.

 ## Section 5 Review

1. List three methods that farmers can use to increase crop yields.
2. Explain how genetic engineering may help farmers grow more food.
3. How does precision farming benefit farmers? How does it benefit the environment?
4. **Thinking Critically Applying Concepts** How are plants that are grown using hydroponics able to survive without soil?

Check Your Progress
CHAPTER PROJECT 5

Your plants should be near the end of their growth cycle. Continue to observe them. Harvest the seeds carefully, observe them, and compare them with the original seeds. If you have time, plant a few of these new seeds to begin the life cycle again.

Program Resources

 Science Explorer Series *Environmental Science,* Chapter 1
◆ **Interdisciplinary Exploration Series** "Fate of the Rain Forest," p. 42
◆ **Teaching Resources** 5-5 Review and Reinforce, p. 137; 5-5 Enrich, p. 138

Media and Technology

 Interactive Student Tutorial CD-ROM A-5

Exploring Life Science Videodisc Unit 1, Side 2, "Can We Still Get What We Need?" Chapter 4

SECTION 1 The Characteristics of Seed Plants

Key Ideas

- All seed plants have vascular tissue and produce seeds. All seed plants also have leaves, stems, and roots.
- A seed has three important parts: an embryo, stored food, and a seed coat.
- Photosynthesis occurs mainly in leaves. Stems support plants and transport materials between the roots and leaves. Roots anchor plants and absorb water and minerals.

Key Terms

phloem	cotyledon	transpiration
xylem	germination	cambium
seed	stomata	root cap
embryo		

SECTION 2 Gymnosperms

Key Ideas

- All gymnosperms produce naked seeds. Many gymnosperms also have needlelike or scalelike leaves, and grow deep root systems.
- To reproduce, gymnosperms produce pollen in male cones and egg cells in female cones. Pollen falls onto a female cone. In time, a sperm cell and an egg cell join. The zygote develops into the embryo of the seed.

Key Terms

gymnosperm	ovule
cone	pollination
pollen	

SECTION 3 Angiosperms

Key Ideas

- Two characteristics of angiosperms are that they produce flowers and fruits.
- To reproduce, the male parts of the flower produce pollen, while the female parts produce eggs. Pollen falls on the stigma. In time, the sperm cell and egg cell join in the ovule. The zygote develops into the seed's embryo.

Key Terms

angiosperm	sepal	fruit
ovary	stamen	monocot
flower	pistil	dicot
petal		

SECTION 4 Plant Responses and Growth

Key Ideas

- A tropism is a plant's growth response toward or away from a stimulus. Plants respond to touch, light, and gravity.
- Plant hormones control tropisms and many other plant functions.

Key Terms

tropism	hormone	auxin

SECTION 5 Feeding the World

INTEGRATING TECHNOLOGY

Key Ideas

- Genetic engineering, precision farming, and hydroponics can help farmers produce more crops to feed the world's growing population.

Key Terms

genetic engineering	hydroponics

USING THE INTERNET

ACTIVITY

www.science-explorer.phschool.com

Program Resources

- **Teaching Resources** Chapter 5 Project Scoring Rubric, p. 118; Chapter 5 Performance Assessment Teacher Notes, pp. 184–185; Chapter 5 Performance Assessment Student Worksheet, p. 186; Chapter 5 Test, pp. 187–190

Reviewing Content:
Multiple Choice
1. d 2. b 3. c 4. a 5. b

True or False
6. roots 7. true 8. angiosperms
9. biennials 10. true

Checking Concepts
11. Seeds can be dispersed by wind, water, or animals. Some plants shoot out their seeds.
12. Stomata open and allow carbon dioxide to enter the leaf and also allow the oxygen and water vapor produced during photosynthesis to escape into the air. Stomata close and retain water in leaf cells during warm temperatures.
13. Annual rings are the circular pattern of xylem cells that form each year in a woody plant stem. Xylem cells that grow in the spring are large and have thin walls because they grow rapidly, producing a wide light-brown ring. Xylem cells that grow in the summer are small and have thick walls because they grow slowly, producing a thin dark ring.
14. Female cones are larger than male cones. The outside is covered by scales which contain at least one ovule at the base of their inner side. The scales close after pollination, and fertilization occurs inside. When the seeds are ready, the scales open, and the cones often hang upside-down on a branch.
15. Pollination is the process by which pollen, containing male reproductive cells, is transferred to the female reproductive structures. Fertilization is the joining of a sperm and egg cell.
16. The plant hormone auxin is involved in phototropism. Auxin speeds up the rate at which plant cells grow. Auxin moves into stem cells on the shadier side of a plant, causing those cells to grow faster than the cells on the sunny side of the plant. With longer cells on one side than the other, the stem bends toward the light.
17. Food can be grown in places on Earth that have poor soil conditions.
18. Answers will vary. Students should describe how the seed is removed from the fruit and should include a description of the conditions under which the seed finally germinates.

Reviewing Content

 For more review of key concepts, see the Interactive Student Tutorial CD-ROM.

Multiple Choice
Choose the letter of the best answer.

1. The process by which a seed sprouts is called
   a. pollination. b. fertilization.
   c. dispersal. d. germination.
2. In woody stems, new xylem cells are produced by
   a. bark. b. cambium.
   c. phloem. d. pith.
3. Which of the following is the male part of the flower?
   a. pistil b. ovule
   c. stamen d. petal
4. What kind of tropism do roots display when they grow into the soil?
   a. positive gravitropism
   b. negative gravitropism
   c. positive phototropism
   d. negative thigmotropism
5. The process of growing crops in a nutrient solution is called
   a. genetic engineering.
   b. hydroponics.
   c. precision farming.
   d. satellite imaging.

True or False
If the statement is true, write true. If it is false, change the underlined word or words to make the statement true.

6. <u>Stems</u> anchor plants and absorb water and minerals from the soil.
7. The needles of a pine tree are actually its <u>leaves</u>.
8. The seeds of <u>gymnosperms</u> are dispersed in fruits.
9. Plants that complete their life cycle in two years are called <u>perennials</u>.
10. The four basic food crops of the world are wheat, corn, rice, and <u>potatoes</u>.

Checking Concepts

11. Describe four different ways that seeds can be dispersed.
12. Explain the role that stomata play in leaves.
13. What are annual rings? Explain how they form.
14. Describe the structure of a female cone.
15. What is the difference between pollination and fertilization?
16. What role do plant hormones play in phototropism?
17. How can the use of hydroponics help increase the amount of food that can be grown on Earth?
18. **Writing to Learn** Imagine that you are a seed inside a plump purple fruit that is floating in a stream. Describe your experiences on the journey you take to the place where you germinate.

Thinking Visually

19. **Concept Map** Copy the concept map about seed plants onto a separate piece of paper. Then complete the map and add a title. (For more on concept maps, see the Skills Handbook.)

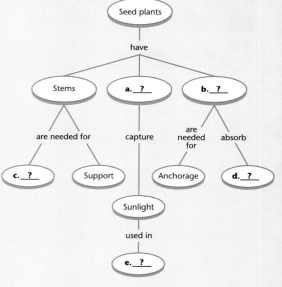

Thinking Visually
19. a. Leaves b. Roots c. Transportation
d. Water and nutrients e. Photosynthesis

Applying Skills
20. Transpiration is at its highest at about 1:00 P.M. Water uptake is at its highest at about 6:00 P.M.
21. The transpiration rate increases throughout the morning until early afternoon, then starts to decrease because most evaporation occurs during the hot middle part of the day.

Not much water evaporates in the cool evening.
22. The maximum amount of transpiration occurs about 5 hours before the peak in water uptake.

Thinking Critically
23. The innermost part of bark is phloem. If the bark is stripped around the entire base of a tree, all the phloem is removed in that space. Food made in the leaves can no longer reach the lower stem cells and root cells. These cells die, followed by the entire tree.

Applying Skills

A scientist measured the rate of transpiration in an ash tree over a 24-hour period. She also measured how much water the tree's roots took up during the same period. Use the data in the graph below to answer Questions 20–22.

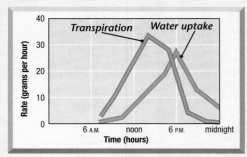

20. Interpreting Data At what time during the day is transpiration at its highest? At what time is water uptake at its highest?

21. Inferring Why do you think the transpiration rate increases and decreases as it does during the 24-hour period?

22. Drawing Conclusions Based on the graph, what is one possible conclusion you can reach about the pattern of water loss and gain in the ash tree?

Thinking Critically

23. Relating Cause and Effect When a strip of bark is removed all the way around the trunk of a tree, the tree dies. Explain why.

24. Applying Concepts Explain why people who grow houseplants on windowsills should turn the plants every week or so.

25. Predicting Pesticides are designed to kill harmful insects. Sometimes, however, pesticides kill helpful insects as well. What effect could this have on angiosperms?

26. Making Judgments Suppose you were a scientist using genetic engineering to increase crop yields. What improvements would you try to introduce? How would they be beneficial?

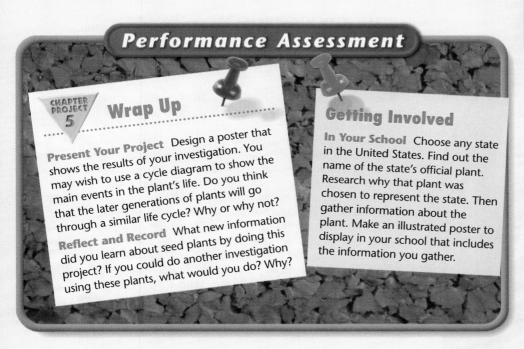

Performance Assessment

CHAPTER PROJECT 5 — Wrap Up

Present Your Project Design a poster that shows the results of your investigation. You may wish to use a cycle diagram to show the main events in the plant's life. Do you think that the later generations of plants will go through a similar life cycle? Why or why not?

Reflect and Record What new information did you learn about seed plants by doing this project? If you could do another investigation using these plants, what would you do? Why?

Getting Involved

In Your School Choose any state in the United States. Find out the name of the state's official plant. Research why that plant was chosen to represent the state. Then gather information about the plant. Make an illustrated poster to display in your school that includes the information you gather.

---

24. If plants near the window are not turned often, they will not grow evenly, and all their leaves will grow toward the window.
25. If helpful insects are killed by a pesticide, the plants that depend on these insects for pollination may not be pollinated.
26. Answers will vary, but students should be able to explain how their improvements would increase crop yield. They should also be able to identify the benefits of their suggestions.

Program Resources

◆ **Inquiry Skills Handbook** Provides teaching and review of all inquiry skills

Performance Assessment

CHAPTER PROJECT 5

Wrap Up
Present Your Project
Encourage students to use the cycle diagram to describe their observations during the life span of the plant in this project. Remind students to include what will happen after the new seeds are germinated. Find a space for students to display their exhibits.
Reflect and Record Discuss the project with students. Make sure they understand the cyclic nature of plant life. Students may suggest using their plants to investigate tropisms or hydroponics. If there is time, allow students to try their new experiments after you approve their plans.

Getting Involved

In Your School Have students work independently or in small groups. If possible, have students organize their choices so that they are researching many states, or states from many regions. Encourage students to use resources such as encyclopedias and the official state home pages on the Internet. For example, the state of Colorado home page is at **www.state.co.us/**.

Corn: The Amazing Grain

This interdisciplinary feature presents the central theme of corn by connecting four different disciplines: science, social studies, mathematics, and language arts. The four explorations are designed to capture students' interest and help them see how the content they are studying in science relates to other school subjects and to real-world events.

1 Engage/Explore

Activating Prior Knowledge

To help students recall what they learned in Chapter 5, Section 1, The Characteristics of Seed Plants, ask: **What two characteristics do all seed plants share?** *(They have vascular tissue; they use seeds to reproduce.)* **What is the function of the seed coat?** *(To protect the seeds and keep them from drying out)*

Introducing the Unit

Have students brainstorm a list of foods made from corn. *(corn on the cob, cornbread)* Then have students think of other products derived from corn. *(Cornstarch is used as a smoothing and thickening agent in many products.)* Ask students whether they know where corn originated. Write students' ideas on the board, and tell them that they will learn about the origin of corn in the Interdisciplinary Exploration. Suggest that students begin making a bulletin board display about corn. Students can add to their display as they work through the unit and learn about more ways that corn is used.

Have a volunteer read the caption about Machu Picchu on page 174. Invite students to find the Andes on a map and find where in the Andes the Incan ruins are located.

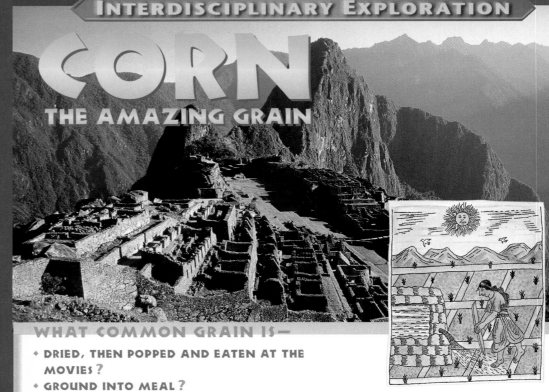

CORN
THE AMAZING GRAIN

WHAT COMMON GRAIN IS—

* DRIED, THEN POPPED AND EATEN AT THE MOVIES?
* GROUND INTO MEAL?
* ROLLED THIN AND FILLED WITH VEGETABLES?
* EATEN IN FLAKES FOR BREAKFAST?

The ruins of Machu Picchu, an Incan city (above left), are in the Andes Mountains of Peru. In the drawing at right, an Incan farmer irrigates a field of maize.

People have been eating corn in hundreds of different ways for thousands of years—since corn was first grown for food by ancient cultures in Mexico.

Because corn is useful, people have valued it throughout history. It tastes good, is nourishing, and stores well. Over time, knowledge of corn has spread among people and cultures. Christopher Columbus introduced corn to Europe. Columbus called it mahiz, meaning "a kind of grain." There have been corn myths, corn dances, corn palaces, shucking contests, corn medicines, and corn mattresses.

Today in many countries of the world, corn is a basic part of people's diet, whether in the form of kernels, meal, oil, syrup, or flour. The United States grows billions of bushels a year. But people eat only a tiny portion of this yield as corn. About 80 percent of the United States corn crop is fed to livestock to supply eggs, milk, and meat. Hundreds of other products—from chewing gum to fireworks—are also made from parts of the plant.

◄ This silver maize was crafted by the Incas.

174 ♦ A

Program Resources

♦ **Teaching Resources** Interdisciplinary Explorations, Social Studies, pp. 144–146; Language Arts, pp. 147–149; Science, pp. 150–152; Mathematics, pp. 153–155.

Maize Through the Ages

Some people say, "Wherever corn went, civilization followed." Corn—or maize—was probably cultivated from a wild grass in Mexico around 8000 B.C. Early farmers planted seeds and harvested crops in planned spaces. They passed on their knowledge of corn to their children and to other farmers. Having plenty of corn is believed to be one reason the ancient agricultural empires of the Mayas and Incas developed and flourished.

In Central America the Mayan civilization was at its height between A.D. 300 and A.D. 800. In Mayan cities, the people built pyramid-shaped temples where they worshipped gods of the sun, rain, and corn. Maize was grown in fields around the cities. The timing of the stages for growing corn affected all Mayan activities. The life cycle of maize and its plant parts—leaves, silk, tassels, and kernels—became the basis for words in the Mayan language.

In South America, the Incan empire thrived between the 1400s and 1535. A powerful ruler of the Incas came to power in Peru in 1438. In less than a century, the Incas expanded their territory from a small area around Cuzco, Peru, to a vast empire. The Inca empire stretched through the Andes Mountains, from Chile to Ecuador. It was the last of Peru's thriving ancient civilizations. The Incan empire was destroyed by Spaniards who arrived in the 1530s in search of gold. In Cuzco, they found an eye-dazzling garden where corn stalks, leaves, husks, and cobs were crafted in silver and gold. To the Incas, corn was more precious than the metal the Spaniards sought.

Though the empires of the Mayas and Incas collapsed, corn-growing spread to other regions. Eventually, the plant was brought north to the Mississippi and Ohio river valleys and east to the Caribbean islands.

Early Civilizations of Central and South America

KEY

Mayan Empire
A.D. 300–A.D. 900

Incan Empire
A.D. 1400s–A.D. 1535

The Mayan civilization in Central America and the Incan civilization in South America flourished before Europeans arrived.

Social Studies Activity

Use a map of Central and South America today.
- Trace the approximate boundaries of the Mayan and Incan empires.
- Name the countries that are now located in these areas.
- Identify the geographical features within the empires.
- Find out about the climate. Why were these lands well suited to growing corn?

A ◆ 175

2 Facilitate

- Direct students' attention to the corn husk mask on page 176. Some students may not know that the husk is the outer leaves of the corn cob. You might point out that there are several crafts that use corn husks, such as the making of corn husk dolls.

- Ask students the meaning of *dishonored* in the second paragraph of the folk tale. If students do not know its meaning, have them look up the word using a dictionary or thesaurus. *(treated in a degrading way)*

- Ask students: **Why did the wife leave?** *(Because the hunter's brother insulted the Great Spirit's gift.)*

- Because the brother disliked the bread, the hunter's wife left and the ears fell off the corn. Ask students: **Do you think it is fair to punish a group of people for the behavior of one person?** *(Lively debate may result. Encourage students to express their ideas, but make sure they debate without being disrespectful of each other's opinions.)*

- Ask: **What does *game* mean near the end of this page?** *(wild animals that people hunt for sport or food)*

- Ask: **How might the hunter have known at that time which direction east was?** *(The sun rises in the east.)*

- Ask: **What motivated the wife to give corn to her husband?** *(Samples: He had gone to the trouble of finding her; it was not his fault that his brother was ungrateful; she felt sorry for the suffering people.)*

Language Arts

From the Garden in the Sky

The word for corn in some Native American languages means "that which gives us life." How did humans discover corn? No one knows, but many cultures have myths and stories to explain how the plant came to be. To the Pawnee on the Nebraska plains, corn was Evening Star, the mother of all things. Evening Star gave corn from her garden in the sky. The Navajo in the southwestern United States tell a story of a turkey hen that flew in a straight line. As it traveled from the morning star, it shook an ear of corn from its feathers. The following folk tale comes from the Iroquois in Canada.

The Corn Goddess

Iroquois corn husk mask

THE GREAT SPIRIT gave seeds of corn to a mysterious maiden who became the wife of a great hunter. The wife taught the hunter's people how to plant and harvest the corn, and how to grind it and bake it into bread. The people were pleased.

But the great hunter's brother disliked the bread and threw it to the ground. The wife was alarmed that he had dishonored the gift of the Great Spirit. That night she told her husband that she must leave his people.

Shortly before dawn, the people heard the sound of falling rain. But it was not rain. It was the sound of thousands of kernels dropping from the ears of corn. Soon all the stalks were empty. The men hunted but found little game. Before long the children cried because they were so hungry.

Background

Facts and Figures Maize, to the English speakers who colonized North America, was another kind of grain. They used the word corn to indicate any grain, even wheat. They called the new food "Indian corn."

Centuries ago, the Inca grew as many as 300 varieties of corn. Today there are thousands of varieties grown throughout the world.

The Spaniards who invaded Mexico in the early 1500s called the thin bread made by the people *tortilla* meaning "small and flat." Mayans and Aztecs, among many other indigenous peoples, had their own names for the bread. *Wej* is the Mayan name. In the Aztec language, the name is *tlaxcalli*.

The word for corn in some Native American languages means "that which gives us life." In traditional Cherokee culture, the moon is called the Mother of Corn.

The great hunter was sad. He decided to leave and find his wife. She had told him, "If ever you want to find me, walk east. When you reach a lake, rest and listen for the cry of a child. Then you should plant an arrow in the ground, point it in the direction of the sound, and sleep. When you wake, the arrow will show you the way."

The great hunter went east to the big lake and lit a fire. Late that night he heard crying. He planted his arrow and lay down to sleep. At dawn, he walked as the arrow pointed. He walked all day, then stopped to rest at night. He lit another fire. Again he heard crying, placed his arrow, and slept. On the third night, his wife appeared.

He said his people were starving and he asked for her help. When winter passed, the great hunter returned to his people with corn from his wife. That year, the harvest was abundant. He rejoiced, but he missed his wife and left to find her again. He traveled to the lake and listened for crying, but he did not hear it. He traveled another day, and another, thinking he knew the direction to go. He searched day after day, listening for the cry. Perhaps he is still looking for her.

Adapted from The Corn Goddess and Other Tales from Indian Canada, *National Museum, Canada*

Language Arts Activity

A folk tale is a story that is passed down from person to person. It may explain something in nature, as this story does, or teach a lesson. Find words and phrases that show that this tale was created a long time ago.

Write your own story about how corn came to be found in nature. Use a modern-day setting and characters in your story.

Program Resources

◆ **Teaching Resources** The following worksheets correspond with these pages: Write a Letter, p. 147; Got an "Ear" for Corny Words?, p. 148; and Cornucopia, p. 149.

◆ Ask: **In what ways is the wife mysterious?** *(Samples: She is the only person who has been given corn by the Great Spirit; when she leaves, the corn stops growing; her husband never finds her.)* Ask: **Why do you think the wife never returns to the husband or his people?** *(Elicit students' ideas. Some may think that the wife was too insulted by the brother's behavior to return; others may think that she is a mysterious spirit rather than a real person, and therefore she was not destined to live permanently among humans.)*

◆ Ask: **What moral lesson do you think this folk tale is trying to teach?** *(Sample: If a gift is not appreciated, it may be taken away.)*

◆ To extend this exploration, invite interested students to find out more about the Pawnee, the Navajo, and the Iroquois. Have students research what regions of the continent they live in, how their cultures are similar, and how they are different.

Language Arts Activity

Stress that students' folk tales should somehow explain where corn came from. Students can be as creative as they wish. For example, in their folk tale, corn could be a gift from a god, could be brought by an animal, or any number of other explanations.

Remind students that if their tale includes dialogue, students should use quotation marks and begin a new paragraph every time the person speaking changes.

3 Assess

Activity Assessment

The words and phrases that students choose from the story may vary. Reference to the Great Spirit indicates a time long ago, as does the fact that the husband walks when he searches for his wife. Accept all reasonable answers that students can justify.

2 Facilitate

- Ask students: **How might corn seeds be dispersed without humans?** (*Animals eating the corn could disperse the seeds around the corn plant; animals who took the whole cob away to eat elsewhere would likely drop some seeds along the way.*)
- Point out that there is one silk strand for each kernel on the cob.
- Some students in the class may have experience growing corn at home. Ask students questions such as these: **How did you take care of the corn plants? How did you know when the corn was ready to eat? How much sun and water did the plants need?**
- After students read the article on the corn plant, ask: **How is corn pollinated?** (*Pollen from the male tassels are caught in the female silks and fertilize the seeds.*) **What would happen if no silks in one corn plant were pollinated?** (*The seeds would not be fertilized, and there would be no kernels on the corn cob.*)
- Explain what centrifugal force is and how it can be used to separate different materials in a mixture.
- If students are making a bulletin board display, give them time to add to their display things they have learned from this section of the unit.
- To extend this exploration, have students research different varieties of corn, how many days the varieties take to mature, and what soil and weather conditions they need. Suggest that students consult gardening books, seed catalogs, and seed packets to find this information.

Tassels to Silks

Corn must be planted by humans. Unlike many plants, a corn plant cannot disperse its own seeds: they stay inside the husk or modified leaves. For thousands of years, farmers have removed the husks and taken out the kernels to plant them. Today huge machines plant, irrigate, harvest, and shuck corn.

After a corn seed is planted, it begins to grow into a corn plant. An ear of corn begins with an arrangement of several hundred female flowers inside the husk. Each flower has a very long style, or silk, that grows outside the husk. The stigma at the end of the silk traps pollen grains. For pollination to occur, the corn silks must grow out of the husk during the time that the pollen is shed. So the timing of pollination is important in the growth of a corn plant.

Male flowers bloom on the plant's tassels and release pollen. One plant's tassels can shed millions of pollen grains in a period of 5 to 8 days. But it only takes one grain of pollen caught on a silk for fertilization to occur. Fertilization begins the process that results in kernels.

How long a corn plant takes to grow and how well it grows depends on the warmth, moisture, and quality of soil. Too much heat or too little water can damage the plant's flowers and result in poor crops. Depending on the climate, sweet corn takes about 125 days to mature from planting to harvesting.

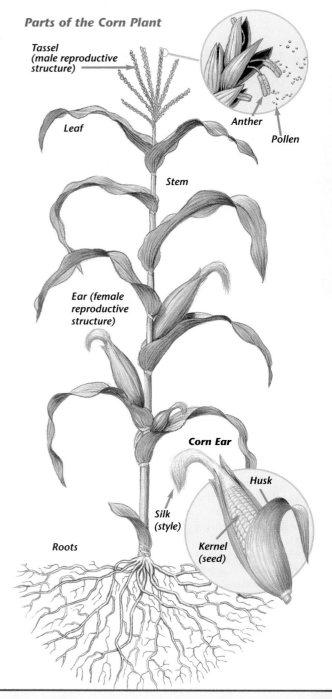

Parts of the Corn Plant

Tassel (male reproductive structure)

Anther

Pollen

Leaf

Stem

Ear (female reproductive structure)

Corn Ear

Husk

Silk (style)

Kernel (seed)

Roots

Background

Facts and Figures Most ears of corn have about 800 kernels arranged in 16 rows.

Farmers have bred new varieties of corn since ancient times. A new variety might be developed to thrive in a harsh climate or in poor soils. Most new varieties are intended to yield more kernels per ear and more ears per acre, meaning more corn produced in a growing season.

Not all corn grows to the same height. In some areas of Central America, it is harvested on horseback because the stalks are so tall. In some cornfields of the southwestern United States, farmers must bend over to pick ears off the stalks. Most corn, however, is harvested and shucked by machine.

According to Guinness Book of Records, the tallest corn plant in the United States was grown in Iowa in 1946. It was 9.3 meters tall.

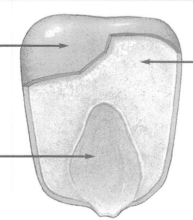

Seed coat
protects the kernel
Bran is made from the seed coat

Embryo
the part of the seed that will develop into a new corn plant
Corn oil is made from the embryo

Stored food
inner starchy part that feeds the embryo
Many things are made from the starchy part of the corn kernel, including:
• *cornstarch*
• *corn sugar*
• *corn syrups*
• *ice cream*
• *animal feed*
• *glue*
• *fuel*

Corn is the main food for cattle and many other farm and ranch animals.

A Kernel Goes a Long Way

Did you know that corn and corn products are used as fuel? Or that corn is found in some brands of baby food, crayons, soap, and tires? It's even found in ketchup, hot dogs, and toothpaste.

Today, only a small portion of the corn that is planted is sweet corn. Sweet corn is sold fresh or used to produce canned or frozen corn. But millions of bushels of field corn, which is less sweet, are trucked to refineries. There the kernels are turned into oil, starch, sugar, or fuel.

When ears of field corn arrive at a refinery, the corn is cleaned and soaked. Next, corn kernels are milled—crushed and ground. The milled substance is spun in giant tanks to separate out the embryos. Oil is extracted from the embryo of the kernel. The seed coat may be removed by sifting and can be dried to produce corn bran.

The remaining substance—the stored food—is ground into corn meal. One part of the ground meal is rich in proteins and is used for animal feed. The other part of the corn meal is the starch.

From cornstarch, corn sugars and syrups are processed. You eat these in breads, breakfast cereals, colas, ice cream, and salad dressings, to name only a few products. Cornstarch is also processed into glues and powders for the paper and textile industries, and into ethanol, a fuel.

Science Activity

When you're at the supermarket, how do you decide which brand of a particular product to buy? What criteria do you use? Working with a partner, choose a corn product, such as tortillas, corn flakes, or popcorn to investigate.

◆ Collect several brands of the product to test.
◆ Decide what you will test for. For example, you might want to test which brand of popcorn produces more popped kernels.
◆ Before you begin, predict what your results will be.
◆ Design your own experiment. Write out the step-by-step procedure you will follow. Make sure that you keep all variables the same as you test each product.
◆ Make observations and collect data.
◆ Interpret the data and draw your conclusion. How did your results compare with your prediction?

A ◆ 179

Program Resources

◆ **Teaching Resources** The following worksheets correspond with these pages: How to Plant Corn, p. 150; How Does Popcorn Pop?, p. 151; and Build a Maize Maze, p. 152.

◆ If possible, arrange a class trip to a corn field, mill, or corn processing factory. Alternatively, find a corn farmer, a university extension agent, or a Department of Agriculture staff member to talk to the class about how to grow corn.

Science Activity

Have students work in pairs. For students not testing popcorn, suggest that they compare the nutritional information between different brands of the same product. For example, they might test the assumption that the most expensive product has the most nutritional value.

Check students' written procedures for safety and practicality before allowing them to perform any experiments. The following is a sample procedure for an experiment testing which brand of popcorn produces more popped kernels: Count out 100 kernels of each brand and pop the kernels from each brand separately, using identical conditions for all brands (for example, amount of oil, type of container, and time allowed for popping). Then count the popped kernels in each sample. Repeat this procedure three times and calculate average figures.

3 Assess

Activity Assessment

Give student pairs a set amount of time to describe to the class their experiment and the results.

Look for students who clearly recorded what they were testing and how they planned to conduct their tests. Students' results should be clearly recorded in a table or chart. Students' conclusions should be clearly stated and supported by their test data. Lead students to understand that if the test results do not support their initial assumption, their experiment was still a success.

2 Facilitate

◆ You may want to help students determine the size of one of the slices of their circle graph. Explain that, for each slice of the graph, they will need to set up a proportion where x equals the number of degrees in a slice. As an example, write the following proportion on the board:

$$\frac{\text{production of major corn belt states}}{\text{total corn production}}$$

$$= \frac{x}{\text{degrees in a circle}}$$

Then help students to solve for x by substituting in the known values and rearranging the equation.

$$\frac{5,242,600}{9,293,400} = \frac{x}{360}$$

$$9,293,400x = 5,242,600 \times 360$$

$$x = \frac{5,242,600 \times 360}{9,293,400}$$

$$x = 203$$

Therefore, the slice for the major corn belt states should contain 203 degrees. The number of degrees for the other slices are as follows: other corn belt states, 115 degrees; states outside the corn belt, 42 degrees.

◆ To extend this exploration, encourage interested students to find out what weather conditions are needed to grow corn. Have students find out why the corn belt is ideal for growing corn.

◆ **Teaching Resources** The following worksheets correlate with this page: World Corn Production and Consumption, pages 153–154 and Volume Increase of Popcorn, page 155.

Mind-Boggling Corn Data

Every continent in the world except Antarctica produces some corn each year. The largest corn-producing country is the United States, growing 41 percent of the world's corn. The graph shows the leading corn-producing countries. China is next largest, growing 20 percent. The other countries in the world grow smaller amounts.

In the United States, corn is grown in nearly every state, producing over 9 billion bushels of corn a year. A bushel of corn contains about 72,800 kernels. Most of that corn is grown in a group of midwestern states known as the "Corn Belt." Iowa, Illinois, Nebraska, and Minnesota are the four major corn-growing states. Indiana, Missouri, Kansas, Ohio, South Dakota, Wisconsin, Michigan, and Kentucky are the other Corn Belt states.

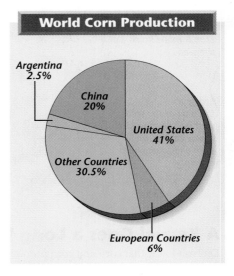

World Corn Production

Argentina 2.5%
China 20%
United States 41%
Other Countries 30.5%
European Countries 6%

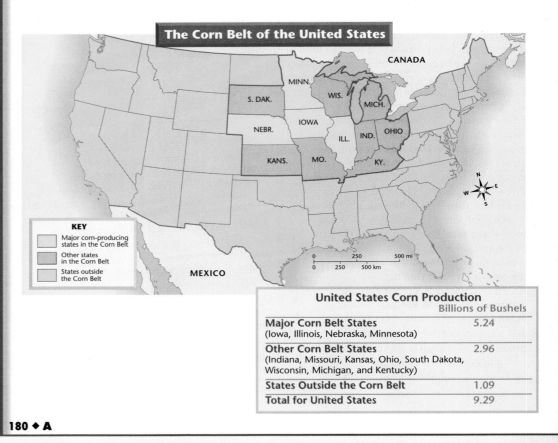

The Corn Belt of the United States

KEY
- Major corn-producing states in the Corn Belt
- Other states in the Corn Belt
- States outside the Corn Belt

United States Corn Production	Billions of Bushels
Major Corn Belt States (Iowa, Illinois, Nebraska, Minnesota)	5.24
Other Corn Belt States (Indiana, Missouri, Kansas, Ohio, South Dakota, Wisconsin, Michigan, and Kentucky)	2.96
States Outside the Corn Belt	1.09
Total for United States	9.29

Background

Facts and Figures Field corn, flint corn, and waxy corn are grown for animal feed or for their byproducts. Corn byproducts are used in making crayons, paints, inks, and camera film. In addition, a corn byproduct is used in some types of antifreeze. Corn byproducts are also found in some brands of baby food, peanut butter, candy, chewing gum, cake icing, margarine, ketchup, potato chips, soup, baking powder, foot powder, cloth, deodorants, tape, glue, soap, fireworks, tires, and many other products.

Corn growers are only a small part of the United States corn industry. There are also corn processors, millers, corn sellers, and exporters. These industries include scientists and corn breeders among their workers.

The Mitchell Corn Palace in South Dakota is decorated with about 3,000 bushels of corn. Corn repairs are made each year.

Math Activity

Make a circle graph to show corn production in the United States. To create your graph, follow the steps in the Skills Handbook.

◆ Use the data in the table on the previous page to set up proportions to find the number of degrees in each slice. Then figure percents for Major Corn Belt States, Other Corn Belt States, and States Outside the Corn Belt. Round to the nearest tenth.

◆ Use a compass to draw a circle.

◆ Determine the size of each of the 3 slices.

◆ Measure out and mark off each slice in the circle.

What percent should you get when you add up these numbers?

Tie It Together

Plan a Corn Ball

Organize a corn carnival for your school. To advertise the carnival, create a huge popcorn ball with popped corn and glue made from a cornstarch and water mixture. (The largest popcorn ball on record weighed over a ton.) Here are some suggestions for activities.

◆ Display a variety of products made from corn.

◆ Bring in food made from corn.

◆ Set up a booth to explain how popcorn pops.

◆ Have a contest for visitors to guess the number of popcorn kernels in a jar.

◆ Set up a booth for telling corny jokes.

◆ Collect corn facts, pictures, and photographs that show corn in art or in history.

◆ Collect information on agriculture in the Mayan or Incan cultures.

A ◆ 181

Math Activity

Point out that the circle graph should have three slices, not four. Ask: **What is the fourth line in the table?** *(the total)* Challenge interested students to find out what percent of the United States total is grown in your state.

3 Assess

Activity Assessment

Major Corn Belt States, 56%; Other Corn Belt States, 32%; States Outside the Corn Belt, 12%. The total is 100%. Make sure the size of each segment is the right size for the percent.

Tie It Together

Time 1 week (2 days for research, 2 days for preparing booths, 1 day for the carnival)

Tips Have students work in groups of three or four. Assign groups a booth or have them draw slips of paper to determine their booth. If necessary, help groups divide up the tasks and make a plan for compiling materials and preparing for the carnival.

◆ Most of the information that students must research should be readily available from encyclopedias or gardening books. However, point out that there is an enormous wealth of information on the Internet. If your school has access to the Internet, students may use it for research. Closely supervise students so that they do not connect to inappropriate sites.

Extend If your carnival is a success, students may wish to keep their materials and ideas to hold the carnival again as a fund-raiser for the school.

READING STRATEGIES

Further Reading

◆ **Magazines** Rhoades, Robert E., "Corn, the Golden Grain," *National Geographic,* June 1993, pp. 92–117.

◆ **Books** Hunter, Sally M., Joe Allen, and Carly Bordeau. *Four Seasons of Corn: A Winnebago Tradition.* Lerner Publications Company, 1996.

◆ Johnson, Sylvia A. *Tomatoes, Potatoes, Corn, and Beans: How the Foods of the Americas Changed Cooking Around the World.* Atheneum, 1997.

Developing scientific thinking in students is important for a solid science education. To learn how to think scientifically, students need frequent opportunities to practice science process skills, critical thinking skills, as well as other skills that support scientific inquiry. The *Science Explorer* Skills Handbook introduces the following key science skills:

◆ Science Process Skills
◆ SI Measuring Skills
◆ Skills for Conducting a Scientific Investigation
◆ Critical Thinking Skills
◆ Information Organizing Skills
◆ Data Table and Graphing Skills

The Skills Handbook is designed as a reference for students to use whenever they need to review a science skill. You can use the activities provided in the Skills Handbook to teach or reinforce the skills.

Think Like a Scientist

Observing

ACTIVITY

Before students look at the photograph, remind them that an observation is only what they can see, hear, smell, taste, or feel. Ask: **Which senses will you use to make observations from this photograph?** *(Sight is the only sense that can be used to make observations from the photograph.)* **What are some observations you can make from the photograph?** *(Answers may vary. Sample answers: The boy is wearing sneakers, sport socks, shorts, and a tee shirt; the boy is sitting in the grass holding something blue against his knee; the boy is looking at his knee; there is a soccer ball laying beside the boy.)* List the observations on the chalkboard. If students make any inferences or predictions about the boy at this point, ask: **Can you be sure your statement is factual and accurate from just observing the photograph?** Help students understand how observations differ from inferences and predictions.

Inferring

ACTIVITY

Review students' observations from the photograph. Then ask: **What inferences can you**

Think Like a Scientist

Although you may not know it, you think like a scientist every day. Whenever you ask a question and explore possible answers, you use many of the same skills that scientists do. Some of these skills are described on this page.

Observing

When you use one or more of your five senses to gather information about the world, you are **observing.** Hearing a dog bark, counting twelve green seeds, and smelling smoke are all observations. To increase the power of their senses, scientists sometimes use microscopes, telescopes, or other instruments that help them make more detailed observations.

An observation must be factual and accurate—an exact report of what your senses detect. It is important to keep careful records of your observations in science class by writing or drawing in a notebook. The information collected through observations is called evidence, or data.

Inferring

When you explain or interpret an observation, you are **inferring,** or making an inference. For example, if you hear your dog barking, you may infer that someone is at your front door. To make this inference, you combine the evidence—the barking dog—and your experience or knowledge—you know that your dog barks when strangers approach—to reach a logical conclusion.

Notice that an inference is not a fact; it is only one of many possible explanations for an observation. For example, your dog may be barking because it wants to go for a walk. An inference may turn out to be incorrect even if it is based on accurate observations and logical reasoning. The only way to find out if an inference is correct is to investigate further.

Predicting

When you listen to the weather forecast, you hear many predictions about the next day's weather—what the temperature will be, whether it will rain, and how windy it will be. Weather forecasters use observations and knowledge of weather patterns to predict the weather. The skill of **predicting** involves making an inference about a future event based on current evidence or past experience.

Because a prediction is an inference, it may prove to be false. In science class, you can test some of your predictions by doing experiments. For example, suppose you predict that larger paper airplanes can fly farther than smaller airplanes. How could you test your prediction?

 ACTIVITY Use the photograph to answer the questions below.

Observing Look closely at the photograph. List at least three observations.

Inferring Use your observations to make an inference about what has happened. What experience or knowledge did you use to make the inference?

Predicting Predict what will happen next. On what evidence or experience do you base your prediction?

---

make from your observations? *(Students may say that the boy hurt his knee playing soccer and is holding a coldpack against his injured knee.)* **What experience or knowledge helped you make this inference?** *(Students may have experienced knee injuries from playing soccer, and they may be familiar with coldpacks like the one the boy is using.)* **Can anyone suggest another possible explanation for these observations?** *(Answers may vary. Sample answer: The boy hurt his knee jogging, and he just happened to sit beside a soccer ball his sister*

left in the yard.) **How can you find out whether an inference is correct?** *(by further investigation)*

Predicting

ACTIVITY

After coming to some consensus about the inference that the boy hurt his knee, encourage students to make predictions about what will happen next. *(Students' predictions may vary. Sample answers: The boy will go to the doctor. A friend will help the boy home. The boy will get up and continue playing soccer.)*

Classifying

Could you imagine searching for a book in the library if the books were shelved in no particular order? Your trip to the library would be an all-day event! Luckily, librarians group together books on similar topics or by the same author. Grouping together items that are alike in some way is called **classifying.** You can classify items in many ways: by size, by shape, by use, and by other important characteristics.

Like librarians, scientists use the skill of classifying to organize information and objects. When things are sorted into groups, the relationships among them become easier to understand.

Classify the objects in the photograph into two groups based on any characteristic you choose. Then use another characteristic to classify the objects into three groups. ACTIVITY

Making Models

Have you ever drawn a picture to help someone understand what you were saying? Such a drawing is one type of model. A model is a picture, diagram, computer image, or other representation of a complex object or process. **Making models** helps people understand things that they cannot observe directly.

Scientists often use models to represent things that are either very large or very small, such as the planets in the solar system, or the parts of a cell. Such models are physical models—drawings or three-dimensional structures that look like the real thing. Other models are mental models—mathematical equations or words that describe how something works.

This student is using a model to demonstrate what causes day and night on Earth. What do the flashlight and the tennis ball in the model represent? ACTIVITY

Communicating

Whenever you talk on the phone, write a letter, or listen to your teacher at school, you are communicating. **Communicating** is the process of sharing ideas and information with other people. Communicating effectively requires many skills, including writing, reading, speaking, listening, and making models.

Scientists communicate to share results, information, and opinions. Scientists often communicate about their work in journals, over the telephone, in letters, and on the Internet. They also attend scientific meetings where they share their ideas with one another in person.

On a sheet of paper, write out clear, detailed directions for tying your shoe. Then exchange directions with a partner. Follow your partner's directions exactly. How successful were you at tying your shoe? How could your partner have communicated more clearly? ACTIVITY

On what did you base your prediction? *(Scientific predictions are based on knowledge and experience.)* Point out that in science, predictions can often be tested with experiments.

Classifying ACTIVITY

Encourage students to think of other common things that are classified. Then ask: **What things at home are classified?** *(Clothing might be classified by placing it in different dresser drawers; glasses, plates, and silverware are grouped in different parts of the kitchen; screws, nuts, bolts, washers, and nails might be separated into small containers.)* **What are some things that scientists classify?** *(Scientists classify many things they study, including organisms, geological features and processes, and kinds of machines.)* After students have classified the different fruits in the photograph, have them share their criteria for classifying them. *(Some characteristics students might use include shape, color, size, and where they are grown.)*

Making Models ACTIVITY

Ask students: **What are some models you have used to study science?** *(Students may have used human anatomical models, solar system models, maps, stream tables.)* **How did these models help you?** *(Models can help you learn about things that are difficult to study, either because they are too big, too small, or complex.)* Be sure students understand that a model does not have to be three-dimensional. For example, a map in a textbook is a model. Ask: **What do the flashlight and tennis ball represent?** *(The flashlight represents the sun, and the ball represents Earth.)* **What quality of each item makes this a good model?** *(The flashlight gives off light, and the ball is round and can be rotated by the student.)*

Communicating ACTIVITY

Challenge students to identify the methods of communication they've used today. Then ask: **How is the way you communicate with a friend similar to and different from the way scientists communicate about their work to other scientists?** *(Both may communicate using various methods, but scientists must be very detailed and precise, whereas communication between friends may be less detailed and precise.)* Encourage students to communicate like a scientist as they carry out the activity. *(Students' directions should be detailed and precise enough for another person to successfully follow.)*

Making Measurements

Measuring in SI

Review SI units in class with students. Begin by providing metric rulers, graduated cylinders, balances, and Celsius thermometers. Use these tools to reinforce that the meter is the unit of length, the liter is the unit of volume, the gram is the unit of mass, and the degree Celsius is the unit for temperature. Ask: **If you want to measure the length and width of your classroom, which SI unit would you use?** *(meter)* **Which unit would you use to measure the amount of matter in your textbook?** *(gram)* **Which would you use to measure how much water a drinking glass holds?** *(liter)* **When would you use the Celsius scale?** *(To measure the temperature of something)* Then use the measuring equipment to review SI prefixes. For example, ask: **What are the smallest units on the metric ruler?** *(millimeters)* **How many millimeters are there in 1 cm?** *(10 mm)* **How many in 10 cm?** *(100 mm)* **How many centimeters are there in 1 m?** *(100 cm)* **What does 1,000 m equal?** *(1 km)*

Length *(Students*
ACTIVITY
should state that the shell is 4.6 centimeters, or 46 millimeters, long.) If students need more practice measuring length, have them use meter sticks and metric rulers to measure various objects in the classroom.

Liquid Volume
ACTIVITY
(Students should state that the volume of water in the graduated cylinder is 62 milliliters.) If students need more practice measuring liquid volume, have them use a graduated cylinder to measure different volumes of water.

Making Measurements

When scientists make observations, it is not sufficient to say that something is "big" or "heavy." Instead, scientists use instruments to measure just how big or heavy an object is. By measuring, scientists can express their observations more precisely and communicate more information about what they observe.

Measuring in SI

The standard system of measurement used by scientists around the world is known as the International System of Units, which is abbreviated as SI (in French, *Système International d'Unités*). SI units are easy to use because they are based on multiples of 10. Each unit is ten times larger than the next smallest unit and one tenth the size of the next largest unit. The table lists the prefixes used to name the most common SI units.

Common SI Prefixes

Prefix	Symbol	Meaning
kilo-	k	1,000
hecto-	h	100
deka-	da	10
deci-	d	0.1 (one tenth)
centi-	c	0.01 (one hundredth)
milli-	m	0.001 (one thousandth)

Length To measure length, or the distance between two points, the unit of measure is the **meter (m).** One meter is the approximate distance from the floor to a doorknob. Long distances, such as the distance between two cities, are measured in kilometers (km). Small lengths are measured in centimeters (cm) or millimeters (mm). Scientists use metric rulers and meter sticks to measure length.

Common Conversions

1 km = 1,000 m
1 m = 100 cm
1 m = 1,000 mm
1 cm = 10 mm

The larger lines on the metric ruler in the picture show centimeter divisions, while the smaller, unnumbered lines show millimeter divisions. How many centimeters long is the shell? How many millimeters long is it?
ACTIVITY

Liquid Volume To measure the volume of a liquid, or the amount of space it takes up, you will use a unit of measure known as the **liter (L).** One liter is the approximate volume of a medium-sized carton of milk. Smaller volumes are measured in milliliters (mL). Scientists use graduated cylinders to measure liquid volume.

Common Conversion

1 L = 1,000 mL

The graduated cylinder in the picture is marked in milliliter divisions. Notice that the water in the cylinder has a curved surface. This curved surface is called the *meniscus*. To measure the volume, you must read the level at the lowest point of the meniscus. What is the volume of water in this graduated cylinder?
ACTIVITY

Mass

Mass To measure mass, or the amount of matter in an object, you will use a unit of measure known as the **gram (g)**. One gram is approximately the mass of a paper clip. Larger masses are measured in kilograms (kg). Scientists use a balance to find the mass of an object.

Common Conversion

1 kg = 1,000 g

The electronic balance displays the mass of an apple in kilograms. What is the mass of the apple? Suppose a recipe for applesauce called for one kilogram of apples. About how many apples would you need?

Temperature

Temperature To measure the temperature of a substance, you will use the **Celsius scale**. Temperature is measured in degrees Celsius (°C) using a Celsius thermometer. Water freezes at 0°C and boils at 100°C.

What is the temperature of the liquid in degrees Celsius?

Converting SI Units

To use the SI system, you must know how to convert between units. Converting from one unit to another involves the skill of **calculating**, or using mathematical operations. Converting between SI units is similar to converting between dollars and dimes because both systems are based on multiples of ten.

Suppose you want to convert a length of 80 centimeters to meters. Follow these steps to convert between units.

1. Begin by writing down the measurement you want to convert—in this example, 80 centimeters.
2. Write a conversion factor that represents the relationship between the two units you are converting. In this example, the relationship is *1 meter = 100 centimeters*. Write this conversion factor as a fraction, making sure to place the units you are converting from (centimeters, in this example) in the denominator.

3. Multiply the measurement you want to convert by the fraction. When you do this, the units in the first measurement will cancel out with the units in the denominator. Your answer will be in the units you are converting to (meters, in this example).

Example

80 centimeters = ___?___ meters

$$80 \text{ centimeters} \times \frac{1 \text{ meter}}{100 \text{ centimeters}} = \frac{80 \text{ meters}}{100}$$

$$= 0.8 \text{ meters}$$

Convert between the following units.

1. 600 millimeters = _?_ meters
2. 0.35 liters = _?_ milliliters
3. 1,050 grams = _?_ kilograms

A ◆ 185

Mass *(Students should state that the mass of the apple is 0.1 kilograms. They would need 10 apples to make 1 kilogram.)* If students need practice determining mass, have them use a balance to determine the mass of various common objects, such as coins, paper clips, and books.

Temperature *(Students should state that the temperature of the liquid is 35°C.)* If students need practice measuring temperature, have them use a Celsius thermometer to measure the temperature of various water samples.

Converting SI Units

Review the steps for converting SI units and work through the example with students. Then ask: **How many millimeters are in 80 centimeters?** *(Students should follow the steps to calculate that 80 centimeters is equal to 800 millimeters.)*

Have students do the conversion problems in the activity. *(1. 600 millimeters = 0.6 meters; 2. 0.35 liters = 350 milliliters; 3. 1,050 grams = 1.05 kilograms)* If students need more practice converting SI units, have students make up conversion problems and trade with a partner.

Conducting a Scientific Investigation

Posing Questions

Before students do the activity on the next page, walk them through the steps of a typical scientific investigation. Begin by asking: **Why is a scientific question important to a scientific investigation?** *(It is the reason for conducting a scientific investigation and how every investigation begins.)* **What is the scientific question in the activity at the bottom of the next page?** *(Is a ball's bounce affected by the height from which it is dropped?)*

Developing a Hypothesis

Emphasize that a hypothesis is a prediction about the outcome of a scientific investigation, but it is *not* a guess. Ask: **On what information do scientists base their hypotheses?** *(Their observations and previous knowledge or experience)* Point out that a hypothesis does not always turn out to be correct. Ask: **In that case, do you think the scientist wasted his or her time? Explain your answer.** *(No, because the scientist probably learned from the investigation and maybe could develop another hypothesis that could be supported.)*

Designing an Experiment

Have a volunteer read the Experimental Procedure in the box. Then call on students to identify the manipulated variable *(amount of salt added to water)*, the variables that are kept constant *(amount and starting temperature of water, placing containers in freezer)*, the responding variable *(time it takes water to freeze)*, and the control *(Container 3)*.

Ask: **How might the experiment be affected if Container 1 had only 100 mL of water?** *(It wouldn't be a fair comparison with the containers that have more water.)* **What if Container 3 was not included in the experiment?** *(You wouldn't have anything to compare the other two containers to know if their freezing times were faster or slower than normal.)* Help students understand the importance of

Conducting a Scientific Investigation

In some ways, scientists are like detectives, piecing together clues to learn about a process or event. One way that scientists gather clues is by carrying out experiments. An experiment tests an idea in a careful, orderly manner. Although all experiments do not follow the same steps in the same order, many follow a pattern similar to the one described here.

Posing Questions

Experiments begin by asking a scientific question. A scientific question is one that can be answered by gathering evidence. For example, the question "Which freezes faster—fresh water or salt water?" is a scientific question because you can carry out an investigation and gather information to answer the question.

Developing a Hypothesis

The next step is to form a hypothesis. A **hypothesis** is a prediction about the outcome of the experiment. Like all predictions, hypotheses are based on your observations and previous knowledge or experience. But, unlike many predictions, a hypothesis must be something that can be tested. A properly worded hypothesis should take the form of an *If…then…* statement. For example, a hypothesis might be *"If I add salt to fresh water, then the water will take longer to freeze."* A hypothesis worded this way serves as a rough outline of the experiment you should perform.

keeping all variables constant except the manipulated variable. Also be sure they understand the role of the control. Then ask: **What operational definition is used in this experiment?** *("Frozen" means the time at which a wooden stick can no longer move in a container.)*

Designing an Experiment

Next you need to plan a way to test your hypothesis. Your plan should be written out as a step-by-step procedure and should describe the observations or measurements you will make.

Two important steps involved in designing an experiment are controlling variables and forming operational definitions.

Controlling Variables In a well-designed experiment, you need to keep all variables the same except for one. A **variable** is any factor that can change in an experiment. The factor that you change is called the **manipulated variable.** In this experiment, the manipulated variable is the amount of salt added to the water. Other factors, such as the amount of water or the starting temperature, are kept constant.

The factor that changes as a result of the manipulated variable is called the responding variable. The **responding variable** is what you measure or observe to obtain your results. In this experiment, the responding variable is how long the water takes to freeze.

An experiment in which all factors except one are kept constant is a **controlled experiment.** Most controlled experiments include a test called the control. In this experiment, Container 3 is the control. Because no salt is added to Container 3, you can compare the results from the other containers to it. Any difference in results must be due to the addition of salt alone.

Forming Operational Definitions
Another important aspect of a well-designed experiment is having clear operational definitions. An **operational definition** is a statement that describes how a particular variable is to be measured or how a term is to be defined. For example, in this experiment, how will you determine if the water has frozen? You might decide to insert a stick in each container at the start of the experiment. Your operational definition of "frozen" would be the time at which the stick can no longer move.

EXPERIMENTAL PROCEDURE

1. Fill 3 containers with 300 milliliters of cold tap water.

2. Add 10 grams of salt to Container 1; stir. Add 20 grams of salt to Container 2; stir. Add no salt to Container 3.

3. Place the 3 containers in a freezer.

4. Check the containers every 15 minutes. Record your observations.

Interpreting Data

The observations and measurements you make in an experiment are called data. At the end of an experiment, you need to analyze the data to look for any patterns or trends. Patterns often become clear if you organize your data in a data table or graph. Then think through what the data reveal. Do they support your hypothesis? Do they point out a flaw in your experiment? Do you need to collect more data?

Drawing Conclusions

A conclusion is a statement that sums up what you have learned from an experiment. When you draw a conclusion, you need to decide whether the data you collected support your hypothesis or not. You may need to repeat an experiment several times before you can draw any conclusions from it. Conclusions often lead you to pose new questions and plan new experiments to answer them.

> Is a ball's bounce affected by the height from which it is dropped? Using the steps just described, plan a controlled experiment to investigate this problem. **ACTIVITY**

A ◆ 187

Interpreting Data

Emphasize the importance of collecting accurate and detailed data in a scientific investigation. Ask: **What if the students forgot to record the times that they made their observations in the experiment?** *(They wouldn't be able to completely analyze their data to draw valid conclusions.)* Then ask: **Why are data tables and graphs a good way to organize data?** *(They often make it easier to compare and analyze data.)* You may wish to have students review the Skills Handbook pages on Creating Data Tables and Graphs at this point.

Drawing Conclusions

Help students understand that a conclusion is not necessarily the end of a scientific investigation. A conclusion about one experiment may lead right into another experiment. Point out that in scientific investigations, a conclusion is a summary and explanation of the results of an experiment.

Tell students to suppose that for the Experimental Procedure described on this page, they obtained the following results: Container 1 froze in 45 minutes, Container 2 in 80 minutes, and Container 3 in 25 minutes. Ask: **What conclusions can you draw about this experiment?** *(Students might conclude that the more salt that is added to fresh water, the longer it takes the water to freeze. The hypothesis is supported, and the question of which freezes faster is answered—fresh water.)*

You might wish to have students work in pairs to plan the controlled experiment. **ACTIVITY** *(Students should develop a hypothesis, such as "If I increase the height from which a ball is dropped, then the height of its bounce will increase." They can test the hypothesis by dropping balls from varying heights (the manipulated variable). All trials should be done with the same kind of ball and on the same surface (constant variables). For each trial, they should measure the height of the bounce (responding variable).)* After students have designed the experiment, provide rubber balls and invite them to carry out the experiment so they can collect and interpret data and draw conclusions.

A ◆ 187

Thinking Critically

Comparing and Contrasting

Emphasize that the skill of comparing and contrasting often relies on good observation skills, as in this activity. *(Students' answers may vary. Sample answer: Similarities—both are dogs and have four legs, two eyes, two ears, brown and white fur, black noses, pink tongues; Differences—smooth coat vs. rough coat, more white fur vs. more brown fur, shorter vs. taller, long ears vs. short ears.)*

Applying Concepts

Point out to students that they apply concepts that they learn in school in their daily lives. For example, they learn to add, subtract, multiply, and divide in school. If they get a paper route or some other part-time job, they can apply those concepts. Challenge students to practice applying concepts by doing the activity. *(Antifreeze lowers the temperature at which the solution will freeze, and thus keeps the water in the radiator from freezing.)*

Interpreting Illustrations

Again, point out the need for good observation skills. Ask: **What is the difference between "interpreting illustrations" and "looking at the pictures"?** *("Interpreting illustrations" requires thorough examination of the illustration, caption, and labels, while "looking at the pictures" implies less thorough examination.)* Encourage students to thoroughly examine the diagram as they do the activity. *(Students' paragraphs may vary, but should describe the internal anatomy of an earthworm, including some of the organs in the earthworm.)*

Thinking Critically

Has a friend ever asked for your advice about a problem? If so, you may have helped your friend think through the problem in a logical way. Without knowing it, you used critical-thinking skills to help your friend. Critical thinking involves the use of reasoning and logic to solve problems or make decisions. Some critical-thinking skills are described below.

Comparing and Contrasting

When you examine two objects for similarities and differences, you are using the skill of **comparing and contrasting.** Comparing involves identifying similarities, or common characteristics. Contrasting involves identifying differences. Analyzing objects in this way can help you discover details that you might otherwise overlook.

> Compare and contrast the two animals in the photo. First list all the similarities that you see. Then list all the differences.

Applying Concepts

When you use your knowledge about one situation to make sense of a similar situation, you are using the skill of **applying concepts.** Being able to transfer your knowledge from one situation to another shows that you truly understand a concept. You may use this skill in answering test questions that present different problems from the ones you've reviewed in class.

> You have just learned that water takes longer to freeze when other substances are mixed into it. Use this knowledge to explain why people need a substance called antifreeze in their car's radiator in the winter.

Interpreting Illustrations

Diagrams, photographs, and maps are included in textbooks to help clarify what you read. These illustrations show processes, places, and ideas in a visual manner. The skill called **interpreting illustrations** can help you learn from these visual elements. To understand an illustration, take the time to study the illustration along with all the written information that accompanies it. Captions identify the key concepts shown in the illustration. Labels point out the important parts of a diagram or map, while keys identify the symbols used in a map.

Blood vessels
Reproductive organs
Hearts
Brain
Mouth
Bristles
Digestive tract
Nerve cord
Waste-removal organs
Intestine

▲ Internal anatomy of an earthworm

> Study the diagram above. Then write a short paragraph explaining what you have learned.

Relating Cause and Effect

If one event causes another event to occur, the two events are said to have a cause-and-effect relationship. When you determine that such a relationship exists between two events, you use a skill called **relating cause and effect.** For example, if you notice an itchy, red bump on your skin, you might infer that a mosquito bit you. The mosquito bite is the cause, and the bump is the effect.

It is important to note that two events do not necessarily have a cause-and-effect relationship just because they occur together. Scientists carry out experiments or use past experience to determine whether a cause-and-effect relationship exists.

ACTIVITY You are on a camping trip and your flashlight has stopped working. List some possible causes for the flashlight malfunction. How could you determine which cause-and-effect relationship has left you in the dark?

Making Generalizations

When you draw a conclusion about an entire group based on information about only some of the group's members, you are using a skill called **making generalizations.** For a generalization to be valid, the sample you choose must be large enough and representative of the entire group. You might, for example, put this skill to work at a farm stand if you see a sign that says, "Sample some grapes before you buy." If you sample a few sweet grapes, you may conclude that all the grapes are sweet—and purchase a large bunch.

ACTIVITY A team of scientists needs to determine whether the water in a large reservoir is safe to drink. How could they use the skill of making generalizations to help them? What should they do?

Making Judgments

When you evaluate something to decide whether it is good or bad, or right or wrong, you are using a skill called **making judgments.** For example, you make judgments when you decide to eat healthful foods or to pick up litter in a park. Before you make a judgment, you need to think through the pros and cons of a situation, and identify the values or standards that you hold.

ACTIVITY Should children and teens be required to wear helmets when bicycling? Explain why you feel the way you do.

Problem Solving

When you use critical-thinking skills to resolve an issue or decide on a course of action, you are using a skill called **problem solving.** Some problems, such as how to convert a fraction into a decimal, are straightforward. Other problems, such as figuring out why your computer has stopped working, are complex. Some complex problems can be solved using the trial and error method—try out one solution first, and if that doesn't work, try another. Other useful problem-solving strategies include making models and brainstorming possible solutions with a partner.

A ◆ 189

Relating Cause and Effect

Emphasize that not all events that occur together have a cause-and-effect relationship. For example, tell students that you went to the grocery and your car stalled. Ask: **Is there a cause-and-effect relationship in this situation? Explain your answer.** (*No, because going to the grocery could not cause a car to stall. There must be another cause to make the car stall.*) Have students do the activity to practice relating cause and effect. (*Students should identify that the flashlight not working is the effect. Some possible causes include dead batteries, a burned-out light bulb, or a loose part.*)

Making Generalizations

Point out the importance of having a large, representative sample before making a generalization. Ask: **If you went fishing at a lake and caught three catfish, could you make the generalization that all fish in the lake are catfish? Why or why not?** (*No, because there might be other kinds of fish you didn't catch because they didn't like the bait or they may be in other parts of the lake.*) **How could you make a generalization about the kinds of fish in the lake?** (*By having a larger sample*) Have students do the activity to practice making generalizations. (*The scientists should collect and test water samples from a number of different parts of the reservoir.*)

Making Judgments

Remind students that they make a judgment almost every time they make a decision. Ask: **What steps should you follow to make a judgment?** (*Gather information, list pros and cons, analyze values, make judgment*) Invite students to do the activity, and then to share and discuss the judgments they made. (*Students' judgments will vary, but should be supported by valid reasoning. Sample answer: Children and teens should be required to wear helmets when bicycling because helmets have been proven to save lives and reduce head injuries.*)

Problem Solving

Challenge student pairs to solve a problem about a soapbox derby. Explain that their younger brother is building a car to enter in the race. The brother wants to know how to make his soapbox car go faster. After student pairs have considered the problem, have them share their ideas about solutions with the class. (*Most will probably suggest using trial and error by making small changes to the car and testing the car after each change. Some students may suggest making and manipulating a model.*)

A ◆ 189

Organizing Information

Concept Maps

Challenge students to make a concept map with at least three levels of concepts to organize information about types of transportation. All students should start with the phrase *types of transportation* at the top of the concept map. After that point, their concept maps may vary. *(For example, some students might place* private transportation *and* public transportation *at the next level, while other students might have* human-powered *and* gas-powered. *Make sure students connect the concepts with linking words. Challenge students to include cross-linkages as well.)*

Compare/ Contrast Tables

Have students make their own compare/contrast tables using two or more different sports or other activities, such as playing musical instruments. Emphasize that students should select characteristics that highlight the similarities and differences between the activities. *(Students' compare/contrast tables should include several appropriate characteristics and list information about each activity for every characteristic.)*

Organizing Information

As you read this textbook, how can you make sense of all the information it contains? Some useful tools to help you organize information are shown on this page. These tools are called *graphic organizers* because they give you a visual picture of a topic, showing at a glance how key concepts are related.

Concept Maps

Concept maps are useful tools for organizing information on broad topics. A concept map begins with a general concept and shows how it can be broken down into more specific concepts. In that way, relationships between concepts become easier to understand.

A concept map is constructed by placing concept words (usually nouns) in ovals and connecting them with linking words. Often, the most general concept word is placed at the top, and the words become more specific as you move downward. Often the linking words, which are written on a line extending between two ovals, describe the relationship between the two concepts they connect. If you follow any string of concepts and linking words down the map, it should read like a sentence.

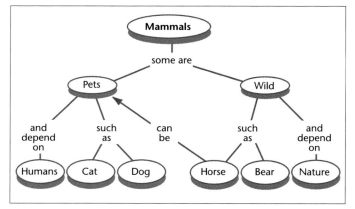

Some concept maps include linking words that connect a concept on one branch of the map to a concept on another branch. These linking words, called cross-linkages, show more complex interrelationships among concepts.

Compare/Contrast Tables

Compare/contrast tables are useful tools for sorting out the similarities and differences between two or more items. A table provides an organized framework in which to compare items based on specific characteristics that you identify.

To create a compare/contrast table, list the items to be compared across the top of a table. Then list the characteristics that will form the basis of your comparison in the left-hand column. Complete the table by filling in information about each characteristic, first for one item and then for the other.

Characteristic	Baseball	Basketball
Number of Players	9	5
Playing Field	Baseball diamond	Basketball court
Equipment	Bat, baseball, mitts	Basket, basketball

Venn Diagrams

Another way to show similarities and differences between items is with a Venn diagram. A Venn diagram consists of two or more circles that partially overlap. Each circle represents a particular concept or idea. Common characteristics, or similarities, are written within the area of overlap between the two circles. Unique characteristics, or differences, are written in the parts of the circles outside the area of overlap.

To create a Venn diagram, draw two over-lapping circles. Label the circles with the names of the items being compared. Write the

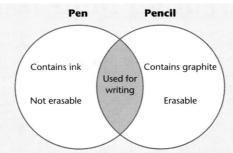

unique characteristics in each circle outside the area of overlap. Then write the shared characteristics within the area of overlap.

Flowcharts

A flowchart can help you understand the order in which certain events have occurred or should occur. Flowcharts are useful for outlining the stages in a process or the steps in a procedure.

To make a flowchart, write a brief description of each event in a box. Place the first event at the top of the page, followed by the second event, the third event, and so on. Then draw an arrow to connect each event to the one that occurs next.

Preparing Pasta

Boil water

↓

Cook pasta

↓

Drain water

↓

Add sauce

Cycle Diagrams

A cycle diagram can be used to show a sequence of events that is continuous, or cyclical. A continuous sequence does not have an end because, when the final event is over, the first event begins again. Like a flowchart, a cycle diagram can help you understand the order of events.

To create a cycle diagram, write a brief description of each event in a box. Place one event at the top of the page in the center. Then, moving in a clockwise direction around an imaginary circle, write each event in its proper sequence. Draw arrows that connect each event to the one that occurs next, forming a continuous circle.

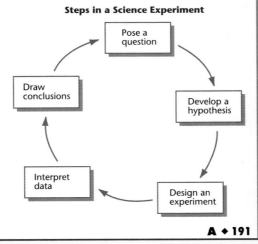

Steps in a Science Experiment

A ◆ 191

Venn Diagrams *ACTIVITY*

Students can use the same information from their compare/contrast tables to create a Venn diagram. Make sure students understand that the overlapping area of the circles is used to list similarities and the parts of the circles outside the overlap area are used to show differences. If students want to list similarities and differences among three activities, show them how to add a third circle that overlaps each of the other two circles and has an area of overlap for all three circles. *(Students' Venn diagrams will vary. Make sure they have accurately listed similarities in the overlap area and differences in the parts of the circles that do not overlap.)*

Flowcharts *ACTIVITY*

Encourage students to create a flowchart to show the things they did this morning as they got ready for school. Remind students that a flowchart should show the correct order in which events occurred or should occur. *(Students' flowcharts will vary somewhat. A typical flowchart might include: got up → ate breakfast → took a shower → brushed teeth → got dressed → gathered books and homework → put on jacket.)*

Cycle Diagrams *ACTIVITY*

Review that a cycle diagram shows a sequence of events that is continuous. Then challenge students to create a cycle diagram that shows how the weather changes with the seasons where they live. *(Students' cycle diagrams may vary, though most will include four steps, one for each season.)*

Creating Data Tables and Graphs

Data Tables

Have students create a data table to show how much time they spend on different activities during one week. Suggest that students first list the main activities they do every week. Then they should determine the amount of time they spend on each activity each day. Remind students to give this data table a title. *(Students' data tables will vary. A sample data table is shown below.)*

Bar Graphs

Students can use the data from their data table above to make a bar graph showing how much time they spend on different activities during a week. The vertical axis should be divided into units of time, such as hours. Remind students to label both axes and give their graph a title. *(Students' bar graphs will vary. A sample bar graph is shown below.)*

Creating Data Tables and Graphs

How can you make sense of the data in a science experiment? The first step is to organize the data to help you understand them. Data tables and graphs are helpful tools for organizing data.

Data Tables

You have gathered your materials and set up your experiment. But before you start, you need to plan a way to record what happens during the experiment. By creating a data table, you can record your observations and measurements in an orderly way.

Suppose, for example, that a scientist conducted an experiment to find out how many Calories people of different body masses burn while doing various activities. The data table shows the results.

Notice in this data table that the manipulated variable (body mass) is the heading of one column. The responding variable (for Experiment 1, the number of Calories burned while bicycling) is the heading of the next column. Additional columns were added for related experiments.

CALORIES BURNED IN 30 MINUTES OF ACTIVITY			
Body Mass	Experiment 1 Bicycling	Experiment 2 Playing Basketball	Experiment 3 Watching Television
30 kg	60 Calories	120 Calories	21 Calories
40 kg	77 Calories	164 Calories	27 Calories
50 kg	95 Calories	206 Calories	33 Calories
60 kg	114 Calories	248 Calories	38 Calories

Bar Graphs

To compare how many Calories a person burns doing various activities, you could create a bar graph. A bar graph is used to display data in a number of separate, or distinct, categories. In this example, bicycling, playing basketball, and watching television are three separate categories.

To create a bar graph, follow these steps.
1. On graph paper, draw a horizontal, or *x*-, axis and a vertical, or *y*-, axis.
2. Write the names of the categories to be graphed along the horizontal axis. Include an overall label for the axis as well.
3. Label the vertical axis with the name of the responding variable. Include units of measurement. Then create a scale along the axis by marking off equally spaced numbers that cover the range of the data collected.
4. For each category, draw a solid bar using the scale on the vertical axis to determine the

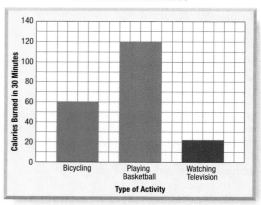

Calories Burned by a 30-kilogram Person in Various Activities

appropriate height. For example, for bicycling, draw the bar as high as the 60 mark on the vertical axis. Make all the bars the same width and leave equal spaces between them.
5. Add a title that describes the graph.

Time Spent on Different Activities in a Week

	Going to Classes	Eating Meals	Playing Soccer	Watching Television
Monday	6	2	2	0.5
Tuesday	6	1.5	1.5	1.5
Wednesday	6	2	1	2
Thursday	6	2	2	1.5
Friday	6	2	2	0.5
Saturday	0	2.5	2.5	1
Sunday	0	3	1	2

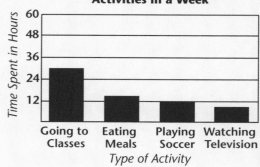

Time Spent on Different Activities in a Week

Line Graphs

To see whether a relationship exists between body mass and the number of Calories burned while bicycling, you could create a line graph. A line graph is used to display data that show how one variable (the responding variable) changes in response to another variable (the manipulated variable). You can use a line graph when your manipulated variable is *continuous*, that is, when there are other points between the ones that you tested. In this example, body mass is a continuous variable because there are other body masses between 30 and 40 kilograms (for example, 31 kilograms). Time is another example of a continuous variable.

Line graphs are powerful tools because they allow you to estimate values for conditions that you did not test in the experiment. For example, you can use the line graph to estimate that a 35-kilogram person would burn 68 Calories while bicycling.

To create a line graph, follow these steps.
1. On graph paper, draw a horizontal, or *x*-, axis and a vertical, or *y*-, axis.
2. Label the horizontal axis with the name of the manipulated variable. Label the vertical axis with the name of the responding variable. Include units of measurement.
3. Create a scale on each axis by marking off equally spaced numbers that cover the range of the data collected.
4. Plot a point on the graph for each piece of data. In the line graph above, the dotted lines show how to plot the first data point (30 kilograms and 60 Calories). Draw an imaginary vertical line extending up from the horizontal axis at the 30-kilogram mark. Then draw an imaginary horizontal line extending across from the vertical axis at the 60-Calorie mark. Plot the point where the two lines intersect.

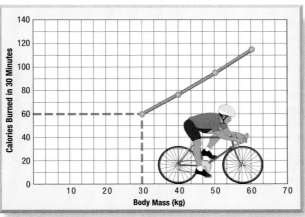

Effect of Body Mass on Calories Burned While Bicycling

5. Connect the plotted points with a solid line. (In some cases, it may be more appropriate to draw a line that shows the general trend of the plotted points. In those cases, some of the points may fall above or below the line.)
6. Add a title that identifies the variables or relationship in the graph.

> Create line graphs to display the data from Experiment 2 and Experiment 3 in the data table. **ACTIVITY**

> You read in the newspaper that a total of 4 centimeters of rain fell in your area in June, 2.5 centimeters fell in July, and 1.5 centimeters fell in August. What type of graph would you use to display these data? Use graph paper to create the graph. **ACTIVITY**

Line Graphs

Walk students through the steps involved in creating a line graph using the example illustrated on the page. For example, ask: **What is the label on the horizontal axis? On the vertical axis?** (*Body mass (kg); Calories Burned in 30 Minutes*) **What scales are used on each axis?** (*3 squares per 10 kg on the x-axis and 2 squares per 20 Calories on the y-axis*) **What does the second data point represent?** (*77 Calories burned for a body mass of 40 kg*) **What trend or pattern does the graph show?** (*The number of Calories burned in 30 minutes of cycling increases with body mass.*)

Have students follow the steps to carry out the first activity. (*Students should make a different graph for each experiment with different y-axis scales to practice making scales appropriate for data. See sample graphs below.*) **ACTIVITY**

Have students carry out the second activity. (*Students should conclude that a bar graph would be best to display the data. A sample bar graph for these data is shown below.*) **ACTIVITY**

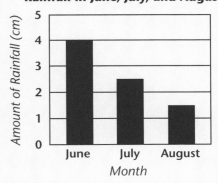

Rainfall in June, July, and August

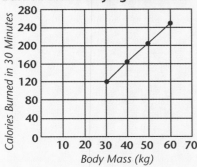

Effect of Body Mass on Calories Burned While Playing Basketball

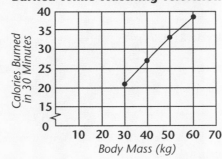

Effect of Body Mass on Calories Burned While Watching Television

Circle Graphs

Emphasize that a circle graph has to include 100 percent of the categories for the topic being graphed. For example, ask: **Could the data in the bar graph titled "Calories Burned by a 30-kilogram Person in Various Activities" (on the previous page) be shown in a circle graph? Why or why not?** (*No, because it does not include all the possible ways a 30-kilogram person can burn Calories.*) Then walk students through the steps for making a circle graph. Help students to use a compass and a protractor. Use the protractor to illustrate that a circle has 360 degrees. Make sure students understand the mathematical calculations involved in making a circle graph.

You might wish to have **ACTIVITY** students work in pairs to complete the activity. (*Students' circle graphs should look like the graph below.*)

Circle Graphs

Like bar graphs, circle graphs can be used to display data in a number of separate categories. Unlike bar graphs, however, circle graphs can only be used when you have data for *all* the categories that make up a given topic. A circle graph is sometimes called a pie chart because it resembles a pie cut into slices. The pie represents the entire topic, while the slices represent the individual categories. The size of a slice indicates what percentage of the whole a particular category makes up.

The data table below shows the results of a survey in which 24 teenagers were asked to identify their favorite sport. The data were then used to create the circle graph at the right.

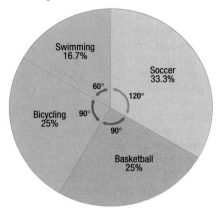

Sports That Teens Prefer

FAVORITE SPORTS	
Sport	Number of Students
Soccer	8
Basketball	6
Bicycling	6
Swimming	4

To create a circle graph, follow these steps.
1. Use a compass to draw a circle. Mark the center of the circle with a point. Then draw a line from the center point to the top of the circle.
2. Determine the size of each "slice" by setting up a proportion where *x* equals the number of degrees in a slice. (NOTE: A circle contains 360 degrees.) For example, to find the number of degrees in the "soccer" slice, set up the following proportion:

$$\frac{\text{students who prefer soccer}}{\text{total number of students}} = \frac{x}{\text{total number of degrees in a circle}}$$

$$\frac{8}{24} = \frac{x}{360}$$

Cross-multiply and solve for *x*.
$$24x = 8 \times 360$$
$$x = 120$$
The "soccer" slice should contain 120 degrees.

3. Use a protractor to measure the angle of the first slice, using the line you drew to the top of the circle as the 0° line. Draw a line from the center of the circle to the edge for the angle you measured.
4. Continue around the circle by measuring the size of each slice with the protractor. Start measuring from the edge of the previous slice so the wedges do not overlap. When you are done, the entire circle should be filled in.
5. Determine the percentage of the whole circle that each slice represents. To do this, divide the number of degrees in a slice by the total number of degrees in a circle (360), and multiply by 100%. For the "soccer" slice, you can find the percentage as follows:

$$\frac{120}{360} \times 100\% = 33.3\%$$

6. Use a different color to shade in each slice. Label each slice with the name of the category and with the percentage of the whole it represents.
7. Add a title to the circle graph.

In a class of 28 students, 12 students **ACTIVITY** take the bus to school, 10 students walk, and 6 students ride their bicycles. Create a circle graph to display these data.

Ways Students Get to School

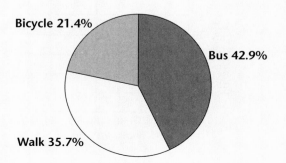

Bicycle 21.4%

Bus 42.9%

Walk 35.7%

Laboratory Safety

Safety Symbols

These symbols alert you to possible dangers in the laboratory and remind you to work carefully.

Safety Goggles Always wear safety goggles to protect your eyes in any activity involving chemicals, flames or heating, or the possibility of broken glassware.

Lab Apron Wear a laboratory apron to protect your skin and clothing from damage.

Breakage You are working with materials that may be breakable, such as glass containers, glass tubing, thermometers, or funnels. Handle breakable materials with care. Do not touch broken glassware.

Heat-resistant Gloves Use an oven mitt or other hand protection when handling hot materials. Hot plates, hot glassware, or hot water can cause burns. Do not touch hot objects with your bare hands.

Heating Use a clamp or tongs to pick up hot glassware. Do not touch hot objects with your bare hands.

Sharp Object Pointed-tip scissors, scalpels, knives, needles, pins, or tacks are sharp. They can cut or puncture your skin. Always direct a sharp edge or point away from yourself and others. Use sharp instruments only as instructed.

Electric Shock Avoid the possibility of electric shock. Never use electrical equipment around water, or when the equipment is wet or your hands are wet. Be sure cords are untangled and cannot trip anyone. Disconnect the equipment when it is not in use.

Corrosive Chemical You are working with an acid or another corrosive chemical. Avoid getting it on your skin or clothing, or in your eyes. Do not inhale the vapors. Wash your hands when you are finished with the activity.

Poison Do not let any poisonous chemical come in contact with your skin, and do not inhale its vapors. Wash your hands when you are finished with the activity.

Physical Safety When an experiment involves physical activity, take precautions to avoid injuring yourself or others. Follow instructions from your teacher. Alert your teacher if there is any reason you should not participate in the activity.

Animal Safety Treat live animals with care to avoid harming the animals or yourself. Working with animal parts or preserved animals also may require caution. Wash your hands when you are finished with the activity.

Plant Safety Handle plants in the laboratory or during field work only as directed by your teacher. If you are allergic to certain plants, tell your teacher before doing an activity in which those plants are used. Avoid touching harmful plants such as poison ivy, poison oak, or poison sumac, or plants with thorns. Wash your hands when you are finished with the activity.

Flames You may be working with flames from a lab burner, candle, or matches. Tie back loose hair and clothing. Follow instructions from your teacher about lighting and extinguishing flames.

No Flames Flammable materials may be present. Make sure there are no flames, sparks, or other exposed heat sources present.

Fumes When poisonous or unpleasant vapors may be involved, work in a ventilated area. Avoid inhaling vapors directly. Only test an odor when directed to do so by your teacher, and use a wafting motion to direct the vapor toward your nose.

Disposal Chemicals and other laboratory materials used in the activity must be disposed of safely. Follow the instructions from your teacher.

Hand Washing Wash your hands thoroughly when finished with the activity. Use antibacterial soap and warm water. Lather both sides of your hands and between your fingers. Rinse well.

General Safety Awareness You may see this symbol when none of the symbols described earlier appears. In this case, follow the specific instructions provided. You may also see this symbol when you are asked to develop your own procedure in a lab. Have your teacher approve your plan before you go further.

A ◆ 195

Laboratory Safety

Laboratory safety is an essential element of a successful science class. It is important for you to emphasize laboratory safety to students. Students need to understand exactly what is safe and unsafe behavior, and what the rationale is behind each safety rule.

Review with students the Safety Symbols and Science Safety Rules listed on this and the next two pages. Then follow the safety guidelines below to ensure that your classroom will be a safe place for students to learn science.

- Post safety rules in the classroom and review them regularly with students.
- Familiarize yourself with the safety procedures for each activity before introducing it to your students.
- Review specific safety precautions with students before beginning every science activity.
- Always act as an exemplary role model by displaying safe behavior.
- Know how to use safety equipment, such as fire extinguishers and fire blankets, and always have it accessible.
- Have students practice leaving the classroom quickly and orderly to prepare them for emergencies.
- Explain to students how to use the intercom or other available means of communication to get help during an emergency.
- Never leave students unattended while they are engaged in science activities.
- Provide enough space for students to safely carry out science activities.
- Keep your classroom and all science materials in proper condition. Replace worn or broken items.
- Instruct students to report all accidents and injuries to you immediately.

Laboratory Safety

Additional tips are listed below for the Science Safety Rules discussed on these two pages. Please keep these tips in mind when you carry out science activities in your classroom.

General Precautions

◆ For open-ended activities like Chapter Projects, go over general safety guidelines with students. Have students submit their procedures or design plans in writing and check them for safety considerations.

◆ In an activity where students are directed to taste something, be sure to store the material in clean, *nonscience* containers. Distribute the material to students in *new* plastic or paper dispensables, which should be discarded after the tasting. Tasting or eating should never be done in a lab classroom.

◆ During physical activity, make sure students do not overexert themselves.

◆ Remind students to handle microscopes and telescopes with care to avoid breakage.

Heating and Fire Safety

◆ No flammable substances should be in use around hot plates, light bulbs, or open flames.

◆ Test tubes should be heated only in water baths.

◆ Students should be permitted to strike matches to light candles or burners *only* with strict supervision. When possible, you should light the flames, especially when working with sixth graders.

◆ Be sure to have proper ventilation when fumes are produced during a procedure.

◆ All electrical equipment used in the lab should have GFI switches.

Using Chemicals Safely

◆ When students use both chemicals and microscopes in one activity, microscopes should be in a separate part of the room from the chemicals so that when students remove their goggles to use the microscopes, their eyes are not at risk.

Science Safety Rules

To prepare yourself to work safely in the laboratory, read over the following safety rules. Then read them a second time. Make sure you understand and follow each rule. Ask your teacher to explain any rules you do not understand.

Dress Code

1. To protect yourself from injuring your eyes, wear safety goggles whenever you work with chemicals, burners, glassware, or any substance that might get into your eyes. If you wear contact lenses, notify your teacher.
2. Wear a lab apron or coat whenever you work with corrosive chemicals or substances that can stain.
3. Tie back long hair to keep it away from any chemicals, flames, or equipment.
4. Remove or tie back any article of clothing or jewelry that can hang down and touch chemicals, flames, or equipment. Roll up or secure long sleeves.
5. Never wear open shoes or sandals.

General Precautions

6. Read all directions for an experiment several times before beginning the activity. Carefully follow all written and oral instructions. If you are in doubt about any part of the experiment, ask your teacher for assistance.
7. Never perform activities that are not assigned or authorized by your teacher. Obtain permission before "experimenting" on your own. Never handle any equipment unless you have specific permission.
8. Never perform lab activities without direct supervision.
9. Never eat or drink in the laboratory.
10. Keep work areas clean and tidy at all times. Bring only notebooks and lab manuals or written lab procedures to the work area. All other items, such as purses and backpacks, should be left in a designated area.
11. Do not engage in horseplay.

First Aid

12. Always report all accidents or injuries to your teacher, no matter how minor. Notify your teacher immediately about any fires.
13. Learn what to do in case of specific accidents, such as getting acid in your eyes or on your skin. (Rinse acids from your body with lots of water.)
14. Be aware of the location of the first-aid kit, but do not use it unless instructed by your teacher. In case of injury, your teacher should administer first aid. Your teacher may also send you to the school nurse or call a physician.
15. Know the location of emergency equipment, such as the fire extinguisher and fire blanket, and know how to use it.
16. Know the location of the nearest telephone and whom to contact in an emergency.

Heating and Fire Safety

17. Never use a heat source, such as a candle, burner, or hot plate, without wearing safety goggles.
18. Never heat anything unless instructed to do so. A chemical that is harmless when cool may be dangerous when heated.
19. Keep all combustible materials away from flames. Never use a flame or spark near a combustible chemical.
20. Never reach across a flame.
21. Before using a laboratory burner, make sure you know proper procedures for lighting and adjusting the burner, as demonstrated by your teacher. Do not touch the burner. It may be hot. And never leave a lighted burner unattended!
22. Chemicals can splash or boil out of a heated test tube. When heating a substance in a test tube, make sure that the mouth of the tube is not pointed at you or anyone else.
23. Never heat a liquid in a closed container. The expanding gases produced may blow the container apart.
24. Before picking up a container that has been heated, hold the back of your hand near it. If you can feel heat on the back of your hand, the container is too hot to handle. Use an oven mitt to pick up a container that has been heated.

Using Glassware Safely

◆ Use plastic containers, graduated cylinders, and beakers whenever possible. If using glass, students should wear safety goggles.

◆ Use only nonmercury thermometers with anti-roll protectors.

◆ Check all glassware periodically for chips and scratches, which can cause cuts and breakage.

Using Chemicals Safely

25. Never mix chemicals "for the fun of it." You might produce a dangerous, possibly explosive substance.

26. Never put your face near the mouth of a container that holds chemicals. Never touch, taste, or smell a chemical unless you are instructed by your teacher to do so. Many chemicals are poisonous.

27. Use only those chemicals needed in the activity. Read and double-check labels on supply bottles before removing any chemicals. Take only as much as you need. Keep all containers closed when chemicals are not being used.

28. Dispose of all chemicals as instructed by your teacher. To avoid contamination, never return chemicals to their original containers. Never simply pour chemicals or other substances into the sink or trash containers.

29. Be extra careful when working with acids or bases. Pour all chemicals over the sink or a container, not over your work surface.

30. If you are instructed to test for odors, use a wafting motion to direct the odors to your nose. Do not inhale the fumes directly from the container.

31. When mixing an acid and water, always pour the water into the container first and then add the acid to the water. Never pour water into an acid.

32. Take extreme care not to spill any material in the laboratory. Wash chemical spills and splashes immediately with plenty of water. Immediately begin rinsing with water any acids that get on your skin or clothing, and notify your teacher of any acid spill at the same time.

Using Glassware Safely

33. Never force glass tubing or thermometers into a rubber stopper or rubber tubing. Have your teacher insert the glass tubing or thermometer if required for an activity.

34. If you are using a laboratory burner, use a wire screen to protect glassware from any flame. Never heat glassware that is not thoroughly dry on the outside.

35. Keep in mind that hot glassware looks cool. Never pick up glassware without first checking to see if it is hot. Use an oven mitt. See rule 24.

36. Never use broken or chipped glassware. If glassware breaks, notify your teacher and dispose of the glassware in the proper broken-glassware container. Never handle broken glass with your bare hands.

37. Never eat or drink from lab glassware.

38. Thoroughly clean glassware before putting it away.

Using Sharp Instruments

39. Handle scalpels or other sharp instruments with extreme care. Never cut material toward you; cut away from you.

40. Immediately notify your teacher if you cut your skin when working in the laboratory.

Animal and Plant Safety

41. Never perform experiments that cause pain, discomfort, or harm to mammals, birds, reptiles, fishes, or amphibians. This rule applies at home as well as in the classroom.

42. Animals should be handled only if absolutely necessary. Your teacher will instruct you as to how to handle each animal species brought into the classroom.

43. If you know that you are allergic to certain plants, molds, or animals, tell your teacher before doing an activity in which these are used.

44. During field work, protect your skin by wearing long pants, long sleeves, socks, and closed shoes. Know how to recognize the poisonous plants and fungi in your area, as well as plants with thorns, and avoid contact with them.

45. Never eat any part of an unidentified plant or fungus.

46. Wash your hands thoroughly after handling animals or the cage containing animals. Wash your hands when you are finished with any activity involving animal parts, plants, or soil.

End-of-Experiment Rules

47. After an experiment has been completed, clean up your work area and return all equipment to its proper place.

48. Dispose of waste materials as instructed by your teacher.

49. Wash your hands after every experiment.

50. Always turn off all burners or hot plates when they are not in use. Unplug hot plates and other electrical equipment. If you used a burner, check that the gas-line valve to the burner is off as well.

Using Sharp Instruments

◆ Always use blunt-tip safety scissors, except when pointed-tip scissors are required.

Animal and Plant Safety

◆ When working with live animals or plants, check ahead of time for students who may have allergies to the specimens.

◆ When growing bacteria cultures, use only disposable petri dishes. After streaking, the dishes should be sealed and not opened again by students. After the lab, students should return the unopened dishes to you. Students should wash their hands with antibacterial soap.

◆ Two methods are recommended for the safe disposal of bacteria cultures. *First method:* Autoclave the petri dishes and discard without opening. *Second method:* If no autoclave is available, carefully open the dishes (never have a student do this) and pour full-strength bleach into the dishes and let stand for a day. Then pour the bleach from the petri dishes down a drain and flush the drain with lots of water. Tape the petri dishes back together and place in a sealed plastic bag. Wrap the plastic bag with a brown paper bag or newspaper and tape securely. Throw the sealed package in the trash. Thoroughly disinfect the work area with bleach.

◆ To grow mold, use a new, sealable plastic bag that is two to three times larger than the material to be placed inside. Seal the bag and tape it shut. After the bag is sealed, students should not open it. To dispose of the bag and mold culture, make a small cut near an edge of the bag and cook in a microwave oven on high setting for at least 1 minute. Discard the bag according to local ordinance, usually in the trash.

◆ Students should wear disposable nitrile, latex, or food-handling gloves when handling live animals or nonliving specimens.

End-of Experiment Rules

◆ Always have students use antibacterial soap for washing their hands.

Using the Microscope

The microscope is an essential tool in the study of life science. It allows you to see things that are too small to be seen with the unaided eye.

You will probably use a compound microscope like the one you see here. The compound microscope has more than one lens that magnifies the object you view.

Typically, a compound microscope has one lens in the eyepiece, the part you look through. The eyepiece lens usually magnifies 10×. Any object you view through this lens would appear 10 times larger than it is.

The compound microscope may contain one or two other lenses called objective lenses. If there are two objective lenses, they are called the low-power and high-power objective lenses. The low-power objective lens usually magnifies 10×. The high-power objective lens usually magnifies 40×.

To calculate the total magnification with which you are viewing an object, multiply the magnification of the eyepiece lens by the magnification of the objective lens you are using. For example, the eyepiece's magnification of 10× multiplied by the low-power objective's magnification of 10× equals a total magnification of 100×.

Use the photo of the compound microscope to become familiar with the parts of the microscope and their functions.

The Parts of the Compound Microscope

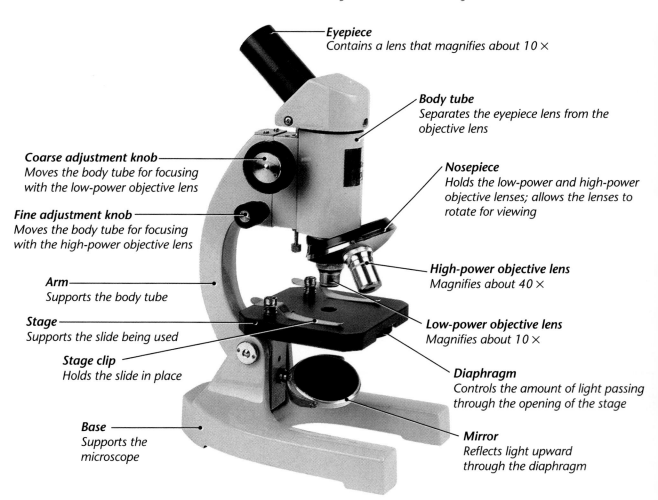

Eyepiece
Contains a lens that magnifies about 10×

Body tube
Separates the eyepiece lens from the objective lens

Coarse adjustment knob
Moves the body tube for focusing with the low-power objective lens

Nosepiece
Holds the low-power and high-power objective lenses; allows the lenses to rotate for viewing

Fine adjustment knob
Moves the body tube for focusing with the high-power objective lens

High-power objective lens
Magnifies about 40×

Arm
Supports the body tube

Stage
Supports the slide being used

Low-power objective lens
Magnifies about 10×

Stage clip
Holds the slide in place

Diaphragm
Controls the amount of light passing through the opening of the stage

Base
Supports the microscope

Mirror
Reflects light upward through the diaphragm

Using the Microscope

Use the following procedures when you are working with a microscope.

1. To carry the microscope grasp the microscope's arm with one hand. Place your other hand under the base.
2. Place the microscope on a table with the arm toward you.
3. Turn the coarse adjustment knob to raise the body tube.
4. Revolve the nosepiece until the low-power objective lens clicks into place.
5. Adjust the diaphragm. While looking through the eyepiece, also adjust the mirror until you see a bright white circle of light. **CAUTION:** *Never use direct sunlight as a light source.*
6. Place a slide on the stage. Center the specimen over the opening on the stage. Use the stage clips to hold the slide in place. **CAUTION:** *Glass slides are fragile.*
7. Look at the stage from the side. Carefully turn the coarse adjustment knob to lower the body tube until the low-power objective almost touches the slide.
8. Looking through the eyepiece, very slowly turn the coarse adjustment knob until the specimen comes into focus.
9. To switch to the high-power objective lens, look at the microscope from the side. Carefully revolve the nosepiece until the high-power objective lens clicks into place. Make sure the lens does not hit the slide.
10. Looking through the eyepiece, turn the fine adjustment knob until the specimen comes into focus.

Making a Wet-Mount Slide

Use the following procedures to make a wet-mount slide of a specimen.

1. Obtain a clean microscope slide and a coverslip. **CAUTION:** *Glass slides and coverslips are fragile.*
2. Place the specimen on the slide. The specimen must be thin enough for light to pass through it.
3. Using a plastic dropper, place a drop of water on the specimen.
4. Gently place one edge of the coverslip against the slide so that it touches the edge of the water drop at a 45° angle. Slowly lower the coverslip over the specimen. If air bubbles are trapped beneath the coverslip, tap the coverslip gently with the eraser end of a pencil.
5. Remove any excess water at the edge of the coverslip with a paper towel.

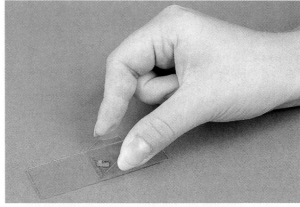

Glossary

A

accessory pigment A yellow, orange, or red pigment found in plant cells. (p. 121)

alga A plantlike protist. (p. 86)

algal bloom The rapid growth of a population of algae. (p. 90)

angiosperm A plant that produces seeds that are enclosed in a protective structure. (p. 156)

antibiotic A chemical that can kill bacteria without harming a person's cells. (p. 72)

asexual reproduction The reproductive process that involves only one parent and produces offspring that are identical to the parent. (p. 59)

autotroph An organism that makes its own food. (p. 21)

auxin The plant hormone that speeds up the rate of growth of plant cells. (p. 165)

B

bacteriophage A virus that infects bacteria. (p. 50)

binary fission A form of asexual reproduction in which one cell divides to form two identical cells. (p. 59)

binomial nomenclature The naming system for organisms in which each organism is given a two-part name—a genus name and a species name. (p. 30)

bog A wetland where sphagnum moss grows on top of acidic water. (p. 127)

budding A form of asexual reproduction of yeast in which a new yeast cell grows out of the body of a parent. (p. 98)

C

cambium The layer of cells in a plant that produces new phloem and xylem cells. (p. 147)

cell The basic unit of structure and function in an organism. (p. 17)

cell wall The boundary that surrounds the cell membrane in some cells. (p. 111)

cellulose A chemical that makes the cell walls of plants rigid and strong. (p. 111)

chlorophyll A green pigment found in the chloroplasts of plants as well as in algae and some bacteria. (p. 112)

chloroplast The structure of plant cells in which food is made. (p. 111)

cilia The hairlike projections on the outside of cells that move in a wavelike manner. (p. 83)

classification The process of grouping things based on their similarities. (p. 28)

cone The reproductive structure of a gymnosperm. (p. 152)

conjugation The process in which a unicellular organism transfers some of its genetic material to another unicellular organism. (p. 60)

contractile vacuole The cell structure that collects extra water from the cytoplasm and then expels it from the cell. (p. 82)

controlled experiment An experiment in which all factors are identical except one. (p. 19)

cotyledon A seed leaf that stores food. (p. 142)

cuticle The waxy, waterproof layer that covers the leaves and stems of some plants. (p. 113)

cytoplasm The region of a cell located inside the cell membrane (in prokaryotes) or between the cell membrane and nucleus (in eukaryotes); contains a gel-like material and cell organelles. (p. 57)

D

decomposer An organism that breaks down large chemicals from dead organisms into small chemicals and returns important materials to the soil and water. (p. 63)

development The process of change that occurs during an organism's life to produce a more complex organism. (p. 18)

dicot An angiosperm that has two seed leaves. (p. 157)

E

embryo The young plant that develops from a zygote. (p. 142)

endospore A small, rounded, thick-walled, resting cell that forms inside a bacterial cell. (p. 61)

eukaryote An organism with cells that contain nuclei and other cell structures. (p. 41)

eutrophication The buildup over time of nutrients in freshwater lakes and ponds that leads to an increase in the growth of algae. (p. 92)

evolution The process by which species gradually change over time. (p. 34)

F

fertilization The joining of a sperm cell and an egg cell. (p. 116)

flagellum A long, whiplike structure that extends out through the cell membrane and cell wall. (p. 58)

flower The reproductive structure of an angiosperm. (p. 157)

fossil The trace of an ancient organism that has been preserved in rock or other substance. (p. 27)

frond The leaf of a fern plant. (p. 132)

fruit The ripened ovary and other structures that enclose one or more seeds of an angiosperm. (p. 159)

fruiting body The reproductive hypha of a fungus. (p. 98)

gamete A sperm cell or an egg cell. (p. 117)

gametophyte The stage in the life cycle of a plant in which the plant produces gametes, or sex cells. (p. 117)

genetic engineering The process of altering an organism's genetic material to produce an organism with qualities that people find useful. (p. 169)

genus A classification grouping that consists of a number of similar, closely related species. (p. 30)

germination The early growth stage of the embryo plant in a seed. (p. 144)

gymnosperm A plant that produces seeds that are not enclosed by a protective covering. (p. 150)

heterotroph An organism that cannot make its own food. (p. 22)

homeostasis The maintenance of stable internal conditions despite changes in the surroundings. (p. 23)

hormone A chemical that affects growth and development. (p. 165)

host An organism that provides a source of energy or a suitable environment for a virus or for another organism to live. (p. 49)

hydroponics The method of growing plants in a solution of nutrients instead of in soil. (p. 170)

hypha One of many branching, threadlike tubes that make up the body of a fungus. (p. 96)

hypothesis A prediction about the outcome of an experiment. (p. 186)

infectious disease An illness that can pass from one organism to another. (p. 68)

lichen The combination of a fungus and either an alga or an autotrophic bacteria that live together in a mutualistic relationship. (p. 104)

manipulated variable The one factor that a scientist changes during an experiment. (p. 187)

monocot An angiosperm that has only one seed leaf. (p. 157)

multicellular A type of organism that is made up of many cells. (p. 17)

mutualism A type of symbiosis in which both partners benefit from living together. (p. 84)

nonvascular plant A low-growing plant that lacks vascular tissue. (p. 125)

nucleus The dense area in a eukaryotic cell that contains nucleic acids, the chemical instructions that direct the cell's activities. (p. 41)

operational definition A statement that describes how a particular variable is to be measured or how a term is to be defined. (p. 187)

organism A living thing. (p. 16)

ovary A protective structure in plants that encloses the developing seeds. (p. 157)

ovule A plant structure in seed plants that contains an egg cell. (p. 153)

parasite An organism that lives on or in a host and causes harm to the host. (p. 49)

peat The blackish-brown material consisting of compressed layers of dead sphagnum mosses that grow in bogs. (p. 127)

petal The colorful, leaflike structures of a flower. (p. 157)

phloem The vascular tissue through which food moves in some plants. (p. 141)

photosynthesis The process by which plants and some other organisms capture light energy and use it to make food from carbon dioxide and water. (p. 111)

pigment A chemical that produces color. (p. 87)

pistil The female reproductive parts of a flower. (p. 158)

pollen Tiny particles produced by plants that contain the microscopic cells that later become sperm cells. (p. 152)

pollination The transfer of pollen from male reproductive structures to female reproductive structures in plants. (p. 153)

prokaryote An organism whose cells lack a nucleus and some other cell structures. (p. 41)

protozoan An animal-like protist. (p. 81)

pseudopod A "false foot" or temporary bulge of the cell membrane used for feeding and movement in some protozoans. (p. 81)

red tide An algal bloom that occurs in salt water. (p. 91)

reproduce The production of offspring that are similar to the parents. (p. 19)

respiration The process of breaking down food to release its energy. (p. 60)

responding variable The factor that changes as a result of changes to the manipulated variable in an experiment. (p. 187)

response An action or change in behavior that occurs as a result of a stimulus. (p. 19)

rhizoid The thin, rootlike structure that anchors a moss and absorbs water and nutrients for the plant. (p. 126)

ribosome A tiny structure located in the cytoplasm of a cell where proteins are made. (p. 57)

root cap A structure that covers the tip of a root, protecting the root from injury. (p. 149)

seed The plant structure that contains a young plant inside a protective covering. (p. 142)

sepal A leaflike structure that encloses the bud of a flower. (p. 158)

sexual reproduction The reproductive process that involves two parents who combine their genetic material to produce a new organism, which differs from both parents. (p. 60)

species A group of similar organisms that can mate and produce fertile offspring in nature. (p. 30)

spontaneous generation The mistaken idea that living things arise from nonliving sources (p. 19)

spore A tiny cell that is able to grow into a new organism. (p. 85)

sporophyte The stage in the life cycle of a plant in which the plant produces spores for reproduction. (p. 117)

stamen The male reproductive parts of a flower. (p. 158)

stimulus A change in an organism's surroundings that causes the organism to react. (p. 18)

stomata The small openings on the undersides of most leaves through which oxygen and carbon dioxide can move. (p. 144)

symbiosis A close relationship between two organisms in which at least one of the organisms benefits. (p. 84)

taxonomic key A series of paired statements that describe the physical characteristics of different organisms. (p. 36)

taxonomy The scientific study of how living things are classified. (p. 29)

tissue A group of similar cells that perform a specific function in an organism. (p. 112)

toxin A poison that can harm an organism. (p. 70)

transpiration The process by which water is lost through a plant's leaves. (p. 146)

tropism The growth response of a plant toward or away from a stimulus. (p. 164)

unicellular A type of organism that is made up of a single cell. (p. 17)

vaccine A substance that stimulates the body to produce chemicals that destroy viruses, bacteria, or other disease-causing organisms. (p. 73)

vacuole A large sac-like storage area in a cell. (p. 112)

variable Any factor that can change in an experiment. (p. 19)

vascular plant A plant that has vascular tissue. (p. 131)

vascular tissue The internal transporting tissue in some plants that is made up of tubelike structures. (p. 116)

virus A small, nonliving particle that invades and then reproduces inside a living cell. (p. 48)

xylem The vascular tissue through which water and nutrients move in some plants. (p. 141)

zygote A fertilized egg. (p. 116)

accessory pigments 121
active viruses 51–52
adaptations of plants 113, 114–115
AIDS (acquired immunodeficiency syndrome) 54, 71
air pollution, lichens as indicators of 104
Alexandrium tamarense 90
alfalfa mosaic disease 54
algae 86–89, 112, 113
   brown 89
   defined 86
   green 88, 92, 112
   lichens formed by fungus and 104
   red 81, 89
algal blooms 90–94
   eutrophication and 92, 94
   freshwater 92
   saltwater 91
algins 89
amebas 82–83
ancient cultures, food preservation in 62–63
Anemone patens 114
angiosperms 156–163
   defined 156–157
   flowers, structure of 157–158, 162–163
   life cycle of 159
   life spans of 165–166
   reproduction in 157, 158, 159
   types of 160
   uses of 161
Animalia (kingdom) 33, 42
animal-like protists 81–85
animals 42
   disease spread by bites of 69
   living space of 23
   pollination of angiosperms and 158
   seed dispersed by 143
annual rings of trees 147–148
annuals 165
Anopheles mosquitoes 85
anther 157
antibiotic resistance 72–73, 74
antibiotics 72, 74, 99
   limiting non-medical uses of 74
   penicillin 72, 74, 103
antitoxin 70
applying concepts, skill of 188
archaebacteria 40–41, 58, 61
Aristotle 29, 30, 32
asexual reproduction
   in bacteria 59
   defined 59
   in fungi 98
   in paramecium 83
aspirin, source of 161
athlete's foot 97, 102
atmosphere of Earth, early 25–26
autotrophic bacteria 59, 60
autotrophs 21, 22, 41, 111 See also **algae**
auxin 165
Aves (class) 32, 33

bacteria 19, 26, 56–65, 72
   autotrophic 59, 60

bacterial cells 56–58
   decomposers 63–64
   defined 57
   heterotrophic 60
   infectious disease and 68–74
   kingdoms of 58–59
   lichens formed by fungus and 104
   living world and 61–65
   reproduction in 59–60
   salmonella 10, 11–13, 70
   survival needs of 60–61
bacterial diseases 72–73
bacteriophage 49, 50
baobab trees 146
bark 147
barnacles, homeostasis in 23
biennials 165–166
binary fission 59, 60, 83
binomial nomenclature 30–31
biologists 29
bird's nest fungi 99
bites, animal 69
bladderwort 164
body temperature 23
bog 127
Borrelia burgdorferi 57
botulism 70
bracket fungi 96
bread molds 24, 98
bristlecone pine tree 114, 152
brown algae 89
Bubo (Genus) 33
Bubo virginianus (species) 33
budding 98

cactus finch 34
calculating, skill of 185
Calvin, Melvin 123
cambium 147
carbohydrate 17
   produced during photosynthesis 123
carbon dioxide 22, 25
   photosynthesis and 124, 145
carrageenan 89
cell(s)
   bacterial 56–58
   chemicals in 17
   defined 17
   energy use of 18
   first 27
   of fungi, structure of 96
   nucleus of 41
   of plants 111–112
cell membrane 57, 81
   in ameba 82
   of bacterial cell 58
cellular organization 17
cellulose 111
cell wall 111
   of bacterium 57
Centers for Disease Control and Prevention (CDC) 10
cheesemaking 62
chemicals of life 17, 26
chicken pox 46–47, 71

childhood diseases 47
Chlamydomonas 41
chlorophyll 112, 121, 122, 123, 144
chloroplasts 111, 122, 144
Chordata (phylum) 33
cilia, protozoans with 83
ciliates 83
classes 32
classification 28–37
   defined 28
   early systems of 29–31
   evolution and 34
   of fungi 99
   kingdoms 32, 40–42
   levels of 32–33
   reasons for 28–29
   of today 34–36
   using system of 36–37
classifying, skill of 183
clear cutting 155
climate changes, red tides and 91
Clostridium botulinum 70
Clostridium tetani 70
club fungi 99
club mosses 133
coal deposits 131
cocoa plants 63
cold sore virus 53, 69
cold viruses 49
colonies of algae 87
colors 120, 121
Columbus, Christopher 174
communicating, skill of 183
compare/contrast tables 190
comparing and contrasting, skill of 188
concept maps 190
cones 152–153, 154
conifers 152
conjugation 60
contact, spread of infectious disease by 69
contaminated object, contact with 69
contractile vacuole 82, 83
controlled experiment 19, 20–21, 187
controlling variables, skill of 187
coral fungus 14–15
corn 174–181
   production data on 180–181
   structure of 178
   uses of 179
Corn Belt 180
corn goddess folk tale, 176–177
corn meal 179
corn smut 102
cornstarch 179
cortisone, source of 161
cotton plants 161
cotyledons 142, 160
cricket-killing fungus 95, 99
critical thinking skills 188–189
Culex nigripalpus 69
cultures 13
curds and whey 62
cuticle 113
   of leaf 145
cycads 151

cycle diagrams 191
cystic fibrosis 54
cytoplasm 81–82
    in ameba 82
    of bacterial cell 58
    defined 57
    of paramecium 83

dandelions 140
Darwin, Charles 34
data tables 192
date palms 115
decomposers
    bacteria as 63–64
    fungi as 102
designing experiments, skill of 187
developing hypotheses, skill of 186
development 18
diabetes 65
diatomaceous earth 88
diatoms 80, 86, 88
dicots 160
digitalis, source of 161
dinoflagellates 88, 90
diphtheria 70
direct contact, spread of disease by 69
disease-causing fungi 102–103
disease-fighting fungi 103
diseases
    childhood 47
    fungal plant diseases 102
    infectious 10, 11–13, 68–74
    viruses causing 54, 68–74
disinfectants 66–67
distemper 54
downy mildews 85
drawing conclusions, skill of 187
droughts 148
Dutch elm disease 97

Earth, early atmosphere of 25–26
Ebola virus 49
egg cells 117
embryo 142, 144
    corn 79
encephalitis 69
endospore 61
energy
    for bacteria 60
    cellular use of 18
    in form of light 120–121
    light as form of 122
    need for 21–22
Engelmann, T.W. 120, 123
environmental cleanup, bacterial for 64
environmental recycling 63–64
    fungi and 102
environmental sources of infectious
    disease 70
Epstein–Barr virus 49
Escherichia coli 57, 59
ethanol 179
eubacteria 41, 59
    recycling by 63–64
euglena 87

euglenoids 87
eukaryotes 41, 80, 96, 111 See also **fungus,**
    fungi; plants; protists
    multicellular 42
eutrophication 92, 94
evergreen plants 152
evolution, classification and 34
evolutionary history of species 35–36
experiment See also **scientific**
    investigations
    controlled 19, 20–21, 187
experimental farms 169

"fairy ring" 103
fall leaves, color of 121
families 32
farming of seed plants 168–170
    improving efficiency of farms 169–170
Felis genus 30, 31
female cones 152, 153, 154
ferns 114, 130–133
    ancient 130–131
    fossil 112, 132
    importance of 133
    reproduction in 133
fertilization
    in angiosperms 158, 159
    in corn 178
    defined 116
    in gymnosperms 153, 154
fertilizers
    eutrophication and 92, 93
    precision farming and 170
fibrous root systems 148
fiddleheads 133
field corn 179
field guides 36
filament 157
finches of Galapagos Islands 34
flagellum, flagella 58
    protozoans with 84
flax plants 161
Fleming, Alexander 103
flowcharts 191
flowers 157, 159
    of dicots 160
    of monocot 160
    structure of 157–158, 162–163
flu virus 69
folk tales 103
    defined 177
    Native American corn 176–177
food
    bacteria and production of 62–63
    fungi and 102
    from plants 124, 148, 168–170
    preserving 62–63
    roots as storage area for 148
food, methods of obtaining
    in bacteria 60
    in fungi 97
food poisoning 70, 71
food vacuole 82, 83
forests, cutting methods in 155
foraminiferans 81

forming operational definitions 187
fossils 27
    evolutionary history from 35
    of gymnosperms 151
    plant 112, 132
foxglove plant 161, 166
freshwater algal blooms 92
Friedman, Cindy 10–13
frond 132, 133
fruiting bodies 98, 103
fruits 156–157, 158, 159
fuel
    bacteria and production of 61
    coal deposits 131
    ethanol, from corn 179
fungus, fungi 14–15, 42, 95–104
    cell structure of 96
    classification of 99
    defined 95–96
    disease-causing 102–103
    disease-fighting 103
    food, obtaining 97
    kingdom of 42, 95
    living world and 102–104
    reproduction in 97–98
funguslike protists 85–86

Galapagos Islands, finches of 34
gametes 117
gametophytes 117, 132, 141
    fern 133
    moss 126
gases in Earth's atmosphere 25
gene therapy 54
genetic engineering 169
genetic material, conjugation in bacteria
    and new 60
genus 30, 31, 32
geologists 29
germination 144
giant kelps 81, 89
giant sequoia trees 150, 152
Giardia 84
ginkgo 151
Ginkgo biloba 151
gnetophytes 151
graphs 192–194
gravitropism 165
gravity, plant response to 165, 167
green algae 88, 92, 112
growth 18
gymnosperms 150–155
    defined 150
    life cycle of 154
    methods of growing 155
    reproduction in 152–153, 154
    types of 151–152
    uses of 155

handwashing, importance of 12, 13
health, bacteria and 64–65
heartwood 147
herbaceous stems 146, 147
heterotrophic bacteria 60

heterotrophs 22, 27, 41, 42, 96 See also
    fungus, fungi; funguslike protists
    animal-like protists 81–85
    defined 22
hidden viruses 52–53
hiker's disease 84
HIV (human immunodeficiency virus) 51
Hoh rain forest 110
homeostasis 23
hormones, plant 165
hornworts 128
horsetails 133
    fossil 112
host 49
house cats (*Felis domesticus*) 30, 31
human body, water in 22
human immunodeficiency virus (HIV) 51
humpback whales 90
hydroponics 170
hyphae 96, 97, 103
    reproductive 97–98
hypothesis 186

Iditarod Trail 70
imperfect fungi 99
Incan Empire 175
indirect contact, spread of disease by 69
infectious diseases 10, 11–13, 68–74
    antibiotics and 72, 74
    common 70–71
    defined 68
    preventing 73
    spread of 68–70, 72–74
    treating 72–73
infectious mononucleosis 49
inferring, skill of 182
influenza (flu) 71
Ingenhousz, Jan 122
insulin-making bacteria 65
interpreting data, skill of 187
interpreting illustrations, skill of 188
Irish potato famine (1845 and 1846) 85
Iroquois corn folk tale 176–177

kingdoms 32, 40–42
    animals 33, 42
    archaebacteria 40–41, 58, 61
    eubacteria 41, 59
    fungi 42
    plant 42, 110–117
    protist 41, 80–89
Komodo dragon 12, 13
kudzu 159

laboratory safety 195–197
Lactobacillus san francisco 63
land, plants on 113–116
large-billed ground finch 34
leaves
    of dicots 160
    fall, color of 121
    of monocot 160
    photosynthesis and 144–145
    of seed plants 144–146
    structure of 144

Leeuwenhoek, Anton van 56–57
lichens 104
life 16–27
    building blocks of 26
    characteristics of living things 16–19
    chemicals of 17, 26
    needs of living things 20–23
    origin of 25–27
    reproduction and 19–20
life cycle
    of angiosperms 159
    complex 117
    of gymnosperms 154
light
    as form of energy 122
    nature of 120–121
    photosynthesis and 120–124
    plants and 121–122, 164–165
Linnaeus, Carolus 30–31, 32, 34
lipids 17
liverworts 128
living space, need for 23
lockjaw (tetanus) 70, 71
lodgepole pines 141
Lyme disease 57, 69, 71

maize (corn) 174–181
    history of 175
    Native American folk tale of 176–177
making generalizations, skill of 189
making judgments, skill of 189
making models, skill of 183
malaria 84–85
male cones 152, 153, 154
mangrove trees 115
Mayan civilization 175
measles 71
measuring, skill of 184
meat preservation 62
medicine
    angiosperms as source of 161
    bacteria and 64–65
Mephitidae (family) 36
methane 25, 61
microscopes 17, 56
mildew 42
    downy 85
Miller, Stanley 26, 27
Mitchell Corn Palace (South Dakota) 181
molds 42, 99, 102
    bread 24, 98
    Penicillium 97, 99, 103
    slime 16, 41, 81, 86
    water 85
monocots 160
mononucleosis, infectious 49, 69
morning glories 166
mosquito bites, disease spread by 69
mosses 109, 126–127, 129
    importance of 127
    structure of 126
mountain lions (*Felis concolor*) 30
multicellular organisms 17, 87
    eukaryotes 42
    plants 112

mushrooms 42, 79, 96, 98, 99, 102
    "fairy ring" of 103
Mustelidae (family) 36
mutualism 84

nanometers (nm) 50
Native American corn folk tale 176–177
natural gas 61
Navajo corn folk tale 176
nectar 158
needs of living things 20–23
    of bacteria 60–61
nerve cells 17
New Zealand pygmy pines 152
nitrogen 25
    bacterial conversion for plants 64
nomenclature, binomial 30–31
nonvascular plants 125–128
nucleic acids 17, 41
nucleus
    in ameba 82
    defined 41
    of paramecium 83
nutrients
    eutrophication and excess 92, 94
    plant adaptations for obtaining 113
    red tides and excess 91

oak tree, roots of 148
observations, classifications based on 29, 30
observing, skill of 182
ocean temperature, red tides and 91
ocelots (*Felis pardalis*) 30, 31
Ochrobactrum anthropi 64
O'Keeffe, Georgia 158
Olympic Mountains in Washington State 110
operational definitions 187
oral groove of paramecium 83
orders 32
organisms
    characteristics of 16–19
    classifying 28–37
    early life forms 26, 27
    fossils of bacteria–like 27
    multicellular 17, 42, 87, 112
    needs of 20–23
    "pioneer," 104
    unicellular 17, 26, 40, 86–87
organpipe cacti 141
origin of life 25–27
ovary 157, 158
over-the-counter medications 72
ovule 153, 154, 158, 159
owl, classifying 32–33
oxygen 25
    algae and production of 86
    autotrophic bacteria and 59
    photosynthesis and 122, 145

papilloma viruses 49
paramecium 82, 83, 84
parasites 49 See also viruses
    sporozoans 84–85

Pasque flower 114
Pasteur, Louis 20, 21, 26
Pawnee corn folk tale 176
peat 127
peat moss 125, 127
pellicle of paramecium 83
penicillin 72, 74, 103
Penicillium **mold** 97, 99, 103
Penicillium roqueforti 102
peonies 166
perennials 166
petals 157
phloem 141, 144, 145, 147, 149
photosynthesis 111, 118–124, 144–145
   chemistry of 123
   defined 111
   discovery of 122–123
   experiment on 118–119
   light and 120–124
phototropism 164–165
phyla 32
pigments
   in algae 87
   plant 121
pine trees 154
Pinus taeda 31
"pioneer" organisms 104
   pioneer plants 127
pistils 158
plant diseases, fungal 102
plant hormones 165
plantlike protists 86–89
plant pigments 121
plants 42, 108–137
   adaptations of 113, 114–115
   cells of 111–112
   complex life cycles 117
   defined 111
   diseases caused by viruses in 54
   ferns and their relatives 114, 130–134
   fixed living space of 23
   fungus-plant root associations 103
   on land 113–116
   light and 121–122, 164–165
   liverworts and hornworts 128
   mosses 109, 126–127, 129
   nonvascular 125–128
   origins of 112
   photosynthesis 111, 119–124, 144–145
   plant kingdom 42, 110–117
   producing better 169
   reproduction in 116
Plasmodium 84–85
poliomyelitis (polio) 71
pollen 152, 153, 154, 158, 159
pollination 153
   of angiosperms 157, 158, 159
   of corn 178
   of gymnosperm 154
pollution
   air, lichens as indicators of 104
   eutrophication and 94
Ponderosa pine 152
posing questions, skill of 186
precision farming 169–170

predicting, skill of 182
Priestley, Joseph 122
prism 120
problem solving, skill of 189
prokaryotes 41, 57 See also *bacteria*
proteins 17
   in coat of virus 51
protists 41, 80–89
   animal–like 81–85
   defined 80–81
   funguslike 85–86
   plantlike 86–89
protozoans 81–84
   with cilia 83
   with flagella 84
   with pseudopods 81–83
pseudopods 81–83
puffballs 98, 99

rabies virus 49, 54, 69, 71
rafflesia 115
rainfall, annual rings and information on 148
rain forest 110
recycling, environmental 63–64, 102
red algae 81, 89
Redi, Francesco 19, 26
red tides 91
relating cause and effect, skill of 189
reproduction 19–20
   in angiosperms 157, 158, 159
   asexual 59
   in bacteria 59–60
   in corn 178
   defined 19
   in ferns 133
   in fungi 97–98
   in gymnosperms 152–153, 154
   of nonvascular plants 126
   in plants 116
   sexual 60, 98, 116
   spores for 132
resistance
   antibiotic 72–73, 74
   engineering plants for 169
respiration 60
responding variable 187
response to surroundings 18–19
rhizoids 126
Rhizopus nigrens 99
ribosomes 57, 58
rice dwarf virus 54
rings of trees, annual 147–148
ringworm 102
rockweed 89
rodlike bacterial cells 57
root cap 149
root hairs 149
roots
   fern 132
   of seed plants 148–149
rubber trees 161

sac fungi 99
Sachs, Julius 123

safety in the laboratory 195–197
salmonella bacteria 10, 11–13, 70
saltwater algal blooms 91
sapwood 147
sarcodines 81, 82–83
scientific investigations 186–187
scientific method See **scientific**
   investigations
seaweeds 41, 86, 89
seed coat 142, 179
seed dispersal 143
   in angiosperms 158
   in gymnosperms 153
seedless vascular plants 130–134
   characteristics of 131–132
   club mosses and horsetails 134
   ferns 114, 130–133
seed plants 138–173
   angiosperms 156–163
   defined 140–141
   farming 168–170
   germination in 144
   gymnosperms 150–155
   leaves of 144–146
   plant responses and growth 164–167
   roots of 148–149
   seed dispersal 143, 153, 158
   seeds 142, 153
   stems of 146–148
   vascular tissue of 141
seedpods, dispersal by bursting of 143
seeds 142
   development of 153
sepals 157
septic systems, eutrophication and leaking 92
sexual reproduction 60
   in bacteria 60
   in fungi 98
   in plants 116
SI units of measurement 184–185
skills, science process 182–194
skunks 36
slime mold 16, 41, 81, 85, 86
sourdough bread 63
soybeans 63
species 31, 32
   defined 30
   evolutionary history of 35–36
sperm cells 117
   of nonvascular plants 126
sphagnum moss 127
spherical bacterial cells 57
spiral shaped bacterial cells 57
spoiled food, prevention of 62–63
spontaneous generation 19–20, 21
spores 97–98, 99, 117
   defined 85
   fern 133
   for reproduction 132
sporophytes 117, 141
   of hornworts 128
   of liverworts 128
   of moss 126
sporozoans 84–85

staghorn fern 114
stamens 157
Staphylococcus aureus 57
stem of seed plants 146–148
   of dicot 160
   of monocot 160
   structure of 146–147
stigma 158, 159
stimulus 18
stomata 144, 145, 146
strep throat 71, 72
Streptococci 41
Strigiformes (order) 32, 33
Strygidae (family) 33
style 158
sunflowers 165
sweet corn 179
symbiosis 84

taproot system 148
taxonomic key 36–37
taxonomy 29, 36 See also classification
temperature
   body 23
   measuring 185
   red tides and ocean 91
termites, zooflagellates in intestines of 84
tetanus (lockjaw) 70, 71, 73
thigmotropism 164
threadlike fungi 99
tick bites, disease spread by 69
tissues 112
tobacco mosaic virus 49
touch, plant response to 164
toxins 70
   algal blooms and 90, 91
transpiration 146
transporting tissue in plants 116

trees 150 See also seed plants
   annual rings of 147–148
tropisms 164–165
tuberculosis (TB) 71
   antibiotic resistance and 72–73
tulip mosaic virus 54

unicellular organism 17, 26, 40, 86–87
United States Centennial Exhibition
   (1876) 159
units of measurement 184–185
Urey, Harold 26, 27

vaccines 73
vacuole 112
   contractile 82, 83
   food 82, 83
Van Helmont, Jean-Baptiste 122
variables 19, 187
vascular plants, seedless 130–134
vascular tissue 116, 141
   of dicots 160
   of monocot stems 160
   of root 149
   of seedless vascular plants 131
vegetables, preserving 62
Venn diagrams 191
Venus fly trap 115
viral diseases 72
viruses 46–55
   active 51–52
   defined 48–49
   hidden 52–53
   infectious disease and 49, 68–74
   living world and 54
   multiplication of 51–53
   naming 49
   shapes of 50
   size of 50, 55
   structure of 50–51

visible spectrum 120, 121
volume, measuring 184
Volvox 22
warbler finch 34
wastewater, eutrophication and 94
water
   in cells 17
   need for 22
   photosynthesis and 124
   plant adaptations for obtaining and
     reducing loss of 113
   as raw material of photosynthesis 122
   seeds dispersed by 143
water lily 114
water loss of leaf, controlling 146
water molds 85
water vapor 25
weasels 36
weather conditions, annual rings and
    information on 148
Weiss Lake 94
wheat plants 141
wheat rust 102
willow trees 161
wind, seed dispersal by 143, 153
woody perennials 166
woody stems 147

xylem 141, 144, 145, 147, 149
   annual rings of 147–148

yam, Mexican 161
yeasts 96, 98, 100–101, 102

zooflagellates 84
zygote 116, 117, 142, 154

Acknowledgments

Illustration

Patrice Rossi Calkin: 35, 52, 53, 82, 83
Warren Cutler: 39
David Fuller: 175
GeoSystems Global Corporation: 70, 180(b)
Keith Kasnot: 87
Martucci Design: 77, 107, 173, 180(t), 192(b), 193, 194,
Morgan Cain & Associates: 17, 20-21, 45, 50(t,b), 51(b), 98, 111, 122, 145, 184 (l,r), 185 (l,r)
Matt Myerchak: 44, 76, 106, 172, 190, 191
Ortelius Design Inc.: 62, 63, 94
Stephanie Pershing: 26-27
Tim Spransy: 176-177
Walter Stuart: 96, 126, 132, 178, 179
Cynthia Turner: 117, 142, 154, 159
J/B Woolsey Associates: 18, 29, 33, 37, 51(t), 89, 97, 124, 149, 157, 163, 167, 188

Photography

Photo Research Paula Wehde
Cover image - Perry D. Slocum/Animals Animals/Earth Scenes

Nature of Science
Page 10, Courtesy of Cindy Friedman; **11,** Michael Dick/Animals Animals; **13l,** Courtesy of Cindy Friedman; **13r,** USDA/S.S./Photo Researchers.

Chapter 1
Pages 14-15, Joe McDonald/DRK Photo; **16t,** Russ Lappa; **16b,** Beatty/Visuals Unlimited; **17,** John Pontier/Animals Animals **19,** Michael Quinton/Minden Pictures; **20,** The Granger Collection, NY; **21,** The Granger Collection, NY; **22l,** James Dell/Science Source/Photo Researchers; **22r,** Zig Leszcynski/Animals Animals; **23,** Jim Brandenburg/Minden Pictures; **25,** Russ Lappa; **27,** Biological Photo Service; **28t,** Russ Lappa; **28b,** Inga Spence/The Picture Cube; **30,** Gerard Lacz/Animals Animals; **31t,** J. Serrao/Visuals Unlimited; **31bl,** Tom Brakefield/DRK Photo; **31br,** Ron Kimball **32-33,** Thomas Kitchin/Tom Stack & Associates; **34 all,** Tui de Roy/Minden Pictures; **36t,** Phil A. Dotson/Photo Researchers; **36b,** Richard Day/Animals Animals; **38,** Mike Ederegger/DRK Photo; **39tl,** Fernandez & Peck/Adventure Photo & Film; **39 all others,** Frans Lanting/Minden Pictures; **40,** Alan L. Detrick/Photo Researchers; **41t,** David M. Phillips/Photo Researchers; **41b,** Microfield Scientific Ltd/Science Photo Library/Photo Researchers; **42,** Ray Coleman/Photo Researchers; **43r,** Frans Lanting/Minden Pictures.

Chapter 2
Pages 46-47, Institut Pasteur/CNRI/Phototake; **48t,** Russ Lappa; **48bl,** Dr. Linda Stannard, UCT/Science Photo Library/Photo Researchers; **48bm,** Lee D. Simon/Science Source/Photo Researchers **48-49,** Dr. Brad Fute/Peter Arnold; **49m,** Tektoff-RM/CNRI/Science Photo Library/Photo Researchers; **49r,** CDC/Science Source/Photo Researchers; **53,** Lee D. Simon/Science Source/Photo Researchers; **54,** Henryk T. Kaiser/Photo Network Tustin; **55,** Custom Medical Stock; **56t,** Richard Haynes; **56b,** Science Photo Library/Photo Researchers; **57l,** Scott Camazine/Photo Researchers; **57m,** David M. Phillips/Visuals Unlimited; **57r,** Oliver Meckes/Photo Researchers; **58,** Dr. Tony Brain/Science Photo Library/Photo Researchers; **59,** Dr. K. S Kim/Peter Arnold; **60,** Dr. Dennis Kunkel/PhotoTake; **61,** Alfred Pasieka/Peter Arnold; **62t,** PhotoDisc; **62b,** Sally Ann Ullmann/FoodPix; **63t,** John Marshall/TSI; **63b,** FoodPix; **64t,** E. Webben/Visuals Unlimited; **64b,** Ben Osborne; **64 inset,** Michael Abbey/Photo Researchers; **65,** Hank Morgan; **67, 68,** Richard Haynes; **69t,** James Darell/TSI; **69b,** David M. Dennis/Tom Stack & Associates; **70,** Kevin Horan/TSI; **72,** American Lung Association of Wisconsin; **73,** B. Daemmrich/The Image Works; **74,** Johnathan Selig/Photo 20-20; **75t,** Biozentrum, University of Basel/Science Photo Library/Photo Researchers; **75b,** Alfred Pasieka/Peter Arnold.

Chapter 3
Pages 78-79, David M. Dennis/Tom Stack & Associates; **80t,** Science VU/Visuals Unlimited; **80b,** Jan Hinsch/Science Photo Library/Photo Researchers; **81l,** O.S.F./Animals Animals; **81tr,** A. Le Toquin/Photo Researchers; **81br,** Gregory G. Dimijian/Photo Researchers; **82,** Astrid & Hanns-Frieder Michler/Science Photo Library/Photo Researchers; **83,** Eric Grave/Science Source/Photo Researchers; **84l,** Jerome Paulin/Visuals Unlimited; **84r,** Michael P. Gadomski/Photo Researchers; **85t,** Oliver Meckes/Photo Researchers; **85b,** Dwight R. Kuhn; **86 both,** David M. Dennis/Tom Stack & Associates; **87l,** Sinclair Stammers Oxford Scientific Films;

87r, Russ Lappa; **88t,** David M. Phillips/Visuals Unlimited; **88bl,** D. P. Wilson/Eric & Daid Hosking/Photo Researchers; **88br,** Andrew Syred/Science Photo Library/Photo Researchers; **90t,** Richard Haynes; **90b,** Doug Perrine/Hawaii Whale Research Foundation - NMFS permit#882/Innerspace Visions; **91,** Sanford Berry/Visuals Unlimited; **92,** Kenneth H. Thomas/Photo Researchers; **94,** Robert P. Falls; **95t,** Russ Lappa; **95b,** Michael Fogden/Animals Animals; **96,** Fred Unverhau/Animals Animals/Earth Scenes; **97,** Nobel Proctor/Science Source/Photo Researchers; **98,** David Scharf/Peter Arnold; **99tl,** E.R. Degginger/Photo Researchers; **99tr,** Rod Planck/Tom Stack & Associates; **99bl,** Michael Fogden/Animals Animals/Earth Scenes; **99br,** Andrew McClenaghan/Sicence Photo Library/Photo Researchers; **101,** Richard Haynes; **102,** David M. Dennis/Tom Stack & Associates; **103,** Rob Simpson/Visuals Unlimited; **104l,** Rod Planck/Tom Stack & Associates; **104r,** Frans Lanting/Minden Pictures; **105l,** Gregory G. Dimijian/Photo Researchers; **105r,** Michael Fogden/Animals Animals/Earth Scenes.

Chapter 4
Pages 108-109, J. Lotter Gurling/Tom Stack & Associates; **110,** Joanne Lotter/Tom Stack & Associates; **111, 112,** Runk/Schoenberger/Grant Heilman Photography; **113,** Kjell B. Sandved/Photo Researchers; **114tl,** Richard J. Green/Photo Researchers; **114tr,** Brenda Tharp/Photo Researchers; **114m,** R. Van Nostrand/Photo Researchers; **114b,** Joe McDonald/Visuals Unlimited; **115tl,** Prenzel/Animals Animals/Earth Scenes; **115tr,** Frans Lanting/Minden Pictures; **115m,** Andrew J. Martinez/Photo Researchers; **115b,** Runk/Schoenberger/Grant Heilman Photography; **116,** Doug Wechsler/Animals Animals/Earth Scenes; **118,** Richard Haynes; **119,** Images International/Erwin C. Bud Nielsen/Visuals Unlimited; **120t,** Richard Haynes; **120b,** Runk/Schoenberger/Grant Heilman Photography; **121,** Carr Clifton/Minden Pictures; **122,** Runk/Schoenberger/Grant Heilman Photography; **123t,** Interfoto-Pressebild-Agentur; **123b,** Georg Gerster/Photo Researchers; **125t,** Russ Lappa; **125b,** Christi Carter/Grant Heilman Photography; **126,** Runk/Schoenberger/Grant Heilman Photography; **127t,** Silkeborg Museum; **127b,** Farrell Grehan/Photo Researchers; **128l,** Runk/Schoenberger/Grant Heilman Photography; **128r** William E. Ferguson; **129, 130t,** Richard Haynes; **132,** Rod Planck/Tom Stack & Associates; **133t,** Milton Rand/Tom Stack & Associates, **133b,** Joanne Lotter/Tom Stack & Associates; **134l,** Runk/Schoenberger/Grant Heilman Photography; **134r,** Frans Lanting/Minden Pictures; **135,** Rod Planck/Tom Stack & Associates.

Chapter 5
Pages 138-139, E.R. Degginger; **140t,** Russ Lappa; **140b,** E. R. Degginger/Animals Animals/Earth Scenes; **141l,** Thomas Kitchin/Tom Stack & Associates; **141m&r,** Carr Clifton/Tom Stack & Associates; **143tl,** D. Cavagnaro/Visuals Unlimited; **143tr,** Frans Lanting/Minden Pictures; **143bl,** E. R. Degginger; **143br,** William Harlow/Photo Researchers; **144 both,** Runk/Schoenberger/Grant Heilman Photography; **146,** Dani/Jeske/Animals Animals/Earth Scenes; **148t,** Runk/Schoenberger/Grant Heilman Photography; **148b both,** Robert Calentine/Visuals Unlimited; **150t,** Richard Haynes; **150b,** Bruce M. Herman/Photo Researchers; **151tl,** Ken Brate/Photo Researchers; **151tr,** Jim Strawser/Grant Heilman Photography; **151b,** Michael Fogden/Animals Animals/Earth Scenes; **152l,** Runk/Schoenberger/Grant Heilman Photography; **152r,** Breck P. Kent/Animals Animals/Earth Scenes; **153,** Breck P. Kent; **155,** C.J. Allen/Stock Boston; **156t,** Russ Lappa; **156b,** Jim Strawser/Grant Heilman Photography; **157,** E. R. Degginger; **158,** Private Collections/Art Resource; **161,** Alan Pitcairn/Grant Heilman Photography; **162,** Richard Haynes; **164,** William J. Weber/Visuals Unlimited; **165,** Porterfield-Chickering/Photo Researchers; **166tl,** E. R. Degginger; **166tr,** Mark E. Gibson/The Stock Market; **166b,** Larry Lefever/Grant Heilman Photography; **168,** Herve Donnezan/Photo Researchers; **169,** William James Warren/West Light; **170,** Arthur C. Smith III/Grant Heilman Photography; **171,** Arthur C. Smith III/Grant Heilman Photography.

Interdisciplinary Exploration
Page 174t, Ed Simpson/TSI; **174 inset,** The Granger Collection, NY; **174b,** Werner Forman Archive/Art Resource; **176,** C.M. Dixon; **179,** Isaac Geib/Grant Heilman Photography; **181,** Peter Essick/Aurora.

Skills Handbook
Page 182, Mike Moreland/Photo Network; **183t,** Foodpix; **183m,** Richard Haynes; **183b,** Russ Lappa; **186,** Richard Haynes; **188,** Ron Kimball; **189,** Renee Lynn/Photo Researchers.

Appendix
Page 198-199 all, Russ Lappa.